Surviving
Lasts
a Lifetime

Surviving Lasts *a* Lifetime

A PARENT'S JOURNEY THROUGH MEDICAL TRAUMA

Astrid Hendren

For

AUDREY *&* **AMY**

And for those who are surviving all around us,

Because surviving lasts a lifetime!

Contents

PART I

Brain Bleed

PART II

Home

PART III
Surviving Is All Around Us

APPENDICES
Resources & Discussion Guide

Foreword

January 2016

An estimated 6 million Americans—one in 50—are living with unruptured aneurysms. Most of these people don't even know they have them. But approximately 1 in 10,000 people suffer brain aneurysm ruptures each year. Aneurysms are small blisters that bulge off the sides of blood vessels in the brain. Enormous trouble arises when one of these little bubbles ruptures, which happens to 30,000 people a year in the United States. Most people would refer to this as a stroke; we neurosurgeons call it a subarachnoid hemorrhage. In this disastrous event, the burst artery gushes blood into the space around the brain, carrying with it a 40 percent risk of immediate death. Sixty-six percent of the lucky survivors suffer some permanent neurological deficit.

Astrid had the bad luck of not just having a brain aneurysm and experiencing a rupture, she also had one of the most unusual aneurysms I'd ever seen. Its location, shape, and anatomy made it different from 99 percent of cerebral aneurysms, and almost all of the usual approaches and procedures I had in my surgical toolbox were useless. Repairing Astrid's extremely difficult aneurysm required an open surgical procedure and a complex skull-base approach, and we faced many technical challenges as we operated. In spite of the complexity of the surgery, everything went beautifully. From a neurosurgeon's perspective, Astrid's outcome has been superb.

Astrid's perspective, of course, is very different from mine—for her this story is not about the success of a surgical procedure but about the process of recovering and reclaiming her sense of self. Her story offers hope to anybody experiencing any kind of brain injury. It's true that recovery involves patience and hard work, but the brain does regain function. Along that journey to recovery the patient may experience cognitive, motor, and sensory issues as well as powerful emotional reactions. A stroke or other brain trauma can change one's perspective on life—it can affect one's very soul.

In this book, Astrid gives us her personal insight into many of the feelings and thoughts she experienced, from the moment of the rupture through her long road to recovery.

Reading her story, I found the kernel of hope that will inspire anyone who experiences a medical trauma. I know the human brain can get through very difficult times. Astrid, and all who read her book, will discover that human beings can get through them, too. It's clear from Astrid's experience that patience, perseverance, hard work, and determination are all necessary ingredients for creating a recovery. More than that, though, she provides great insight into the concept of the "new normal" one must face after a medical trauma. Accepting the "new you" can be hard on both the patient and loved ones, and often requires ongoing therapy to understand and resolve.

Medicine has come a long way in understanding the process of brain injury in the 20 years since Astrid experienced her rupture. A similar patient today would not be left to her own devices the way Astrid was—the best brain and spine facilities now offer integrated, comprehensive care and support that treat the whole patient. We physicians can not only repair the physical damage, we can also provide a wide range of therapeutic options to help a patient fully recover. We can provide neuropsychological assessments and cognitive therapies when needed. By identifying which brain region was injured we can determine its effects on neurotransmitters, allowing us to provide neuro-psychopharmacological assistance along the recovery pathway. Physical and occupational therapy and other meditative therapies have been found to be beneficial for a patient's complete recovery. Psychiatric support can help when a patient and family face difficult emotional times. We now have large teams to address many of the issues Astrid faced, and provide hope to all patients who suffer a medical trauma.

The larger lesson I hope readers take away from this book is one about overall health. Most people take for granted that our neurons will keep firing, our blood will keep flowing, and all the complex processes will go on as they should. But a healthy body requires tending to, in a way most people don't think about until an injury forces them to.

Astrid was very healthy and fit when she faced this difficult surgery, which enabled her body to process the enormous trauma. And while she could not have prevented the rupture of an aneurysm that had been there since birth, it was crucial that she had the healthy body and mind that could fight to survive. The rest of us can learn from her experience without having to repeat it.

Astrid's is a story of survival, adaptation, acceptance and finally, renewal. All of us will have to deal with trauma of some kind in our lives, and the stronger you are both physically and mentally going in, the better your chances for a positive outcome.

—Philip E. Stieg, PhD, MD
Chairman and Neurosurgeon-in-Chief
Weill Cornell Brain and Spine Center

Preface

Four months ago, I contacted Dr. Stieg and asked if he would comment on a draft of the book you're about to read. I had not communicated with him since my follow-up visit after surgery, now 18 years ago, so I was particularly humbled and touched when he offered instead to write the book's foreword.

I'm glad that Dr. Stieg points out in his foreword that today's healthcare system addresses the whole patient better than it did when I had my stroke. His current institution, Weill Cornell Medical Center in New York, and other hospitals around the country are taking an approach different from the one I encountered 19 years ago. State-of-the-art brain, spine, heart, and cancer centers are springing up everywhere. Non-profit organizations such as the American Heart Association and American Cancer Society offer patient support-groups on a large scale. Many advocacy organizations push for legislation to require insurance policies to cover whole-patient care. Institutions such as the Schwartz Center for Compassionate Healthcare in Boston—which promotes a more human connection between patients and caregivers—seek to improve patients' quality of life.

Hopefully, progress and awareness will continue to grow. My goal in writing this book is to help people who are dealing with any kind of trauma to find the strength and courage necessary to ask for help, to keep faith, and to persevere.

—Astrid Hendren
January 2016

Prologue

Turning fifty was an emotional day
Not for the usual reasons
The grey hair, the wrinkles, or forgetfulness
But it was the age I had bargained for that very night
Of course there had been no answer to my plea
And with that, I was sent home
Seventy-six stitches kept my head together
After the skilled hands had taken my skull apart
The nerves severed, veins moved, and brain tissue pushed aside
A bone was taken out to get deeper down
To the Circle of Willis, deep in the brain, to the tip of my brainstem
Where vessels had fused, possibly since birth
And had now exploded in my brain
A bone strangely "floating" behind my ear
Where lesions of scar tissue have formed
A constant sensation of "pins and needles" lining my skin
Headaches, 24/7, make up my day
Sleeping on my belly forever part of the past
Learning to sleep on my back with my head tilted "just so"
Would turn out to be a most challenging task
Anything to avoid that deep cutting pain from that morning

That day when I was told I had suffered a massive brain bleed
Maybe once a month the pain lets me be
That day I can breathe, and hope that my wish has been heard
The other many days of the moon cycle
I would fear, hide, cover up, and live the day
As so many of us would, when given no other choice
Because eighteen years ago, at age thirty-two, I faced death
And made a bargain with God
"Just let me live to be fifty so my kids will be OK"

—Astrid Hendren, January 25, 2015
Medfield, Massachusetts, U.S.A.

PART I

Brain Bleed

Can Butterflies Smell?

The events of that day are etched in my brain. Nothing could have prepared me. On May 7, 1997, I was driving home from Home Depot with my daughter. We'd purchased yet another piece of fencing, which I hoped would help keep my children safe in our backyard, which bordered a small pond. Driving on a small country road in Sharon, Massachusetts, we'd soon pass our favorite local farm, called Wards Berry Farm, a place we often visited, because we lived so close. We loved petting the farm animals and we'd buy fresh fruits and vegetables. When we were just a mile from home, my precocious almost-three-year-old asked, "Mommy, can butterflies smell?" I peered at her in my rearview mirror. I always kept it tilted so I could make eye contact with my girls in the back seat without having to turn my head. Audrey's bright blue eyes gazed at me expectantly, her blond curls framing her face. She was one of those toddlers who capture people's attention with unusually deep questions and observations. She once remarked that crying happened because the clouds inside the person were too full of rain.

She was waiting for an answer. All I could feel was a hot, tingling sensation in the back of my head. I didn't yet label it as pain, but it stopped me from forming a coherent thought. The sensation had come on quickly and overpowered me. Within a few seconds the burning sensation had turned into deep, overwhelming pain. "I'm sorry, honey, Mommy can't answer that right now," I stammered. "I have a bad headache." My intuitive little girl sat back quietly in her seat. I turned my attention back to the road. The last mile home seemed like a journey to another continent.

The sensation in the back of my head was so intense that I would have had difficulty describing it. A "ten" on a medical pain scale would not have done it justice. Pulling into our driveway, I was grateful that my parents, who'd been visiting from Holland for a few weeks, could take over the care of my little girl. She'd been silent for the last five minutes of the ride. I told my parents I had a bad headache and needed to lie down and take some Ibuprofen. Many weeks later I would learn that Ibuprofen, which is a blood-thinner, probably did not help my situation. But I knew nothing about blood thinners, high blood pressure, or disease of any kind. I was thirty-two years old, a mom of two little kids. I was in great shape, and in the prime of my life.

I took the pain killer and filled a rubber water bottle with hot water to try to give my neck some comfort. I lay on my bed for ten minutes, then went to the living room, where I tried to make some phone calls and take care of everyday business. I had an executive search consulting practice, and needed to let my primary client know that I would be out sick the rest of the day. Steve Garfinkle at Chestnut Hill Partners had known me for years. When I told his wife Barbara that I was going to be out, she sounded concerned. She knew how rare it was for me to take a sick day.

Next, I called the doctor's office to make an appointment. "We have no openings left today," the receptionist said.

I said that the pain was terrible; they simply had to make time for me.

She told me if it was that bad to go to the emergency room. I hung up the phone and leaned back in the chair in my living room, the pain in the back of my head so intense that I could barely make a plan for what to do next.

It had just been Easter. The decorations were still all around me: a pretty soft-yellow tablecloth on the dining room table, Easter baskets with leftover candy on the window sill, and a bunny-shaped bowl with fragrant purple hyacinths on the coffee table.

I'd always loved the holiday: it felt like a new beginning. Easter meant spring was almost here, and to me that meant the smell of flowers, blossoming trees, and girls in pretty dresses. But most of all, at Easter I could recreate some of my favorite traditions from childhood. The girls and I colored eggs for a whole day, and on Easter morning we hid them for the girls to find, along with other eggs that held surprises. I took great care in making Easter baskets, and filled them with candy and chocolate eggs, little toys, and sometimes a little stuffed animal. Years ago, I owned a company, "All Things Dutch." At Easter I imported seasonal specialties, including gold, blue, and pink foil-wrapped eggs, and the finest chocolate bunnies. I always made a big deal about inviting family and friends for this holiday, hoping that my daughters would remember Easter as a happy holiday, just as I did.

This year, in which the girls would turn one and three, I'd continued another beloved tradition from my childhood. Just as my mother had done for me, I took them shopping to find new Easter dresses. My mother had always put curls in my long hair, too; I remember feeling so pretty, all dressed up.

Today, sitting in my chair in the living room, my head pounding, I recalled the girls' and my trip to Sears, where I bought them matching pink outfits. They were so proud to wear them. The pictures of that Easter weekend were sitting on my coffee table, a testament to a lovely holiday indeed.

Nobody could have predicted what lay ahead.

Audrey and Amy, December 1996   Astrid and girls 1997, just weeks before the aneurysm ruptured

Just Drop Me Off

My mother looked panicked when she came into the living room to check on me. She told me later that my eyes had been rolling back into my head and all the color had drained from my face.

The Dutch don't meet emergencies with the same urgency that Americans do. At the time, in 1997, the socialist health care system in Holland, for example, didn't provide an equivalent to 911, a way of making emergency calls. When I was growing up, people rarely visited emergency rooms because family physicians still made house calls, and doctors still took patients to the hospital in their own cars if needed. People still don't worry about liability and doctors rarely get sued. If something goes wrong, patients don't blame medical staff; this would be the last thing on their minds. I know of horror stories in which doctors' negligence clearly led to deaths, and yet the families still worshipped and adored the physicians. They continued to trust these family doctors without question.

My parents did not know they could call 911 and I didn't even think of it. So when I asked my dad if he could take me to the nearest hospital, he put on his coat and found the car keys, just as he would have in Holland.

I'd been to an emergency room several times before, and knew that I probably had hours of waiting and tests ahead of me.

"Just drop me off," I said to my dad when we got there. I

promised to call when the tests were done.

My sweet father drove home. He has probably regretted it ever since. I hobbled to the receptionist's window. "My headache is so bad I can hardly see," I said.

The receptionist, a plump middle-aged woman with dirty blond hair, looked bored. She handed me a stack of paperwork without looking at me. "Probably a migraine," she said.

Bewildered, I sat in the chair at the registration desk. I felt my body getting heavy. I tried to turn my attention to the questions on the paper, but the letters merged together. I felt frustrated and very nauseous. How could they ask me to do this when I was in so much pain?

"I can't do this," I said. "Please get me a doctor."

The woman insisted I needed to get the paperwork filled out, as it would give the hospital permission to treat me. I felt the urge to vomit. I could feel myself beginning to faint. From the corner of my eye I spied a man in a white coat striding past me. I leaned back and grabbed his coat. I muttered, "Please help me. The pain in my head is so bad."

Then I vomited all over him.

He screamed at the woman behind the window: "Get this woman into a scanner!"

My world went blank.

Bad News

A few hours later, the same doctor stood at my bedside. He had a pleasant face, blue eyes, red hair, and a strong Irish accent. I'll never forget his words: "I have bad news for you," he said. "You had a massive brain bleed and are scheduled to have emergency brain surgery within the next two hours." I took those words in, while studying his face; this gentle man was fighting tears. It seemed that his news should have caused an emotional response from me. And yet, it triggered an opposite reaction in me, one that would ultimately save my life: a fierce practicality.

"Well, don't you think I should be transported to one of the major hospitals then?" I said.

He seemed taken aback. "Of course, that is your choice," he said. "We'll wait for your husband. I called him and he should be here in forty-five minutes."

I had asked my dad to drive me to the nearest hospital. I'd wanted to make things easy for him. So here I lay in our small, local hospital. Despite my pain and confusion, I still had the presence of mind to realize that this might not be the best place to have surgery. I was fortunate, after all, to live near Boston, home to many of the best hospitals in the world.

About a half hour later, the same doctor reappeared with what seems in retrospect like astonishing news: He said that the brain surgeon on call had decided, after studying the angiogram that he would not need to operate. Instead, my body needed to absorb the blood that had flooded both ventricles of my brain. This doctor with the strong Irish accent was clearly struggling with his emotions; he told me that nurses would help me get up, and that I would most likely be going home the next day.

Lying in bed, listening to his words, I wasn't sure what to think. Going home seemed like a positive development. But, I asked him, how could I be sent home when I still had such excruciating pain? He explained that a lot of blood was pressing against my brain, causing symptoms similar to those associated with encephalitis. The nurses would give me pain medication, he said. I tried to describe how severe this was: I had given birth to two children, without any pain medication. I told him that I would rather give birth ten more times than have another minute of this searing pain. He didn't answer.

My Bargain

My husband appeared in the doorway about an hour later. Before he said a word, I reassured him: "Don't worry, I've already paid the co-payment." He was easily frustrated and often called me a hypochondriac. The thought of his coming down on me right then was more than I could handle, so I tried to play things cool. He said he'd called a friend of ours, a doctor in a post-acute rehab facility, to get his opinion. He asked my nurse where we could get a copy of the images that had been taken when my head had been scanned; she directed him to an office in the basement.

I don't remember seeing him much after that. I honestly don't know where he was. At the time, I assumed he was with our kids most of the time. But I discovered years later that my parents took care of the kids; they'd assumed that my husband was with me in the hospital.

Late in the afternoon, they moved my bed from the emergency floor to a "regular" room. I was by myself that night, contemplating the idea that I might die. I realized that I'd never prepared for this. I was young and healthy, after all, and while the thought of writing a will had crossed my mind, I'd always been comforted by the notion that because I didn't own much, a will wasn't much necessary. I had arrived in the United States at the age of nineteen, with one suitcase and $100 in cash, and had worked many jobs. I'd managed to live the American dream in my own way, through hard work and careful saving. But in this moment, thoughts of my mortality took on new meaning: I had two children who needed me for guidance and care. I became painfully aware that I hadn't told anyone the things I wanted my kids to know: practical things, intimate details, and the lessons I had learned in my life. I wondered who might tell them for me if I was not here.

I asked the nurse if I could make a phone call. In 1997, few people had cell phones yet, and the room did not have a TV or a phone. Later that night she brought one and plugged it into the wall of my room. I left a message for the one person I felt I could trust with such heavy and troubling thoughts. Not my mother or a good friend; I didn't want to worry them even more. Instead, I called the marriage counselor my husband and I had visited after I had initiated a separation before our children had even been born. This was after just seven years of marriage. We had decided to give our relationship another try.

This counselor had become a crucial person in my life; he knew more about my emotional wellbeing, worries, and fears than anyone else. When he called back, he was clearly touched by my request to make sure my girls would get counseling if something happened to me. But he explained that professional ethics would bar him from reaching out to my children or husband if I died. My husband would have to initiate the contact.

I felt anxious. At the end of the call, I said, "Well, I will just have to stick around."

This conversation, difficult as it was, strengthened my resolve to survive; I realized that I *couldn't* die—there was too much to do in life. I was needed. My only option was to live.

I asked the nurse for a pen and paper and wrote a letter to

a high school friend in the Netherlands named Agnes whom I hadn't seen in many years. She was on my mind because she had visited me for a couple months when I was building "All Things Dutch" years earlier, before my children were born. During her visit, Agnes had received a phone call informing her that her older brother had suffered a rupture of an aneurysm and died shortly after. Now, in hindsight, having suffered a brain bleed myself, I realized that I hadn't been much of a friend to her during her great sadness and loss. It was strange to think that my family could be in her shoes in the next day or so, grieving my death. I never actually sent the three-page letter I wrote to Agnes that night in my hospital bed. It was lost in the shuffle of my illness, and somehow stored away in my attic. I found it this past January. My handwriting in the letter is almost illegible, most likely due to the pressure and pain the blood was causing in my brain when I wrote it.

That night, lying in my hospital bed, my head pounding, I prayed. I promised the universe that I would give back if I was allowed to live. I promised that my life would be valuable to others, and that I would serve. I promised that I would be kind, and true to myself, and to the world—that I would "do good" in my life.

I asked God to please let me live. To allow me to turn fifty, so my daughters would be 18 and 20, so they could take care of themselves, and I could be the example they needed. I asked God to let me live long enough to teach them, while I taught others. I would serve, should my silent prayers to survive be answered. I cried softly until the sheets around me were wet from tears. Finally I fell asleep.

Circle of Willis

The next morning a group of doctors stopped by and told me that I apparently had no specific neurological damage from the brain bleed. They said this was a miracle compared to what was expected under the circumstances. The stroke I had suffered would have to resolve itself. They explained nothing more, and I didn't probe. I had no idea what to ask; they were the experts, after all. Meanwhile the pain had subsided some—but the idea of getting up and putting on my clothes to go home seemed absurd. I needed assistance just getting out of bed and making it to the bathroom.

It would be many months before I learned about the different types of strokes. An "ischemic stroke" is the most common; it's caused by a clot, which blocks the supply of blood to the brain. The clot usually results from high cholesterol or high blood pressure. My stroke however, was a "hemorrhagic stroke"—a fancy term for a brain bleed. This type of stroke is less common but far more deadly. Mine resulted from a ruptured aneurysm inside my brain. An aneurysm can occur anywhere in the brain (as well as in other places like the abdomen or heart). It's like a garden hose that weakens and bulges, and finally leaks or bursts. Aneurysms are often located in the frontal lobe, in places that can be fairly easily operated on and "clipped" or "coiled." When it is clipped, the surgeon clamps the base of the weakened or ruptured vessel. Scar tissue forms there and reinforces the wall, preventing (one

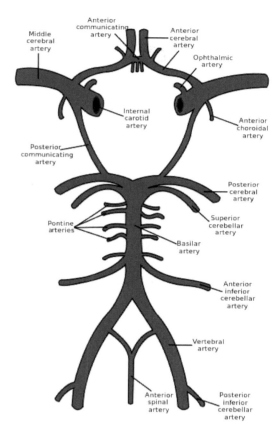

"Circle of Willis en" by Rhcastilhos - Gray519.png. Licensed under Public Domain via Commons—
https://commons.wikimedia.org/wiki/File:Circle_of_Willis_en.svg#/media/File:Circle_of_Willis_en.svg

hopes) a new rupture. Instead of a clip, a surgeon may insert a coil into the weakened artery and achieve the same results.

Sometimes the aneurysm, unfortunately, is located in a more difficult location. It could be inside a malformation called an AVM—a tangle of blood vessels that complicates blood flow. An AVM is a complex area, and I have since learned that surgery inside such a malformation is exceeding difficult. To make matters worse, sometimes an AVM forms right at the tip of the brainstem, which is basically the command center of the body. The vessels in this area are called the Circle of Willis—a group of arteries in a circular shape, which supply blood to the brain and surrounding structures. An aneurysm may grow there over time. If it ruptures, it's in a uniquely dangerous location both for a bleed as well as for surgery. This type of aneurysm has a very high mortality rate. It was probably a good thing that I didn't know all this at the time. I heard much later from someone that the surgeon who had seen my first angiogram concluded that, if his reading of the scans was accurate, he could not do anything for me, it was considered inoperable. This meant that in essence my first husband who called our friend Robert Van Strien had saved my life because of that initiative.

Crayons

I had arrived at the small local hospital on a Tuesday morning, and would have been sent home on Wednesday if not for our friend Dr. Robert Van Strien. He was the rehabilitation doctor my husband had thought to consult. My husband had received a copy of my angiogram that first day at the hospital, and had brought it home. Robert, our friend, took a look at it. My parents would say later that Robert had sat in our living room, studying the images, not saying much. But he mumbled things like, "Something doesn't look right." This made them very worried.

He took the stack of images to Boston, where, late that night, Dr. Philip Stieg scrutinized them. Dr. Stieg was the Associate Chief of Neurosurgery at the Brigham and Women's Hospital, one of the flagship Harvard teaching hospitals. He determined that I would need a three-dimensional angiogram for him to confirm what he suspected—that I had a ruptured aneurysm inside an AVM—and to determine if he could even attempt surgery.

At the time, a three-dimensional angiogram could be done in only a couple of hospitals in the world, one of which was the Brigham and Women's Hospital in Boston. A typical angiogram showed a two-dimensional picture, which they had done at the local hospital, and which did not show the aneurysm inside the malformation in my brain. On Wednesday afternoon, the nurses at the local hospital were trying to get me up and dressed to go home. But we got news that Dr. Stieg wanted me to transfer from the local hospital to "the Brigham." The plan was to transfer me the next morning. Staying in place one more night would allow my brain to absorb some more of the blood that had flooded both my ventricles; I could "stabilize" a bit more.

I was now in a room on the regular floor of the local hospital. I remember feeling as if I'd been alone for hours—I got much less attention here than in the ICU—but I took comfort in thinking that the lack of attention meant I was out of danger.

Since I would be transferred to Boston the next day, my parents stopped by with the girls in this nearby small hospital. When they appeared in the door of my hospital room, they were each holding one of my girls. I had just received my pain medications and felt confused and irritable. I hugged each of my girls, but I could feel their little bodies stiffen, and felt them almost push me away. I held them tight, but I could see the fear in their eyes. I fought tears, and pretended that I suddenly had to go to the bathroom. I let them go and they sat on my parents' lap in the chairs next to my bed. In the bathroom I did my best to pull myself together and went back to the bed. Audrey brought crayons and asked if I would draw pictures with her. I told her my head still hurt too much. I saw worry and surprise in her eyes. It suddenly occurred to me that I had not considered what my kids and my parents would feel, seeing me in this scary place.

I hadn't been concerned about my girls' care and wellbeing: My parents were such wonderful grandparents. But now, together in this hospital room, I saw myself through my daughters' eyes, in this bed, IVs sticking out of me, monitors beeping constantly. The girls were clearly horrified. After a short visit, I took my mom aside. I told her in a thick voice that I needed her to take care of my babies by taking them away from me. She looked at me, tears in her eyes, and promised she would. I knew that my mom would protect and nurture my girls as if they were her own. Both my parents would also use the task I entrusted them with to distract themselves from the horrible events that had unfolded—from the possible death of their daughter. The knowledge that my parents would take care of my daughters was all I needed to resign myself to the fact that I needed to do this on my own. I had quickly decided I should not see my girls again until I could walk into my house on my own two feet. Seeing their mother like this was traumatic; I had to get through this myself.

Ride to Heaven

I arrived at Brigham and Women's Hospital by ambulance on Thursday morning. The pain in my head seemed more intense with every bump in the road. The soft-spoken EMT, a middle-aged woman with hazel green eyes, and thick, short, black hair, attended to my every groan with concern. Every few minutes she updated me on how much longer I'd have to endure the ride. We passed familiar landmarks: the Faulkner Hospital, The Arnold Arboretum in Jamaica Plain, and Jamaica Pond, which was across the street from the home of my husband's older brother, his wife, and their child. I could see through the back window that cars were pulling over, but I couldn't hear any sirens or see the lights.

Arriving at the Brigham and Women's Hospital Emergency Room entrance on Francis Street, I felt the gurney lurch as the EMTs rolled me inside. People were already waiting to take me to the Intensive Care Unit on the ninth floor of the "hospital tower." I felt exhausted. In my new room, they lifted me into bed and hooked me up to an array of monitors and IVs. Before long, a young resident came by. He was quite tall, had short light brown hair and bore a striking resemblance to the son of our Queen in Holland, Crown Prince Willem Alexander. In any case, he "looked Dutch," and therefore had already made me feel better just though his presence; he felt familiar. He was gentle when performing a neurological exam, which consisted of a series of questions and tests. He asked me my name, how old I was, what day it was, and he asked me why I was here. Then he told me to follow his finger with my eyes as he moved it to the far right of my field of vision; next he moved it to the left. He asked me to squeeze his hands and he looked in my eyes with a special instrument.

The whole exam took about ten minutes. His manner was calm and patient. "I don't find any neurological damage, which is great," he finally said. The resident was Craig Van Horne; he'd later become a respected neurosurgeon. As I consider his name these years later—"Van Horne," which is kind of like "Smith" or "Jones" for an American—I realize that he probably is of Dutch descent. He would stop by many times that day, ask me the same questions, and test me for neurological changes.

About an hour after he left, I was taken down to the lower level of the hospital to have the three-dimensional angiogram. The process entailed making an incision in my groin and sliding a tiny catheter into a main artery. The catheter slid through my artery up to my neck, where it delivered radioactive dye, through which a device captured images from inside my head. The imaging took about forty-five minutes. Performing the test would allow the medical staff to see a three-dimensional picture of my brain and the blood vessels around it and supplying it. It was the only kind of imaging that could detect my aneurysm, let alone pinpoint it inside the malformation. The test itself was quite risky; I was somewhat sedated to make sure I didn't move much.

I knew this test was intended to confirm and clarify diagnostic information and would tell the doctors at the Brigham and Women's Hospital what was really going on in my head and what could be done about it.

That Thursday morning seemed endless—getting transported, settling in my new bed, the tests, the probing. At one o'clock an attractive doctor walked into the room. His name-tag read: "Dr. Philip Stieg, Associate Chief of Neurosurgery." Slender and tall, he had friendly blue eyes, blond hair, and an engaging and reassuring smile. His confident demeanor put me at ease. His bedside manner was direct and honest. This style worked well for me; I'd never liked to sugarcoat things. In hindsight, I am sure that, by the time patients get to Dr. Stieg, he knows he can only save those who have the attitude to face the dire statistics that come with the diagnoses and risks associated with his work.

Dr. Stieg looked serious as he stood by my bed and said: "I'm not going to lie to you, this will be a very tough surgery. I'll need every top person on this team and they'll need to be well rested." He went on to tell me that he'd found what he'd feared: I indeed had an AVM—a malformation of blood vessels—at the tip of my brainstem. My ruptured aneurysm was inside that AVM, two inches deep into my brain.

He told me that since the malformation was located at the tip of the brain stem, it would be extremely difficult and risky to access. I learned that the majority of people with this particular kind of aneurysm die immediately when it ruptures. Most of those who survive have subsequent bleeds soon after—and this kills them. Dr. Stieg made it clear that if I did not have surgery, I would be one of those people. Meanwhile, he explained those survivors who underwent surgery, and survived it, have a high risk of disability because of the complicated location, and possible death from vascular spasms in the weeks after the surgery. I got the message loud and clear: my chances for survival were slim, and my chances of fully functioning if I did survive were even slimmer.

Dr. Stieg told me that he would open my skull on the back, left side of my head. He planned to remove a piece of bone from behind my ear and move all the layers of nerves and brain tissue until he could get to the aneurysm. He took a slight breath, looked directly at me, and turned very serious, "Worst case scenario," he said, "I won't be able to get to it, in which case I will sew you back up and you will go home and most likely have only a few weeks to live." He paused for a minute to let me take in those words.

I think he was encouraged that I hadn't broken down in tears so far. I waited for his next words, which I hoped would be the good news. He gently put his arm on the bed railing and touched my hand. He continued in a soft voice. "Best case scenario: I get to the malformation, and to the aneurysm, and I'm able to clip it. I sew you back up and you could possibly go home on Friday."

I took a deep breath. "Well, I hear you're the best in town," I said. "Why don't you do your job and I'll do mine."

He smiled. "That's a plan. We will do another angiogram this afternoon and monitor you closely."

The strategy, he said, was to allow more of the blood that had invaded my ventricles to be absorbed before the operation. This was painful, but it would allow my body to stabilize and my blood pressure, which was high, to come down a bit. The team would be ready for surgery on Monday morning at 7. Dr. Stieg assured me, "If anything happens in the meantime, like another bleed, we will perform emergency surgery right away. I'll check on you every day, and Dr. Van Horne will be in charge of the neurological exams. Any questions?"

I managed a smile. "No, just get it done."

Heaven or Hell

On Saturday morning, things seemed to be getting worse. The
pain had become unbearable. Only closing my eyes brought any
relief. When I did shut my eyes, I no longer felt anything. Later I
was told that I'd been slipping in and out of a coma. In that state,
with my eyes closed, I felt first as if I were on a long slide. Next
the slide's angle changed; it straightened out ahead of me, like a
tunnel. The tunnel changed; it became a large open space, somehow circular and multi-dimensional. I noticed people from my
past and current life, and people I didn't know. My husband was
working on something I couldn't see: he had his back turned to
me. I saw my grandmother clearly; she had died at age 59 from
cancer. She had not been involved much in our lives because she
had treated my mother badly. I had always missed not having a
grandmother present in my life. Her dog Lassie stood by her. It
was as if I passed these people or figures and floated toward a soft
light ahead of me. The floating figures had light blond hair and
were dressed in flowing white robes—a soothing image. They all
seemed to be surrounded by warm light. Everything I saw was
peaceful and beautiful—a lovely experience.

I tried to reach the end of the road, but the way went on and on.
The distance didn't change, but the light and the surroundings did.
The soft light surrounded me; the floating figures were coming
close. I gazed at the soft colors and at the people I passed. A man

with a small beard and a robe the color of burlap bags—Jesus, or perhaps what I imagined he would look like—floated in the large open space. He smiled kindly, but was too far away to reach. I recall vividly that the journey through the first part of the tunnel seemed fast, as if I were twirling through it and past the floating images. All around me, I saw people—ones I'd played with when I was little, and others whom I did not recognize; all of them had gentle and kind expressions on their faces. My own two girls were there, just as I had left them a few days before, in their present form and at their present age.

Moving through the multidimensional space, with the soft light surrounding me, activity seemed to slow down, and with that, the space around me became larger, and ever more beautiful.

The images from that day have stayed with me. I haven't told a lot of people about the experience because it didn't seem news-worthy. I was too busy trying to survive. Also, I couldn't find words for the experience. I was not a particularly religious person, although spiritual, and had never experienced God as a presence in my everyday life. But I was worried about dying, and I needed help. It seems plausible to me that I was trying to find hope, and the strength to survive.

I decided to put the vivid memory aside after my surgery. But it kept coming back into my awareness, whenever I had time to reflect. Eventually—about two years after my stroke—I started looking for a medical explanation. I read a bunch of books. *How We Die* by Sherwin Nuland made the most sense to me. It helped me understand, from a medical perspective, how the brain and body shut down when dying. It explained why and how im-ages such as the ones I had experienced might arise. Perhaps surprisingly, the scientific explanation didn't make the memory less comforting. In fact, it validated my experience as real; I discovered how close I had been to death.

I didn't read Nuland's and the other books in order to explore the possibility of an afterlife. I didn't feel the need to. My near-death experience occupied my thoughts because it had showed me that dying itself is peaceful and painless and, most important, timeless. This was a powerful and comforting revelation. My near-death experience happened during a time of pain so unbearable, that I couldn't open my eyes or move one tiny muscle. Yet those moments in the tunnel, with its soft white light and floating people, were peaceful and happy. I felt no fear, nor pain. The moment seemed infinite; I was outside of time; I felt no hurry and no suffering. My knowledge and memory of that place and its magic will forever be a comfort to me: both in preparation for my own death, as well as the death of loved ones.

Code Red

That Saturday morning, something had gone wrong. I've never asked anyone what triggered the next events, but I remember being wheeled down the hallway so fast that my hospital bed nearly hit the double doors at the end of the hallway. The elevator ride down to L2 was difficult. I felt like my surroundings were buzzing and loud. Two people pushed my bed into a dark room. Someone told me that I was about to have another angiogram. In hindsight, I wonder if the "slipping into a coma" was concurrent with my experience in the tunnel, and triggered this decision for another angiogram. Perhaps they worried I had suffered another brain bleed.

At this point, I had undergone at least four angiograms and remember the technicians from each one. In fact, the faces of these acute caregivers will be with me forever. After each procedure, they'd put a heavy lead blanket on my leg. They'd leave it there for four hours to apply pressure and keep the leg still. This practice helped ensure that the incision in my groin closed up. A couple of times a doctor even sat on my leg to help speed the process. During one of the angiograms, a technician came to my bedside and asked if I would allow them to use a new technology, a plug made of cow bladder or something. I declined, explaining that I already felt like an experiment, thank you, and would rather not gamble with my odds. I was pretty drugged each time they performed an angiogram. On this last, urgent occasion, having been rushed down to the lower floor of the hospital, I vaguely noticed panic on the faces of people around me, but could focus only on my terrible headache.

On Saturday afternoon, after the angiogram, Dr. Stieg came to visit. He brought his children to say hi. I was secretly shocked that he would bring such young children into my hospital room. I felt bad for them, having to come in on a Saturday to see someone as sick as me, a complete stranger to them. But I have to admit that it was a welcome sight to see young life and genuine smiles. They reminded me of Tommy and Annika from the Pippi Longstocking movies I'd loved as a child—perhaps seven and nine years old, with blond hair, blue eyes, and fair skin. Dr. Stieg said that everything was still on schedule for Monday morning and to rest as much as I could.

Mother's Day

The nurses in the intensive care unit at the Brigham were wonderful. I particularly remember two sweet-souled male nurses, and my gratitude for their small gestures of kindness, their gentle care. My brother Ron had flown in on Friday from Texas, where he was a flight instructor "on loan" from the Dutch Air Force to the U.S. Air Force. But he'd been grounded due to his worries and distress over my brain bleed. Here in the hospital, he was a godsend, sitting next to my bed for what seemed like endless hours, day and night. I felt safe in his presence; he provided peace and comfort in a strange, sterile, noisy place. Meanwhile, my parents were still at home with my babies. Apparently my twin brother and his wife had flown from Holland and arrived sometime that weekend, but I don't remember seeing them. The doctors may have limited visitors to keep me quiet in preparation for the surgery. Johanneke, the wife of our doctor-friend Robert Van Strien, had called my twin brother and said to come immediately. He'd replied that he would rather come when I was recovering; they did not have enough money to come twice. She told him he needed to come now; I might not recover, and there was a good chance he wouldn't see me again.

Robert Van Strien had stopped by on Friday night, and I'd asked that visitors stay away. I was worried that I'd see fear in their eyes, which would not be helpful to me. In sum, their visits would complicate things: I was trying to go about this matter-of-factly. There was a job to be done and I needed to focus and believe it was possible.

In the middle of the night I was awakened by loud noises and commotion.

Nurses rushed by in the hall. I could see from my bed that something was happening that had everyone in uproar. Much later that night, I asked a nurse what had happened. He looked at me sadly and answered, "The young mom next door who suffered a stroke while trying to deliver a baby passed away." The sorrow in his eyes undoubtedly reflected his concern for the poor mother and her family, but in my small world here in the hospital tower—a place reserved for the worst cases—it felt like death was almost expected. I could be next.

I didn't sleep the rest of the night, and in the morning was glad to hear my brother's voice as he arrived. He kissed my cheek.

"Happy Mother's Day!" he said.

This wish, while well-intended, hit me like a brick. For the first time since my massive brain bleed five days earlier, I felt fear and anger. I answered bitterly. "Yes, what a great Mother's day," I said, closing my eyes, trying to keep myself together. My only comfort in that moment was the notion that this painful ordeal had happened to me and not to one of my kids. I lay there with my eyes closed, thankful they were spared, and knew deep down that I could only handle this challenge *because* it happened to me. I convinced myself this was much easier. I had a job to do *because* I was a mother. I needed to use my energy to survive, not allow myself to feel despair, anger, or fear.

Worrier or Warrior?

When your native language is different from the one you use every day, it's fascinating to watch which words the brain chooses to describe a particular emotion or situation. The choice of words often comes up short in either language, a curse, for me, of learning a first language at birth, immigrating to another country as a young adult, and learning the second language in which I conduct my life. People like me have learned mostly child-like words—and few adult or business words—in our first language; we stopped learning new words in our native tongue when we left our home country. The trouble is compounded because we learn the new language without having ever learned the formal foundation of grammar and vocabulary for that second language.

Another interesting phenomenon is that in English, the slightest difference in spelling of a word can translate into a completely different meaning. Because English is my second language these slight differences come up in my life almost daily, and it is something I wonder about often. For example, in my journal-writing about my stroke, I reflect on how I am a "worrier"; I tend to worry a lot about the people I care for. Yet when writing about it, my brain constantly wanted to choose the word "warrior." Of course, both applied, and it would make me ponder the meaning of each word for a long time after writing it.

PART II

Home

The First Day of the Rest of My Life

I don't recall much of the morning they saved my life. They must have sedated me: I didn't feel worried at all. I don't recollect saying goodbyes or thinking that "good luck" was needed. I was just eager to get this thing done. Perhaps I have blocked those memories or was just focused on what lay ahead. I do remember being wheeled to and arriving in the operating room; it seemed pleasant. I recall seeing Dr. Stieg before he'd been scrubbed and gowned. The room seemed very bright, the people around me in good spirits. This reassured me. I am not sure if medical professionals realize how much their body language at such crucial moments affects the mental status of patients and their ability to fight; I will say that it made a big difference to me. The pleasant atmosphere and the air of confidence in the room helped me trust, relax, breathe, and let them do their job.

—

Regaining consciousness, while still in the operating recovery room, I found panic all around me. At least three people were screaming and yanking on belts and handles near me. I heard a man scream in a deep voice, "Are you stupid? Are you kidding me? She survived the surgery and now she is going to die of pneumonia!"

A face with a concerned expression appeared near my eyes,

and I felt strong hands reach beneath me, lift my body, and slam me back down on my side. I felt a hot sensation on my right shoulder. This turned out to be a belt that had strapped my body to the bed. I retched. Black stuff spewed from my mouth and onto the recovery bed.

From the corner of my eye I spied the nurse they'd been yelling at, who stood by, looking helpless and panicked. She seemed older, and worn out. Her short, reddish, grey hair was mostly covered by her hospital uniform hat; her skin was pale; she looked like she was ready to cry. Then everything went blank.

I awoke to the same burning sensation in my shoulder. I'd discover days later that the flipping of my body had caused a nasty burn on my right shoulder; it would take days to heal. Nobody really had time, of course, to pay attention to such insignificant details. They were just trying to make sure I lived.

That morning, Monday, May 13, 1997, at 7:00 a.m., a surgical team of incredible doctors and anesthesiologists had taken on the mission of saving my life. The skill and resolve required to saw open someone's skull, move brain tissue, cut nerves and muscle, and place a titanium clip on an artery wall, inside a defect that had possibly been there since birth—this, to me, is miraculous. It could lead you to believe that God is at work.

The surgery took seven hours and, aside from the scary event when I had aspirated—inhaling bodily fluids into my lungs, with the risk of drowning, or dying of a pneumonia infection—I don't remember much detail until I was moved to a recovery room in the intensive care unit. My brother Ron would return to my bedside soon after. Nurses came in and out, but Ron would be with me the whole time. He sat in the corner, and if I groaned or moved, he jumped to my bedside. He seemed to know instinctively what I needed, since I could not speak. It was not clear yet why I could not speak, I was told that a breathing tube had been in my body during the surgery. The tube can cause damage to the vocal cords. But the concern about possible damage had already been discussed in context of the enormous complexity of the location of the ruptured aneurysm and the need to move brain tissue to get to it. Even I knew that at this point, it was a waiting game, and my body needed time to heal and recover from the invasive operation. But the frustration I experienced because of the inability to move and speak, and the difficulty I had with simple functions like swallowing and breathing, were petrifying. I could hear and see everything around me, but I couldn't tell anybody what I needed, wanted, or how bad the pain was. I was completely at the mercy of people around me.

My mouth was dry, and every time I moved my lips, my brother would dip a wooden stick into a cup of water. The stick had a tiny, bright-blue piece of sponge attached to its end. Over and over, he ran the moistened sponge along my lips and inside of my mouth. Ron did not talk much, but picked up quickly on my body language, and signaled a nurse when I was in discomfort or needed to be attended to.

The simple gestures with the wooden stick and sponge, with a cool face cloth, his holding my hand—these became welcome ways to occupy my time. I was so grateful to have the interaction with and gentle care from my big brother.

Late in the evening, a nurse entered the room. Seeing her face, I was overcome with a feeling of panic. "I'm the night nurse," she said to my brother. "You can feel free to go home anytime."

I recognized her instantly: This was the woman who was yelled at that morning by the man with the deep voice. He had said that I might die because of what she did, or did not do. I wasn't sure, but flashing back to the chaos, I felt terrified. In retrospect, I can only imagine how enormously stressful the jobs of these acute caregivers are. They must cope with difficult emotions, and are pushed to limits, caring for patients like me. I imagine how high the stress levels must be, trying to care for someone they have just met, who they know has little chance of living a normal life. Any mistake could mean death for that patient. I have also learned in my research that patients with brain trauma sometimes behave aggressively, lashing out, rattling even the most seasoned practitioners.

Seeing the nurse come in, I was reminded of hearing those words, "die" and "pneumonia." My heart pounded; I groaned. My brother was talking politely to the nurse, apparently ready to say goodnight. I felt powerless; he was going leave me with this woman and, I was sure, I would die. Hearing my groans, my brother realized that something was upsetting me, but it was hard for him to understand. He reached for my hand. I squeezed it hard.

"She's upset about something and she doesn't want me to leave," he said to the nurse. She left the room. He turned to me. "Do you not want me to leave?" I squeezed his hand again. He knew something was different because I hadn't done this before.

The nurse came back in with medicine. I squeezed Ron's hand hard again. He realized that my distress had something to do with the nurse. "I think she doesn't want you here. I think she's afraid of you. Is there any way we can have a different night nurse?" The woman did not say a word, but left the room.

I calmed down instantly. My brother had understood my fear

and taken care of it. A young male nurse whom I recognized from the weekend came into the room and announced that he would be there for me instead. Grateful, I relaxed and fell asleep.

For the next couple of days I tried to cope with the pain and thirst—and the frustration of not being able to speak. The minutes and hours turned into days, interspersed—in that herky-jerky rhythm of hospital life—with visits from doctors, nurses, teams of residents, and administrators.

A Beethoven symphony replayed in my brain day and night, even though there was no background music in my hospital room. I would hear incessant symphonic music for many months after my surgery. I had no idea why. Later I was told this was the sort of music Dr. Stieg liked to play when he performed surgery. Fortunately, for me, I enjoyed classical music. I imagine that this non-stop "elevator music" might easily drive someone else crazy during recovery. Instead, it brought me comfort and order. Sometimes the constancy of the music in my head felt like the only thing I could count on.

Rehab

Given the choice between entering a rehabilitation hospital and going home, I chose home. I now know this was not the wisest decision. But all I wanted was to get back to my children and to normal. I wished desperately to put this horrible chapter behind me, to go home and get on with my life. But I'd given no thought to how I'd achieve "normal"—how I would cope. Nobody else raised these questions, either. I think everyone at the hospital assumed that I had caregivers waiting for me at home.

I did have the insight that going straight home on Friday, just four days after my brain surgery, was probably not the best choice. But I had remembered my conversation with Dr. Stieg before the surgery when he told me about my chances of survival. When he said that best-case scenario meant I would go home on Friday, so it secretly became the day I wanted to be send home, as competitive as I am, to be seen as that "best-case scenario. So I asked to go to my husband's childhood home in Wellesley, Massachusetts, instead, for the weekend. His aunt, who was widowed, had raised him and his brothers after their mother had passed away when my husband was 13. She lived alone. In my distorted thinking, her beautiful one-level home, surrounded by peaceful gardens, would be an ideal place to spend a few days. I imagined myself going to a Swiss recovery resort, like the ones I'd read about in novels when I was a teenager. I'd rest and recuperate, and prepare for the reunion with my girls.

I complicated matters by asking if I could invite my husband's godmother, Pril, to drive down from Maine to help take care of me. Whenever we visited Pril in her house in Maine, she and I laughed a lot. Pril had treated me occasionally to special outings—to cities, dinners out, Broadway shows. I thought having her positive energy would help speed my recovery. I gave no thought to the fact that it was insensitive of me to invite myself to Aunt Caroline's house and then ask someone else to come and take care of me. I'm sure these kind women wanted only to accommodate my odd wishes. Of course I wasn't in the frame of mind to consider other people's feelings; I was in survival mode. And I was completely unprepared for the serious problems I'd encounter in the aftermath of brain surgery.

I hadn't considered the possibility that Pril wouldn't have the stomach for my fragile state and intense pain. Instead of caring for me as I vomited all night, she got sick herself. I ended up feeling lonely and scared. My pain was as bad as, if not worse than, the day I had gone to the hospital when my father dropped me off. I began to wonder if once again I was facing my end.

The prospect of getting home to my kids was my one comfort—and my driving motivation to keep faith. But my mind got stuck on the question of whether I should have "faith" or if this was my "fate." I felt tortured by word play. I also felt powerless—and irritated over my lack of control in the simplest things, like going to the bathroom and eating a meal.

A physical therapist came to Aunt Caroline's house on Saturday morning. She insisted that I do sit ups to strengthen the weakened muscles in my stomach. I could do no such thing, of course. I told her that my pain was excruciating, that my first night home had been horrible, and that I was getting sicker every hour. Still she insisted. I was intensely frustrated, trying to defend myself against this supposed expert, and wept.

I finally asked to call Sarah, the head nurse and assistant to Dr. Stieg, who had given us her personal number in case of an emergency. Sarah rushed to the house and called Dr. Stieg. His response was, "She just had brain surgery, of course she is having a lot of pain! She should be resting. No physical therapy!" Sarah fired the physical therapist.

It was probably just an administrative detail, but unfortunately, as a result of this incident, I believed I was no longer eligible for such services. Having grown up in the socialist system in Holland, I didn't even think to ask. Therapy of any kind was never really discussed; my case kind of fell through the cracks.

You Look Like a Biafran

Monday, just three days after being released from the hospital and one week post-surgery, my husband picked me up at his aunt's house in Wellesley. The ride home to Sharon, our small commuters town, would take just twenty minutes. We had moved to Sharon less then a year before. We knew few people because the girls were not even in preschool yet, and we did not belong to a church.

Lost in thought, hunched in the passenger seat of the car, I braced myself. Bumps and turns moved my head, which increased my agony. I took in the sights around me. During the last thirteen days, nature had burst forth: cherry blossoms and forsythia had bloomed; tulips and daffodils had sprung up everywhere. It was a bright sunny day. I felt incredible relief, and a near-desperation to get on with life. Going home meant I had survived. I could not wait to get home! It was May 20th, the day my oldest daughter, Audrey, had been born three years before. I realized that my sweetheart would not get the usual cake and party, but I promised myself we would celebrate soon. Driving down our street, seeing our house, my eyes welled with tears. I couldn't wait to be reunited with my two beautiful children. They had given me my will to survive.

We pulled into the driveway and I pulled myself out of the car. I stepped onto our driveway, leaning on my walker. The front door opened. Audrey stood in the doorway, holding my mother's hand.

Anxious as I'd been to get home to my babies, I hadn't considered that they might be scared by my appearance. I'd changed drastically in the two weeks I'd been away. My voice had a strange high pitch. I leaned on a walker. But I *could* talk, and I *could* walk.

I had also lost a lot of weight and muscle mass. My cheekbones were sticking out, and my nose seemed even more pronounced. My husband would admit a few days later that he couldn't hug me because of the drastic weight loss. He said that I looked "like a Biafran," referring to the sad images on TV of Biafran people dying of hunger as a result of the civil war in Nigeria. The comment was a bitter pill to swallow.

Fortunately, I didn't need to wear a hat or scarf to cover my surgical wound. Dr. Stieg had been proud that he'd left the outer layer of my long brown hair intact. He'd shaved the entire left side of my skull, but left a long sort of "comb-over" on top, which covered my enormous wound. The fact that he'd had the sensitivity to think of such a detail—so insignificant to my survival, yet so important to my emotional recovery—made him, to me, not only a great surgeon, but also an amazing human being. I'm sure that my children would have been terrified had they seen my shaved head with its enormous scar and seventy-six stitches.

Letting go of my mother's hand, Audrey screamed "Mommy!" I knelt. She hugged me, and I felt her warm little body, her tiny arms wrapped around me. Tears flowed down my cheeks. I remembered her birth, the midwife handing her to me, her little head resting on my chest. The gratitude and responsibility I felt to care for my girls was overwhelming. It was an incredible gift of joy to be here now, to hold my precious child.

My mother was holding Amy, my strawberry blond one-year-old

with beautiful green eyes. Amy clung to my mother's shoulder. I reached for my baby daughter. She turned towards me. Her deep green eyes scanned me from head to toe, finally resting on my face. I'll never forget the moment our eyes met. Her face showed sheer surprise and disbelief, as if she had seen a ghost, even though we'd been apart for only thirteen days. But her dark look quickly changed. She opened her eyes wide, smiled big, and squirmed to get out of my mom's arms and into mine. My heart raced, processing the wave of emotions. I felt weak in my knees as I reached out to hold my baby.

Standing there in the driveway with my three-year-old wrapped around my legs and my one-year-old safely in my arms, I felt as good as I ever could. It didn't matter that I was still in pain. It didn't matter that the world was spinning around me. I just wanted to comfort them, reassure them, that I was OK. I wanted to ensure that they knew that Mom was here, ready to protect them and to teach them to protect themselves.

This would prove to be both my strength and my weakness. To show my girls I was capable of surviving anything, I would end up foregoing a chance to be vulnerable, to ask for help when I needed it. I would feel hurt, lonely, and abandoned. I would grow deeply disappointed with people in my life I thought I could count on but who did not come to my aid. Aside from my parents— who stayed for two weeks after my surgery before going back to the Netherlands, where my dad had to return to work—and one friend from Holland who came to help for a week—I received little to no support. I would struggle to recover from major brain surgery while not one member of my husband's family—not one of the friends we had made over the years—came to the house to take care of my kids or me. No one took them for an outing, or brought us a meal. Even at the annual four-day vacation in Nantucket with my husband's family in July, I was the one entertaining all the little cousins.

Looking back, it's obvious to me that I desperately needed help. Yet at the time I had no idea how to ask for it. With no support from the community in which we lived, because we had just moved there and knew few people, I found myself isolated and struggling with the emotional and physical trauma.

Strangely, the perception of those around me was that I was doing well and had returned to a normal life.

Scar hidden by a layer of hair

The scar after surgery 1997

After Care

On each of my first three days back home, a nurse stopped by the house for ten minutes and took my vitals—including my blood pressure, which was still high even though I had been put on medication. I realized that my blood pressure had been high for as long as I could remember; shouldn't it have been a red flag to my healthcare providers? I'd always been told that I must have "white-coat syndrome"—which refers to high blood-pressure readings in otherwise healthy people who are anxious in medical settings. Not one doctor had considered that I might actually *have* high blood pressure and should be on medication. I was young, fit, and a non-smoker, after all, who hardly drank alcohol. My high blood-pressure readings had been brushed off for as long as I can remember. In fact, over the years I even provided the "white coat syndrome" explanation myself when a nurse gasped at my reading, often in the 160/95 range. (120-/80 is normal and 140/90 is considered high by American Heart Association standards.)

I did learn at a post-surgery doctor's visit that high blood pressure likely did not cause the brain bleed. But it certainly had not helped the rupture and needed to be managed from that point forward. Of course, I now know that high blood pressure carries many other health risks, and fortunately, doctors today are more aggressive about treating it, no matter what one's other health indicators might be.

I struggled to get through everyday tasks. I realized that nobody had asked me about the care I would receive at home. I think hospital staff assumes that patients go home to family caregivers. Sadly, many people don't *have* family close by—or may be trapped in unhappy marriages in which the partner is not a caregiver. The patient is sent home needing to recover not just from the physical trauma, but the emotional trauma as well.

Here's another commonly overlooked factor: Medical trauma can cause tremendous stress and even irreparable damage to close relationships. Because each person processes emotional trauma differently, it can spark conflict and judgment in a marriage, a family, and even among the best of friends. I have heard stories from other survivors that when the life-threatening situation has passed, the patient's family members often find themselves blaming each other for not stepping up, or for being impatient or unsupportive. The family of the survivor usually needs—but may not have the chance—to process both their traumatic memories of the catastrophe itself and their fears and worries about what lies ahead. These dynamics have a huge impact on a patients' course of recovery. Yet there is little recognition of the loneliness and need for support which patients and their caregivers feel independent of each other.

My parents stayed as long as they could. They had taken care of the girls during my entire hospital stay, grocery shopping and cooking for them, entertaining them, and generally making life for them as normal as possible. My parents had also coped with visitors like my twin brother and wife. All the while they'd dealt with the burden of worrying that their only daughter might die.

Meanwhile, my husband was going through his own struggles.

The day after I came home from surgery, he arrived home from work and became infuriated: My parents had not picked up the children's toys in the front yard. This made him angry. He told me I needed to address it with them.

I was sitting on the couch in the living room. I told my parents that my husband felt irritated about the toys in the front yard. My father, one of the most even-tempered and gentle beings I know, turned red. His body stiffened. He turned to my husband and yelled in broken English, with such force that sprays of spit flew with the angry words: "You should take better care of your wife," he yelled. "How can you show anything but gratitude to us? You have not said thank you, or considered how we have gotten through this terrifying week, taking care of *your* tiny toddlers! Instead you blame us for something as trivial as toys in the front yard. Why don't you do something yourself about the toys!"

I'd never seen my father so angry. I was afraid he'd have a heart attack. I got up from the couch and begged them to stop. My dad turned and looked at me in horror. It was clear from his expression that he couldn't believe he'd lost control so completely. He stepped toward me. "Can I help you back to the couch?" he asked gently, instantly calm at the sight of my distress. I broke down in tears, and the girls who had come running out of their bedrooms and started crying as well. My husband turned and left the house, slamming the door behind him. In hindsight, I can see how the tension had reached such high levels, both because of the incredible dire situation, as well as the language barrier, and the usual stresses of having in-laws visit, on either side! I had not been there to mediate, translate, and facilitate and I am sure it was hard on all of them.

That evening my parents told me they could only stay with me for two more weeks. They worried that one of them might lose control again over my husband's insensitive behavior, that they would just add to the pain. I felt confused and hurt. In the end, I just tried to focus on what I needed to do to get through. I mostly blocked it out, the sadness, the (unjust) feeling that nobody cared. I needed to survive, for everyone's sake.

Thus, being home was a mixed blessing. I was really happy to be home, but it was so much harder than I'd imagined. I still experienced intense headaches. I had bedsores and terrible sciatic nerve pain. To make matters worse, my body, which had been in medical shock for weeks, had kicked back into gear: I got my period the day after I arrived home. In addition, because of the trauma of the surgery on my head and muscles, I couldn't turn my head or move my body much. My parents, who were sleeping in a small bedroom in our basement, suggested I sleep in the playroom next to them so they could help me to the bathroom in the night and otherwise care for me. During the first couple of days, the pain was so intense that I needed two people to hold me up. My mom massaged my back for hours. My parents took shifts taking care of the girls and taking care of me. Seeing my daughters gave me hope and made me feel alive, but it also became clearer every day how difficult the road ahead was going to be. At first, I couldn't lift Amy, although within a few days I was able to comfort her when she cried by sitting in a chair and holding her. She seemed desperate to be held by me.

Unfortunately, her need created tension between my parents and me. They believed that she'd been fine while I was in the hospital. They told me that she'd learned to sleep through the night: They had let her "cry it out" at night. Now her need to be cuddled and held by me, they felt, was causing her to regress. I broke down in tears. "All I wanted when I was in the hospital was to survive so I could hold my girls!" I yelled. "You need to let me be! In fact, I needed to cuddle with my daughters as much as they needed me. I wanted to hold them, to feel their skin against mine, to respond naturally to Amy's cries.

In Holland, people tend to be stoic and not make a fuss. Children don't sleep with their parents and are typically left to cry themselves to sleep. People say that crying "is good for the development of their lungs." But I'd never agreed with this. I had a strong opinion that babies who cried were trying to speak their needs, and I wanted to tend to those needs when my daughters called. So even though Amy was a healthy one-year-old who slept in her own crib, I didn't mind getting up in the middle of the night if she cried. Amy was clearly anxious and wanted to held by me all the time. But I couldn't explain to my worried parents or husband the overwhelming emotions I felt when holding her. Knowing that I was almost separated forever from my precious babies, that they would have been left without my love, care, and guidance, was almost too much to bear.

I was feeling grief over what might have been. I got into the habit of tending to Amy when she cried in the middle of the night. I'd secretly sit with her for hours. I felt the warmth of her body, listened to the sound of her breathing, smelled her baby head. I would whisper in her ear that I loved her. How happy I was that I had survived and could still be her mommy! I imagined what would have happened if I had died—and I cried, rocking my baby.

How Are You Today?

In hindsight, I realize that it would have been smart to check in for a period of recovery at a rehabilitation hospital before going home. Arriving home on Monday, I could walk, talk, and breathe, but that was pretty much all. Just three days later, on Thursday, I decided I was ready to walk by myself to Star Market, a local grocery store. It normally took five minutes to walk there from our little house. That Thursday was a beautiful, sunny day. Once I had said that I was going to get a loaf of bread and I'd set out to walk, I didn't want to give up. Or give in. I was determined to overcome this first test.

It was good to feel the fresh air in my lungs. I tried to focus on the walk and on getting that loaf of bread. I felt that if I completed this simple task, I would better understand that I had survived, and that life would eventually return to normal. The horror and pain of the previous two weeks might simply be erased. Every step I took brought more pain, but I kept reminding myself to set one foot in front of the other, just as I'd always done when times got tough. I wasn't sure how I would make it back to the house after I'd bought my loaf of bread. I knew that I could call my father to pick me up, that he would come in a heartbeat. But I knew I'd feel like I had failed my own test if I called him. I had set the bar pretty high for my first outing, but I had only myself to compete with, and pushed on. My thoughts were occupied with the notion that this was such an ordinary errand, yet so extraordinary for me. I don't know how long it took me to walk, but it seemed like forever. I opened the door to the supermarket. People rushed around under bright lights. It was around noon, busy lunch-break time. I found my way to the bread aisle, grabbed a loaf, and made my way to the register.

"How are you today?" asked the girl behind the counter. She was young, had long dark hair and was wearing heavy eye make-up. She looked at me distractedly, and had a faint smile on her face while she pushed the loaf of bread over the scanner.

My life stopped for a split second. Her question, completely innocent and well intended, caught me off guard. I had no idea how to respond. I wanted to scream, "Are you kidding me? How *am* I today? I just had massive brain surgery a week ago. That's how I *am* today!"

Still, her mundane question let me know something important: I looked like everyone else—no better or worse than others who came by her register. She couldn't see the stitches tracking from the bottom of my neck to the top of my head; they were only visible if you pulled away my dark brown hair. She couldn't have known that I'd lost nearly twenty pounds in those two weeks and was scary thin. Nor did she know that the pounding in my head was so loud it overpowered the music playing over the store's speakers. I might even have answered if I had been given another minute, but she'd already focused her eyes back on the register.

She hadn't asked how I was because she'd wanted to know. She was following standard procedure. People in the U.S. say these things. I walked away with my loaf of bread and realized that the question "How are you today?" must evoke strong emotions for anyone who has been through a traumatic experience—an illness, say, or the death of a loved one. We ask such a personal question with so little interest and consideration. This common question suddenly struck me as ridiculous. The reality hit me: My trauma didn't matter to anyone else. It was as if I'd just blinked and awakened from a nightmare.

Astrid, with brother Ron at BC game

Astrid with twin brother Edwin, 2009

One Way Only

The night of my brain bleed I'd made that one phone call to the psychologist who'd come to know me through marriage counseling and private sessions. It's noteworthy that I didn't call my husband, mother, brother, or friend. I wonder if I'm the only one who's turned to their psychologist with their dying wish. Perhaps it's not so unusual. After all, this one person knew my untold stories; I had entrusted him with deep secrets about my marriage, my mistakes, and my fears.

After I had returned home from my surgery, I waited every day for a word from this person I'd called in my most desperate moment. Other people sent flowers, balloons, and cards wishing me a speedy recovery. I didn't receive anything from my therapist. I was hoping for a lifeline, and instead I was drowning. My disappointment was intense, but mitigated by the knowledge of the rules of engagement in a doctor-patient relationship. After all, he had specifically explained the night I'd called him that he could not contact my husband in case I died. Professional ethics probably also prevented him from calling me. He likely couldn't check to see if I was surviving, or to invite me to come to his office to talk.

While I fully accept the fact that you go to a therapy session to dump your trash on the therapist's floor so you can go back to a cleaner house, psychotherapy is of course much more than that. A good therapist gives your trash a home, not just a dumping ground. A good therapist helps you sort through the trash and salvage the recyclables. My therapist had done all that. But now the metaphor shifted: I was looking for him to help me carry my bloody mess, even for just a few feet.

I wondered if he even knew I was alive. I secretly concluded that he must not care. If he cared, I thought, he would have sent a card or placed a call, even if it meant breaking some rules. After all, I reasoned, how often does a patient call you as a last stop before dying? How many psychologists' patients have near-death experiences to begin with?

I was playing a cruel mind-game with myself, but in my lonely world, contact with him was an important missing link in the chain to recovery. I wanted him to be like a priest, who would have had no ethical dilemma about contacting a parishioner. No one would have questioned the intentions on either side. I spent many hours in dialogue with myself about the situation; the dilemma tortured me.

The central problem was that I needed him to reassure me, to become part of my everyday life. But I knew very well he could not. I vacillated between neediness and realism. It took me many weeks to realize that the only way I could put an end to this sad experience was by calling and making an appointment. I imagined telling him that he had screwed up. Big time. I told myself I had an obligation to his other patients—I needed to confront this accomplished therapist. He'd been great, sure, but I'd had him on a pedestal, and he had let me down when I needed him.

I finally met with the psychologist, and asked him why he hadn't sent a card or called. He said that not contacting me and checking in had been very difficult. In fact he *had* called my house and talked to my crying father a couple of times. He knew I had survived. He apologized for not contacting me directly. I asked the question that had been on my mind all this time: "Would you do it differently if you had to do it again?"

I held my breath, waiting for the answer. Yes, he said. Yes, he would have.

Saints and Angels

Six weeks later, I met with Dr. Stieg, my surgeon. He took my stitches out and told me that he thought I wouldn't have survived had it not been for my attitude. He described how during the surgery he discovered another weakening of the wall inside the malformation. But that weakening was too "broad based" and in "too dangerous a location" to put a clip on. Instead he'd put a clip on the ruptured aneurysm and filled the entire malformation with a "fiberglass mesh cloth." He'd hoped the cloth would reinforce the wall and that my body would form scar tissue around the cloth. This sounded reassuring at the time. Dr. Stieg explained that aneurysms usually take from fifteen to forty years to grow, so he was not especially worried that I would have another one. They would do routine angiograms for a while to make sure the clip was still was in place. He said that even if the clip fell off, there would most likely be enough scar-tissue growth to prevent another rupture.

I asked Dr. Stieg why my headaches were still so bad. He didn't seem surprised, but he offered no explanation or solution. I knew what he was trying to say: "You have survived something extraordinary. Pain is the least of your worries." It seemed he wanted to pass me off to someone else—someone who could address my pain and other issues. These were not his expertise. He was a surgeon; he fixed bodies, not lives. Intuitively, this made sense to me. I knew I had to go elsewhere for support.

I asked if he knew anyone else who had survived this kind of brain bleed who was also a mother with kids. Someone I could talk to. Unfortunately, he did not.

Just before I left, I gave Dr. Stieg an oil painting I had made for him. I was eager to give him something to show my apprecia-tion. I didn't have a lot of money, so this oil painting I'd made of a beach path was the best way I could express my gratitude. The paint was still wet when I brought it in; oils take six weeks to dry. Today, thinking about this, I laugh. I can only imagine the sorts of presents grateful patients bring to their doctors. Mine was a sweet gesture, but really, where on earth was a prestigious surgeon going to hang an oil painting done by a thirty-two-year-old housewife recovering from brain surgery? I hope the miracle-workers who receive these gifts know that they are given from the bottom of patients' hearts, to express the inexpressible.

I visited the intensive-care staff that day, too. I brought a box filled with muffins and chocolate croissants from a famous bakery and wrote a card detailing all they'd done for me. I'll forever re-member the faces of each staff member who had seen me through the surgery—my heroes. Theirs were the faces I saw when I was dying and surviving. The slightest changes in their expressions spoke volumes. They'd complimented me on being "the best pill taker" on the floor. Somehow just *that* made me feel better. Their gentle touch when they changed my bedding, their kind words when I was calling yet again for assistance to go to the bathroom— these lifted my spirits. They were my saints and angels in the world of the ninth floor of Brigham and Women's Hospital.

I often think back on those nurses and doctors and marvel:

Strangers cross these clinicians' paths every day, and the nurses and doctors touch these strangers' lives in profound ways. I can only imagine the courage it takes to witness patients' struggles to survive. Patients leave, then, without a trace. These caretakers' healing touch has an enormous impact on trauma patients' chances, and on the patients' courses of survival and recovery.

This reminds me of a comforting story in *Kitchen Table Wisdom* by Dr. Rachel Naomi Remen, a lovely book given to me after my surgery by my sister-in-law. In the story, pieces of a puzzle are missing; the author makes the point that we can see the whole beautiful picture of the puzzle only when both the ugly and pretty pieces are present and assembled. In my puzzle, the caregivers in the hospital were some of the beautiful pieces.

Life Goes On

Those first few weeks after I arrived home from this follow up visit with Dr. Stieg, which turned out to be the only one I would have, I simply coped. I had to handle intense pain and emotions, and move on in a world full of action and new developments. My stitches were out and my head was healing, but the pain remained the same. Pain medications did not relieve the suffering much. Although coping with the pain was challenging, coping with my anxiety and fear was worse. By now, my parents had gone home, my husband was at work, and I was caring for my two toddlers as well as I could.

My consulting business had been put on hold for weeks. Without working, I earned no income. I had no disability insurance, so the financial impact would cut deep very soon. Audrey had started attending pre-school three mornings a week and Amy still took a two-hour nap every day. So six weeks after my surgery, I started working again as an executive search consultant, recruiting C-level executives for my clients. My job required my full attention and quick thinking. It entailed making many phone calls and conducting interviews with high-level executives in order to screen them for a potential position I was hired to help fill. In my high-pitched, crackling voice, I told the potential candidate that I was recovering from a cold. I devoted my attention to working better, smarter, and faster. This work turned out to be the perfect distraction and confidence booster. I couldn't feel sorry for myself when I was working, and making money was crucial to our household. My worries and fears could be put aside for the time I was focused on other people's lives and careers. My ears rang and my vision blurred by the end of my workday, which only lasted as long as Amy's nap. I think that occupying myself constantly by working and mothering my girls was both a curse and a blessing. I simply had to "suck it up."

Of course, this only emphasized the illusion for everyone else—I seemed to have fully recovered and moved on.

A New Normal

Sometimes I felt like saying "surviving isn't everything it's cracked up to be." I'd been operated on by a maverick and knew I was lucky to be alive, but my pain and worries seemed out of sync with the world's expectations of me. My depression and sadness only made me feel worse about myself.

I was struggling with the fear that my stroke could happen again. Or that something else would kill me. I realized within weeks after my surgery that my "new normal" would include abandoning naïve presumptions about life and health. We are all pleasantly oblivious to the potential for pain and devastating events until something happens that brings our lives to a screeching halt. I've spent a lot of time thinking and comparing myself to other people who've survived trauma. Emerging from a near-fatal event, you find that everyone around you is delighted for you. They say things like, "You must feel so happy! You must have a new lease on life." They need you to "get over it," to be happy you survived, and to move on. I felt almost guilty and ashamed that my feelings were quite the opposite from what society was expecting of me.

I'd been sent home without instructions for how to handle what lay ahead. I had no idea that the crippling pain would recur so often. At least a couple times a week I had the same excruciating pain as I'd had when I went to the hospital with my ruptured aneurysm. The pain would set in motion fear and panic. I returned to the emergency room several times that first year, convinced that I'd had another brain bleed. I rode an emotional rollercoaster, knowing that anything could happen at any second and that my worst fear could still come true: I could die and my girls would not have a mom.

I called around to the hospitals in Boston, looking for support groups for survivors such as myself, but even more important, survivors who had lived to grow old after this kind of event. None existed in those days.

A Voice from the Past

But months after my surgery, I received unexpected support from a familiar source. I got an email from my high-school science teacher from Holland. Jan Van De Berg had heard about my brain hemorrhage and was moved to reach out. He asked if I remembered what had happened to him. I didn't. He reminded me that he'd had a hemorrhage as well, back when I was in his class. One day he told my class that he would be out of school for six weeks because he needed brain surgery. The students erupted into cheers. In Holland schools rarely hired substitutes, so when a teacher was absent, students were allowed to go downtown and socialize in little cafés or go home. So a teacher's absence was therefore generally regarded as good news. Sadly, my classmates hadn't listened to the cause for our teacher's sick leave.

Jan was in his early thirties at the time. Apparently, I came to his desk after the lesson and apologized for my classmates' insensitivity. I asked what the surgery was for, what kinds of problems he might face afterwards, and whether he was afraid. It was not that extraordinary for me to step up and show concern. I was the School Counsel Vice President in a school of 1,200 students. I knew every teacher well, and spent much of my free time in meetings with them. It seemed, and even seems in hindsight, not that special, but instead incredibly insensitive on the part of my classmates! But my gesture had made an impression on this teacher. He told me that he'd always been grateful for my kindness. It had stood out for him. When he heard about my surgery, he felt compelled to connect and make sure I knew that he was available to talk. He had survived his surgery eighteen years ago, and it had changed his life dramatically. He told me about the fear and the struggles, so similar to mine.

His first email was a huge gift; it offered me a way to talk safely about my worries and the questions I had about my future and risks. He was not a doctor, of course, but I'm sure other survivors can relate to how reassuring it is to connect with someone who's had a similar experience—perhaps especially if his disaster was long ago and he is doing well. This email connection with Jan gave me hope for my own recovery.

A crucial difference between us was that he didn't have children. This left a gap in my healing because so much of my fear related to the worry of not being there for my girls. But it was a tremendous help to be able to reflect on life and bounce ideas back and forth about how others handle the news, and how to move on. Unfortunately, this supportive relationship, limited to emails over a 3,000-mile distance, became a source of jealousy for my husband. He even purchased a Dutch dictionary to try to read the emails in secret, even after I had translated them for him. He insisted that my email exchange was the same thing as having an affair. So I ended the friendship. I gave up my only outlet and sounding board, in an effort to prevent the complete breakdown of my marriage. Understandably, during this traumatic and difficult time in our lives, issues in our marriage, which had been worked on years ago in counseling, came back in full force and polarized us more then ever.

Alone

That first year, the pain of not feeling understood by anyone often felt as intense as my physical pain. I needed to move on with my life, to close a chapter that would not end, to heal a wound that was not visible to the outside world. I felt ashamed to feel this challenge. For the first time in my life, I was stuck. I had no idea why this suffering was clinging to me so fiercely. I'd always been positive and upbeat, but now I felt only sadness, fear, anger, and emptiness.

Above all, I felt lonely. The loneliness of the experience was, and still is, the most difficult part. The feeling that nobody understood. That nobody cared. The fact that I looked fine and was back at work and taking care of the girls made it seem as though I no longer needed any help or support.

For a long time, I felt devastated after a visit with family or friends because no one asked me about my pain or how I was coping. Their avoidance made me feel worse. If I said that I was having a bad headache, people around me told me about their headaches. Now, eighteen years later, I see that those lovely and compassionate people were probably just trying to reassure me that my headache was not going to cause my death; they, too, had headaches! Now I can see their attempts to make me feel better. Yet at the time I needed to be able to speak aloud that I was in terrible pain, and had many other issues that interfered with life. And even though I "looked great" considering what I'd been through, I was still scared about the possibility of a relapse.

Meanwhile I was overlooking something important: My parents, brothers, other family members, and friends had also just faced their own mortality. Somehow they needed to make sense of it, to recover from their own trauma. Theirs was different from mine, but nevertheless it made them unable to be the beacon of hope and comfort that I needed.

In the winter of 1997, six months after my surgery, I went to Dr. Louis Kaplan, a neurologist at Beth Israel Hospital, for a follow-up care visit. Near retirement age, Dr. Kaplan felt like a grandfather to me. Personable and gentle, he reassured me about my worries. He told me that Dr. Stieg was the most skilled surgeon he had ever seen at work, and that he had done a great job in my case. I had nothing to fret about, Dr. Kaplan said.

When Dr. Kaplan asked if I was interested in starting a support group for stroke survivors, I felt honored. I knew I would enjoy organizing such a group, and said yes.

I worked with a nurse at the Beth Israel, who was also a stroke survivor, but had been disabled by her stroke. We planned our first meeting for January of 1998. Driving there, I felt anxious yet hopeful. The participants included Dr. Kaplan himself, Margie, the nurse who'd survived the stroke, and two other survivors who suffered from severe disabilities. These last two patients brought their devoted family caregivers. During the emotional meeting, it became obvious that the caregivers were struggling, too. They also needed support in coping with their worries and fears.

I'd hoped that the meeting would connect me with survivors I felt I could relate to, but instead it only brought into sharp focus how alone I was: I listened to the survivors' and caregivers' moving stories and thought of my husband. Since marrying him when I was twenty-one, I'd been trying to rescue him from his childhood demons. He was not a caring type and did not usually express compassion. He was limited because of his own past. I was used to it. But now I found myself needing loving care that he could not give. I was having a hard time accepting this. Yet I couldn't leave him because I had nowhere to go. We had small children; I had just nearly died. At that first meeting, reality sank in. I excused myself and rushed out of the building to my car, where I burst into tears. I hadn't even told my husband that I had organized this meeting. I knew he would have been angry that I was "still dwelling on the surgery," as he had said several other times.

I rationalized that my husband was unable to support me because his mother had died when he was young. He must fear similar pain for my kids. I told myself that he didn't understand my pain because it wasn't his. *He* didn't experience the replay of the trauma, involuntarily through flashbacks and emotional triggers, every second of the day as I did. So many of the stories of survival I've heard since my brain bleed speak to the great love and compassion stroke survivors received from their spouses and other caregivers. That love and compassion are the main themes in books with these kinds of stories. My experience was quite the opposite. My husband's lack of compassion and care made me feel unworthy and unimportant. And even though I accepted that our situation was different *because* of my husbands' own painful experiences as a young person, I had a lot of unresolved feelings of anger and pain as a result. In those early years after my stroke, the outside world didn't know because I was covering it up by moving full speed ahead. While I started to learn how to cut off these painful emotions, I had a sense of embarrassment about the lack of connection between myself, and my husband at such a painful time. I would often find comfort in music that highlighted the emptiness I felt, songs such as "Wonderful Tonight" by Eric Clapton.

Cruise Control

Going back to work had exhausted me; fatigue permeated every fiber of my body, and pain reached excruciating levels. I felt like an engine that had little fuel left. But the engine had to become more efficient all the time. I desperately wanted to be on cruise control, even if just for a little while.

Since cruise control was not an option, I had to adapt. First, I decided to send Amy to a small, nearby daycare center, run by a lovely woman named Gail. Amy went two mornings a week so I could work. This arrangement helped me find the time and peace of mind needed to be present as a mom when the girls where both home.

In the first year after my surgery—in which I experienced daily pain and exhaustion—I also had to develop a new way to parent. I had to plan activities smartly; I could do so few and only for a short time. I planned my day as if my girls were babies again. I focused on basic things: I knelt next to them while they took their baths and puttered yellow ducks around in the water. In pain, my world spinning, I could just be silent while they happily played. I became skilled at avoiding tasks I couldn't complete. I didn't have to read books to them if I flipped the pages and asked them to tell me what they saw. Children's books with marvelous illustrations but few words became our favorites. I didn't have to be the center of their attention if I put a blanket on the ground and set up the stuffed animals for special celebrations. Such activities gave me time to take a breath, watch, and enjoy. I didn't take them to the mall, where the fluorescent light was too intense for my traumatized optic nerves. Instead I let the girls create dress-up parties at home. I hardly ever went to the movies; the loud noise was too much to handle for my traumatized brain. Instead I held a film party every Wednesday: I invited a few little ones over and provided microwave popcorn, pillows on the floor, and a movie curtain at the door.

On Saturday mornings, the girls and I listened to the "Children's Classical Hour" on NPR. Settled into one of their bright-red twin beds, surrounded by sunflower-yellow walls and a mural of a white picket fence, which I had painted before my surgery, we listened to wonderful segments such as "Beethoven Lives Upstairs," stories about Mozart's childhood, and lessons about the roles of the instruments in The Nutcracker Suite and Swan Lake. What a gift to tune into these free programs, while being in my own home, and not having to be in a loud social setting that would frazzle my brain. I also valued our annual membership with the Roger Williams Zoo, where the girls could play outside in a safe, fenced-in park. I sat for hours while the animals, just be being themselves, entertained and mesmerized the girls. These became wonderful solutions for me, a parent trying to cope with the everyday challenges of surviving a medical trauma.

Who's Taking Care of Whom?

I tried to prove to the girls and myself that life would go on as usual. I played mind-games with myself to stay positive and be present for my children. It was an uphill battle, but every time we came to the top of a hill the view was breathtaking. I found that I could meet the challenges better because I had always done a lot with the girls and built good memories before my surgery. I doubt my daughters even realized that I had to make so many adjustments.

Although, it was interesting to watch my daughters wanting to comfort me now that I had "a boo-boo," the role reversal of them trying to take care of Mommy was not always easy to accept. The tight hugs from my oldest daughter felt often painful. I've since learned that touch can be uncomfortable after any surgery, and aversion to touch is a common reaction after physical trauma. My nerves had been rattled, and while some hugging was fine, certain touch felt like being scratched; a soft tickle could feel like sandpaper.

I often needed "skin space," in the true sense of the word. My girls, with whom I had always loved snuggling, seemed desperate to continue or even increase the closeness. I was eager to feel them close, but the physical hindrance of pain was a hurdle that would only cease over time. I'd find myself getting restless and agitated when they got too close. My head was definitely off limits. I felt unbearable pain and an unnerving feeling of pins and needles if my head was touched. My girls forgot this daily; they tried to brush my hair as they always had, and startled when I snapped at them. I grieve about the memory of those issues, and wondered for a long time if I did damage to the nurturing instinct of those sweet beings trying to care for their hurt Mommy. I've since learned that they did understand; they just had to learn the new limits of the "new me". Together we seemed to adjust to what was possible and what was not.

Nowadays, my main excuse for anything is: "But I'm a stroke survivor." I use this line when I want my daughters to turn off their horrible, loud, monotonous teen music, and when I need them to clean their rooms because the mess drives me crazy. I also use it when I forget the sort of details about their lives that other parents might have forgotten regarding their own children. As my daughters got older, they could better discern what's really related to the stroke, the result of baggage from my childhood, fallout from other traumas I've endured—or simple irritation.

My girls became my best sounding board. They check in with me and provide great feedback when I have bad days. They say things like, "You deserve to take care of yourself; you're a great mom; you need to let us take care of you, too."

Par for the Course

The new normal included myriad adjustments and reminders. After I came home from surgery, even climbing as few as three stairs left me breathless. I went to many doctors, including pulmonologists to see what could be wrong. I was told that anesthesia from major surgery could take months to process, and it could leave traces of fatigue for a long time. I also was told that it could be damage from the breathing tube used during the surgery, something that is a known risk and just a nuisance. It would be years before I found out from a doctor that my vocal cords had been badly damaged. Vocal cords are like French doors, I was told. One of my "doors" was paralyzed in the closed position; the other one was partially paralyzed. The muscles around the vocal cord had compensated for the damage and I was still able to speak just fine. But any irritation in my esophagus caused more breathing problems. I learned that drinking acidic orange juice and eating a lot of acidic fruit was adding to my breathing issues. I started eating apples and drinking low-acid juices instead, and things improved.

My tongue had been affected, too, and when I stuck it out, it was crooked and leaned to one side. This seems insignificant, but the partial paralysis of my tongue led to terrible self-inflicted bites inside my mouth and my tongue; it would get in the way of my teeth when chewing. My sense of taste had changed, too. If I drank beer, I could taste only the bitterness; if I ate a cookie, I could taste only the sugar, and wine simply tasted sour. Carrots were one of the few things I could eat and enjoy those first few months. I've heard this is common among stroke survivors. Carrots' crunchy texture and flavor made them a comfort food for me. I researched the way taste buds compensate for a deficit such as mine, and learned that less sensitive taste buds now had to "step up to the plate." Another example of body's amazing ability to heal and find new pathways.

Another issue I cope with even today is that if I don't sit perfectly straight when I swallow, I will likely choke. This is a very common phenomenon among stroke survivors and often leads to infections. I still choke regularly but have learned to avoid the obvious hazards: I never drink out of a faucet or tilt my head back to drink or eat something. I try to sit directly across from people I'm dining with so my head is not turned when swallowing. In order to prevent the horrible headaches, I arrive early at business meetings so I can choose a seat that will allow me to avoid having to keep my head turned for long periods of time. These may seem like minor nuisances, but they are a constant reminder of the time I almost died.

A major change was the disruption in my sleeping pattern: Since my surgery, I have had to sleep flat on my back with my head straight. Keeping my head turned for more than twenty seconds meant I'd wake up with such excruciating pain that I couldn't move. I could only close my eyes and suffer until I dozed off again. I'd slept on my belly since I was an infant; I would pull up my right leg under my belly, and it had literally been my sleeping position for as long as I could remember. This adjustment to only sleeping flat on my back was a particularly difficult one.

In the beginning, I propped up pillows around me to prevent my body from rolling and had great difficulty getting good rest. Through the years, my body resigned itself to this new "flat on my back" position, strictly as a pain management strategy, but the emotional toll about something as simple as not being able to be a "belly sleeper" any longer, was huge.

"It's from the surgery." This came to explain all my difficult symptoms. My emotional and physical troubles ranged from annoying to scary. I went to see a psychologist. He told me about Post Traumatic Stress Disorder (PTSD), a common phenomenon after trauma; it can involve anxiety, depression, mood swings, insomnia and many other problems.

I struggled with anxiety, especially when traveling. I understand this fear is common among survivors who needed very specialized medical care when the trauma occurred, or whose life was saved by a particular doctor. We're afraid to leave this lifesaving resource behind. In the months and even first few years after my surgery my PTSD would be triggered by a simple trip out of town. Later it was triggered only when I flew to Europe to visit family. I wanted to feel that "my surgical team" was nearby, that I could reach them in case I needed them. Of course, that fear was always met by the sobering thought that Dr. Stieg had made it quite clear that "this was it" when he performed the miracle of clipping my aneurysm to save my life; he could not fix the other weakened part of that malformation, and the fiberglass mesh he had filled the malformation with was going to have to do. The knowledge that this malformation was still there in my head provided plenty of anxiety on any given day.

I did not think I was depressed, although doctors had offered medication. I had always been someone with a very positive outlook and came to believe meds can be an all-too-easy way for doctors to deal with post-trauma issues, including pain and feeling down. I have wondered many times throughout the years why not a single doctor has asked me a simple question: "what are you most worried about that might happen." I visited the emergency room with terrible headaches, or walked into doctors' offices with excruciating pain. Clinicians did all sorts of tests and prescribed all sorts of medication. In hindsight, with a society that is addicted to pain killers, anti-depressants, and anti-anxiety medications, I wonder how different care would be, if we started asking that one question, and therefore perhaps starting to get to the root of some other issues. Of course, I never offered the answer to that hypothethical question either. Post-traumatic stress evokes a much stronger "fright and flight" response than in someone who does not suffer from PTSD. Nerve pain, muscle pain, and stress-related tension pain, are often the result. Symptoms will vary from person to person, and depend on what kind of trauma occurred. A soldier coming back from war will respond differently to hearing a gun shot than I will. For me, driving by the tower of the intensive care unit of the Brigham and Woman's Hospital is an emotional trigger—even this many years later. Every survivor of trauma has certain triggers. I now believe that for a survivor to free him or herself of these triggers, he or she needs to identify them very specifically, even if the list is long. And the survivor needs to know the symptoms that accompany the triggers, and the situations that cause a response.

My daughter recently called from a new job, feeling overwhelmed. She called me again twenty minutes later, having run out of gas on the highway on her way home while it was dark. She had forgotten her wallet that morning and had only a dollar in her car. I tend to function well in such situations, but inevitably, suffer from severe head pain in the following days—as I did after helping my daughter think through options that day. Any call to action, for my traumatized body, takes "all I have." I now know, nearly twenty years later, that only my high-alert response system works. The less urgent response system, which would have responded to her needs without sounding undue alarms, is lost.

Everything feels "raw" to me. I feel raw to events, to the influences and the impressions events make on me. Light bothers me, noise bothers me, and repetitive tasks like counting money feel like fingernails on a chalkboard. My response system gets so tired and "over-sensitized" that I avoid stressful situations. As a result, my world has become smaller. I have talked to many survivors, especially those who have had a traumatic brain injury or surgery, who recognize these sensitivities. They, too, feel like their brain is on full throttle all the time, and I personally sit often just holding my head in both hands to try to calm "it" down.

I have tried taking anti-depressants and did not find them helpful, but an anti-anxiety medication, which I use from time to time when I travel, has made a big difference. It has been a long road to find the tricks to manage the symptoms.

I never had the luxury of dwelling on my symptoms. I needed to raise children and make a living. Writing this book, I believe, has been the best therapy for creating and recognizing my own list of triggers and symptoms. And with that, I think I have been able to work through my Post Traumatic Stress, even 18 years later.

Full Catastrophe Living

Full Catastrophe Living, by John Kabat-Zinn, changed my life. I'd bought the book on a whim many years before my brain bleed. I'd become interested in meditation, and had read the book soon after buying it. But I hadn't studied it carefully, nor applied the wisdom in the book to my day-to-day life. After my surgery, I took the six-week course described in the book, taught by Doug Philips, a meditation teacher in Newton, Massachusetts. He'd studied with Larry Rosenberg, another well-known meditation and mindfulness practice teacher. Doug recommended other books that helped me understand what I was trying to "accomplish" (a word not quite apt in describing mindfulness practice, which teaches the relinquishment of goals). Doug used helpful phrases that pointed to the ways we unintentionally increase our distress: "watering the seeds of suffering," for example, and "holding on to the hot plate after you have burned your hand." I learned to "listen to and be with my pain," rather than pushing it away. The practice helped me cope, and to feel like I had some control again—not necessarily over the *pain*, but over my response to it. The sitting meditation was difficult and emotionally draining, but I learned invaluable lessons from it.

My meditation practice taught me to soften my reactivity; it helped create space between the moment I felt something and my reaction to it. Through practice, I could find a pause in the moment before I reacted to a thought flashing through my head, whether that reaction was going to be anger, pain, or fear. In the beginning I could only find that pause when I was paying attention during the actual sitting practice. But as I practiced more, it became a more automatic response in my everyday life. I felt much calmer. In particular, in the breathing practice, focusing my attention on the breath was very helpful in my small world filled with fear. I found myself letting go of an unhealthy habit of holding my breath.

I found that there is a moment in every breath that comes closest to the experience I had when I was in a coma the night of my aneurysm. I experience a moment after completely exhaling, and just before inhaling again, as a peaceful pause—without pain, anger, or sadness. This pause happens every time anyone breathes out, but we rarely know it because we rarely bring attention to it.

The pain medications I'd been prescribed had hardly touched my terrible discomfort. But the meditation practice helped me bring awareness to the pain in a way that soothed. I identified four forms of pain in my head, each varying in intensity from a four to a ten (on a scale of ten) on any given day. In the first few years after the surgery, a nearly constant nerve pain plagued my head and shot to places all over my body. This pain came on suddenly and was sharp as a knife. For example, it shot from the back of my head and through both my eyes. A doctor told me that the pain was in the optic nerve, which was healing from the surgery. The nerve pain has gotten better over the years but is still intense at times.

Clinicians told me that the pain on the left side of my head, behind my ear, was caused by scar tissue forming around a "floating bone" that was pulling on the surrounding tissues. Furthermore, since my surgery, I was unknowingly carrying my head like a turtle: I was sticking my neck forward and carrying my head away from my body. This caused muscle problems, but when I tried to hold my head correctly, the pain was excruciating. It was a no-win situation, trying to alleviate that particular pain. My most intense pain seemed to involve the actual brain tissue. It involved the entire backside of my head and felt as if someone were squeezing a sponge, my brain. It was a crippling kind of pain, and fairly constant, for the first many years. It faded sometimes to a level four, but shot up to high levels any time I encountered stress. I sought help from several doctors, looking for pain-management strategies.

It was the meditation practice that dramatically changed the intensity of the pain. This may be surprising, but it makes sense: The body is signaling pain, telling you to stop doing what you are doing. If you don't stop, the body signals more pain in an effort to get the attention it needs. My strategy had been to try to ignore the pain, to push through it. I thought I was being tough, but I was just being ignorant and making the pain worse.

In daily meditation, I directed my attention to the pain, focusing on what it felt like, on where it came from, on the emotions surrounding it. The practice always made the pain subside to a manageable level. Of course, finding the time to sit became a challenge. My life got busier and more "normal," so I tended to make less time for my own healing. I focused my attention on the girls.

I began to develop another habit, which was probably not healthy but appears to be a coping strategy for many survivors of medical trauma. I secretly prepared, in my mind, for the worst-case scenario: my death. I was struck when several friends who'd survived cancer said things like, "I don't think I'll become a very old person." Those who haven't suffered trauma might say, "How can you say such a thing?" or quickly change the subject. But as a survivor myself, I recognize this fear that one won't live to be very old. I know first-hand that something can happen in a split second. I know what this feels like. And even though I've always been an optimistic and upbeat person—and have proved myself to be a fighter—I've had to accept this fear in order to live with it, rather than dismiss it.

Here's an illustration of my fear: After my surgery, I hadn't gone to a dentist for at least seven years—even though I needed $5,000 worth of dental work. This avoidance persisted because I worried that the money would be wasted if I died. Here's another example: Both my feet need surgery; I have such severe bunions that both my big toes are dislocated. The joints are tremendously painful, but I am afraid of both the surgery itself and of the emotions that a surgery, and being in an operating room, will likely trigger. Few survivors will admit to such mind games, for fear of being labeled negative or unstable, but the deep fear—and sometimes even irrational thoughts—are often just below the surface.

PART III

Surviving Is
All Around Us

Anniversaries

My mother and father visited my family here in the U.S recently. One day, driving on an errand with my mother, I brought up, for the first time in many years, the subject of my surgery. "I remember Dad taking me to the hospital," I said. This simple statement triggered an outpouring of emotion. My mother described the days of my hospital stay, the phone ringing all the time, my dad answering, speaking to clinicians, and crying as he passed along the daily updates to family and friends. She said she couldn't let her emotions show when it was all happening because the girls would have figured out that the situation was dire. I think she may have underestimated how very perceptive kids can be.

My twin brother and his wife came and stayed at the house, my mother said, and I understood that it had all been enormously stressful. I reminded her that everyone at that time was coping with the fact that I was likely to die or be severely disabled. It's hard to imagine how she and my father managed to keep their emotions in check, feed the children, and manage the family dynamics.

That day when my mom and dad brought the girls to the local community hospital for a very brief visit—and I had asked my mother to please care for my children while I was at the hospital—this had been an emotional moment. It turns out she and I both remembered it vividly. She tearfully confided that this request had been *her* lifeline; it became her mission during those difficult days in which I was struggling to survive.

Driving in the car that day, my mom described another memory of visiting me on a day I'd taken a turn for the worse. A nurse had told her, "You have to keep talking to your daughter; she's slipping into a coma. Keep talking to her; it doesn't matter what you say." And so my mother did.

All these years later, it's painful to imagine her, facing the prospect of losing her child. My own children grown now, I reflect on her experience and feel enormous compassion for her.

As for my father, he is unable to speak of his experience of those early days after my aneurysm ruptured. Whenever the topic comes up, he withdraws and goes silent. Even eighteen years later, when I smile and try to show him that it's OK to talk about it, he can't. My brothers don't talk about the events either—and really, why would they? Life goes on, and they have traumas and worries of their own.

My children have suffered in their own ways from this chapter in our lives. Right after my surgery, I took Audrey to the local library in Sharon, Massachusetts, where we lived at that time. Walking in, my three-year-old pointed at a magazine rack and asked, "Is that what they did to your brain, Mommy?" There, on the cover of Newsweek, I saw a full-size drawing of a skull with the brains exposed. I had thought she had no idea about what had happened, but she'd clearly put together bits and pieces of information: witnessing my father cry on the phone, hearing him explain my need for brain surgery and, of course, sitting in the car when my aneurysm ruptured.

Others were affected by my experience, too. Some surprised

me with their kindness. Two months after my surgery I received a reminder about my daughters' annual physicals. I had long admired our pediatrician, Dr. John Conway. He clearly loved kids, and I remember his devastation when his son's best friend, Travis Roy, a Boston University hockey player, broke his neck playing in his first college game. I could even call on Dr. Conway over the weekend or late at night if I had a worry—and he always responded with care. Over the years, he'd encouraged me to go back to school and become a doctor myself. He told me he'd recommend me to Brown University, his alma mater. He was always a very positive and encouraging person, who reassured me on many occasions that he trusted the instinct of a parent more than anything.

The day of my daughters' appointments, Dr. Conway noticed us in the hallway where a nurse was checking the kids' height and weight. Later in the examining room, he asked, "What happened to you? You've lost a lot of weight." I filled him in, and showed him my huge scar, still healing and raw.

He wept. "I am so glad you survived," he said. "You are such a wonderful mother and your children need you. Please make sure to take good care of yourself because you're important to people. And you've been through a lot."

His emotion brought me relief. His words made me feel better, important. A couple of days after the visit, I received a letter from him that I treasure. Again, he told me that he knew how difficult this must have been for me and how happy he was that I survived. I've read the letter many times over the years; especially on the days I've felt the loneliest. I've saved all the cards I received the week I returned home. I stored them in a gift bag, along with a deflated "Get Well" helium balloon.

I haven't received a card since. I would have appreciated receiving cards even years later. Anniversaries of traumatic events often stir up distress for survivors. There's a real need for reflection and insight during the weeks leading up to anniversaries. No one in my life talked again about my brain bleed. Every year, I found that the oncoming Spring had a profound impact on me. The tree blossoms and the early flowers triggered powerful memories. On May 7, 2000, at the start of a new century, sitting at the dinner table with my kids and husband, I said aloud that it was the third anniversary of my stroke.

"Is that a reason to celebrate?" was my former husband's cold reply.

A year after my stroke, I had lunch with a new friend who had lost her husband to a brain bleed. I told her a two-minute version of my ordeal. I had learned to adjust the story's length to match the attention span of the average person who wants to know what happened (or thinks he or she does). It seems people usually only want to know when it was, how bad it was, and that you are fine. This new friend I was having lunch with, however—and not surprisingly, given her own experience—asked for more details. I realized during this lunch that I had not been able to sit down and tell someone the whole story. This friend's husband had been a journalist; he had nearly completed a book about his brain trauma before he passed away. Hearing his story felt like a turning point for me. I thought that writing about my fears might help me work through them and close the chapter. I also came to realize that it might be a meaningful way to help others dealing with their own traumas.

My Red Notebooks

Other survivors of medical traumas have told me that, they too, feel like medical trauma makes you refer to most everything in the past as "before (my surgery)" and "after (my surgery)." And of course, many survivors add "because of" if there are disabilities as a result. To a large extent, my near-death experience and bodily trauma came to define me. Sometimes, if I feel defiant, I will use words that are much more blunt, and say: "before my head blew up." Yet no one knew the extent of my pain and suffering. For the first few years after my brain bleed I often wanted to introduce myself by saying, "Hello, my name is Astrid and I had a brain bleed." Other survivors have told me they have had the same impulse. My trauma continued to interfere with my life. My greatest fear was not dying, but that I'd leave my children without a mother.

I found it liberating to realize that fear, founded or unfounded, was my main obstacle to recovery. I could continue to seek reassurance that my head was fine, that the aneurysm was fixed, that I had as good a chance to live a long life as anyone—but my distress was no longer explicitly about my stroke. It had to do with the fact that I'd looked death in the eye and had seen that it was unpredictable and ruthless.

Not long after my stroke, I had decided to try to work through my fear by creating a permanent record for my children of the parent I was planning to be—in case I would die. I bought a couple of red spiral notebooks and one night I sat down and wrote a list of buzzwords, including: relationships, self-image, education, parents, parenthood, marriage, attitude, drugs, hobbies, career, childhood memories, fears, money, and humor. I was planning to use these as prompts for short letters, "my life lessons," to my daughters. Almost every night, I would scan the list, and choose a word that jumped out at me. Since I'd been a teenager, I had recorded my thoughts and kept diaries.

The letters proved to be a wonderful and therapeutic practice; I came to look forward to the writing. Every word on the list provided a window into my life, and food for thought about what I wanted to teach my girls. The letters describe the journey of a young immigrant who moved to "the States" at the age of nineteen and pursued the American Dream. My feelings about the letters' topics have changed somewhat because of real-life experiences, but most of my feelings have endured since I composed the letters in those years after my surgery.

A letter called "The Cause" describes how, at 21, I took on a cause much larger than my own when I married my first husband. He had suffered a tremendously sad childhood. I tried to fill the role of his psychologist, to help him process his feelings of abandonment by his mother. This was a mistake, of course. I wanted my girls to learn that you have to care for yourself before you can care for others.

Another letter testifies to the amazing opportunity available to anyone in the United States who wants to work hard, as I did. At 25, I launched "All Things Dutch," a mail-order company, with just a dollar. I worked with well-known Dutch companies

AHOLD and HEMA to distribute and sell Dutch goods to expatriates who lived in the United States. It was important to me that my daughters understood the privileges and opportunities that came with their American citizenship.

In "Dress Code," I described what felt like my most humiliating experience as a teen: I was ridiculed by a group of wealthy kids at a party because they noticed a loose thread on my homemade skirt. The letter offered a lesson in humility and in recognizing the ways society demands conformity even in something as insignificant as the clothes people wear. I wanted to teach my children, above all, to temper their pride, no matter how much success they had.

Like many immigrants and parents from less-affluent backgrounds, I felt driven to provide my children with opportunities I didn't have. In "The Need for Education," I explained my goals for them. I'd married young and worked from home to help pay for my husband to get his MBA. I took care of the children full time. At the time, it seemed like a good idea to allow him get his advanced degree, yet, as I describe in the letter, my lack of a formal degree hurt my self-respect and prevented me from reaching my own potential. I wanted my daughters to understand that education is more than just a chance to get a better job: being educated brings intellectual growth, choices, and a sense of independence.

The letters also express strong opinions about growing up in a socialist country. "Sex, and Drugs, and Rock and Roll" covered the culture shock I experienced when, shortly after I arrived in America, I saw for the first time people smoking marijuana at a party. It seems like a contradiction—that someone from Holland, where drugs are so prevalent according to American perceptions, would be surprised and turned off by Americans using drugs to escape. But few children in Holland ever use drugs. So I was astonished to see young people in the U.S. hiding in houses, doing illegal activities, rather than socializing, dancing, and meeting people of all ages at clubs and cafes, as we did in Holland.

One letter, which was difficult but important to write, pertained to the death of my aunt. She was the younger sister of my mother. At age 32, she had been diagnosed with breast cancer. At age 49 she was diagnosed with breast cancer in her other breast, (It was surprising to me at that time to learn she had not had a single mammogram since the treatment after her first diagnosis.) She fought the disease, but it was terminal and, after getting the necessary written permission from two doctors (her own, and an independent doctor), she opted to die with help of an injection. Her family gathered with her, and she passed away peacefully. I know of another friend of my parents who was able to communicate after suffering a second stroke that he wanted to die. In the Netherlands, several legal paths allow patients to choose aid-in-dying. My aunt chose "active euthanasia," which means "assisted suicide," as opposed to "passive euthanasia," which means the patient stops eating and drinking and/or refuses treatment. I did a big project on this subject in high school. People in Holland consider and accept these as valid options—a matter of patient choice. In Holland, it is *your right* to choose how to die when you are ill.

In my letter, I specified that I wanted to die peacefully, receiving the comfortable care I wanted in case of another bleed. I feared being severely disabled, and a burden to my loved ones, which is not something I wanted.

I included stories about my own mistakes in the letters to

show my daughters that even their mother had made poor decisions. I hoped the girls might learn from my mistakes.

Of course I know that much of parenting can't be planned ahead and, as children grow into young adults, their peers can hold more influence over the decisions they make, especially when hormones surge! The best I can do is hope that some of my words and example will hold fast as they learn to live more independently each day.

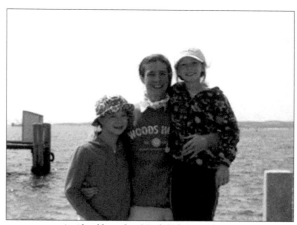

Astrid and her girls in Woods Hole, Massachusetts

It *is* about the Small Stuff

Writing those letters, I was so earnest: I believed if I just told my girls about my past, present, and possible future, I'd cover the necessities. But years later, the anxious calls from college would bring up subjects I couldn't foresee. Of course my kids could have figured out on their own how long to cook a chicken, and which shavings to buy for a bunny's litter box. But such everyday questions are the important things in life; I feel so grateful to be here to answer them. Back in the late 1990s I was busy writing down the Big Life Lessons—drugs and alcohol, relationships, my opinions on social issues—and I overlooked the little stuff.

The hugs and the togetherness my daughters needed when I came back from the hospital "after surgery" have morphed into iPhone texts about every day matters. The girls call me with all sorts of questions; many of them are so specific and personal that my letters could never have resolved them.

I think I'd have liked knowing, back then, that such insignificant details as how to cook a chicken would be important in parenting teenagers. But I didn't dare to dream of mundane rewards when I was faced with death. I wrote the letters to imprint who I was and what I stood for and, to be honest, I wrote them for my own sake. Faced with my own mortality, I was trying somehow to become immortal.

Ready to Die

After writing for nearly a year, I closed the red spiral notebooks in 1998, with the list of buzzwords and the letters in them. I'd written all the warnings and lessons I wanted my kids to know—and my values, memories, hopes, and dreams for them. When I was done, I felt ready to die. I was not *willing* to die, but I was *ready* to die. I had not written a will or built an inheritance, but I'd written a guide, from me to them.

I called the red spiral notebooks "My Red Letters," because I had come to associate red—the color of blood from the brain bleed—with the threat of death and the fury of pain. For me, red was also the color of love, of my intense connection to my children and my passion for living. Red became more than a color. It evoked emotions in me and triggered thoughts. For many years, when creating any kind of art, I found that I was inspired to create modernistic expressions using the color red, rather than the more familiar landscapes I usually painted. For a while, I listened daily to The Red Hot Chili Peppers. Their raw sound and words resonated, even if my ears rang. The girls often drew pictures or made cards with red hearts or red tulips, my favorite flower. I saw red all around me.

Full Circle

I had stored what I saw as the key to my life in my attic in two red notebooks, and the day I turned fifty, my life came full circle. The aneurysm, which had been repaired many years earlier, was no longer a threat in my world. When I read the notebooks to reflect on the letters I had written so long ago, I realized that some of "My Red Letters" contained life lessons I could still pass on, but many already had been. Even though the anniversary of my fiftieth birthday was a true milestone, I had passed many more milestones these last eighteen years that were not about my surgery. There are now new "before" and "after" references.

Now that I've passed 50, my perspective has changed. In 2005, after 19 years of marriage to my first husband, I found the courage to divorce him. I cashed in my retirement funds and purchased the house we had moved to after my surgery in 1999, when the girls were 3 and 5, located in a wonderful suburb of Boston. I gave up my consulting practice, and accepted a full-time job at the American Heart and Stroke Association. Now I could provide for my girls. I continue to work at the American Heart and Stroke Association as Youth Market Director. It has been a very meaningful experience to be involved in the organization that supports and advocates on behalf of my cause.

In 2010, I remarried and still live in the same wonderful house, which has a beautiful backyard. We've built English flower gardens and created fountains and ponds. With help of my parents, we've just finished designing and building a Victorian teahouse made from recycled windows and other materials. This backyard, in every season, is a haven for the whole family and our three Labrador Retrievers and one Dachshund.

Astrid, David, Mom and Dad toast in the backyard 2015

Surviving Lasts a Lifetime

Now that the danger of death from the aneurysm has passed, my passion for living and my wish for good health have only increased. I wrote the "red letters" from the perspective of a young mother who feared death and wanted to leave behind life lessons for her children. I could write fifty more letters—but the lessons would be different now. I am different now.

As a parent, I spent so much time trying to teach my children how to live their lives. I finally recognize that it's time to live my own life. There's power in knowing that surviving a trauma doesn't cease. My stroke will always be with me; it will shape me and make me stronger, and hopefully more compassionate. For many years, I'd sought to just "close the chapter," but came to realize and accept that the chapter will never fully close. Trauma survivors need to survive the rest of their lives. Surviving really lasts a lifetime.

I've learned that we can't choose when we die, but we can choose how we live. My most rewarding moments have been those I devoted to helping others who were also just surviving. It doesn't take a grand gesture to make a difference in someone's life. A home-cooked meal, a warm hug, taking the time to ask sincerely about another's health and well-being—these can provide others with tremendous relief. There's a big difference between needing time to heal and being stuck. Today, I look around and count my blessings. I'm grateful to be able to reach out to others, celebrate life, and embrace all to come in my next fifty years.

David and Astrid with Buddha, Balou,
and Bodhi in Provincetown 2011

Amy senior photo, high school 2014

Audrey senior photo, high school 2012

David and Astrid get married
on Lake Garda 2010

A happy moment 2010

Audrey graduated
University of MD a semester
in early Dec 2015

Amy with sister Audrey at high
school graduation, 2014

Astrid and the kids in Provincetown 2008

Astrid, with twin brother Edwin, older brother Ronald,
at mom and dad's fiftieth anniversary in 2009, Holland

Epilogue

On my fiftieth birthday I wrote in my journal:

January 25, 2015

I wish to bargain for more years
And live to be 100
To see grandchildren
For I think I would be better at it

If you can't grant me my wish
Please let them all know
That I am safe
And without pain
That will be such a relief

It will be a new life
And I will see it all
In a whole new light
From a different place

I can hear the call
And feel the curtain close
The uncertainty of when
Or what to prepare
I am not ready yet
But I know it is time

I know I have done
What I came for
It is set in motion
And time will tell

But my kids are strong
And the others moved on
I have grieved it all
And have feared much more
The pain was intense
The coping tough

I am ok
I am light
It will be lovely
The little child is safe in her young strong arms
The future is good
I can feel the peace
The pain is gone

Suddenly I think
There might be that chance
That it was just the dress rehearsal
That I can be fifty
And even fifty more

—Astrid Hendren

Acknowledgements

I am incredibly thankful for the support I received from so many individuals as I took on the task of putting my story into words. I am deeply grateful to my daughters Audrey and Amy, who crossed my path and made my life worth fighting for. They have taught me about the deepest kind of love, and I can only wish that they too will experience that kind of love in their lifetimes.

Without Dr. Philip Stieg and his medical team at the Brigham and Women's Hospital, or our friend Dr. Robert Van Strien, who looked at my angiogram, saw that something was wrong, and made sure it got to Dr. Stieg at ten o'clock that night: I would not be alive to tell the story. Dr. Stieg is confronted every day with life and death situations of people he has never even met: yet he dedicates his life to saving them. I am forever indebted to the nursing team, who cared for me with great skill and compassion. Their kind words and unwavering support became a lifeline to me on my darkest days. My interactions with them came full circle when I spoke at a neuro-nurse conference in Waltham, MA and unbeknownst to me, several of my caregivers from 18 years earlier were in the audience. I was deeply touched when they came forward to let me know how happy they were that I had survived and was doing well. As a patient, I had believed I was just "passing through" the healthcare system, but I now know that the nurses who cared for me didn't forget me and that my time in the hospital had meaning for them too.

I am eternally grateful to my brother Ron, who was my rock. He helped me speak when I had no voice and made me feel present when I was almost gone. I can never thank my parents enough for supporting me throughout my life, especially at this crucial time. They were the inspiration for my fighting spirit and the positive attitude I needed to survive. Their loving care of my daughters enabled me to rest easier while I was in the hospital and at home recuperating. They always seem to be able to make me laugh and show me the silver lining. Their unconditional love is the foundation on which I was able to rewrite my life and adjust to the new normal after the surgery.

My husband David has been my most devoted fan, providing encouragement and support when I didn't think the story mattered and worried that my writing was insignificant.

A number of people read this book in part or its entirety and gave me good editing advice and constructive criticism. Their questions and feedback helped me focus on the issues that could be most helpful to others who are trying to survive a medical trauma as a parent.

In particular, I am grateful to my friend Susan Murphy, who contributed enormously through her professionalism and expertise in writing, but most importantly, through her friendship and compassion. Her insights enabled me to tell my story in a second language while preserving the integrity of what she called "my voice."

I was incredibly fortunate to be introduced to Nell Lake, my talented editor, who was able to coach a first time author, through the humbling process of getting the book ready for publishing. She provided invaluable input and encouragement when interpreting my doubts about the value of the story into the notion that I was becoming a "real writer" instead, because of it.

I also want to thank others who have inspired me to publish

my story, such as Kristina Hill and Olivia Quickly, young survivors who have visited schools with me to share their stories of survival.

Finally, I wish to express deep gratitude for my meditation teacher Doug Philips who, through the work of John Kabat-Zinn and his teachings, helped me cope through difficult times and taught me invaluable life survival strategies.

The impact of so many others, including the PE Teachers whom I have been privileged to meet through my work as Youth Market Director for the American Heart Association, and who have become friends, cannot be put into words. They all contributed in many ways: in my ability to see light at the end of the tunnel and putting one foot in front of another.

Resources &
Discussion Guide

RESOURCES

Resources for Survivors of Medical Trauma are available through many organizations, including those listed below. In addition, many hospitals offer regular survivor group meetings and other resources for both survivors and their family caregivers.

American Heart and Stroke Association
www.heart.org

Brain Aneurysm Foundation
www.bafound.org

American Brain Foundation
www.americanbrainfoundation.org

American Stroke Association
www.strokeassociation.org

American Cancer Society
www.cancer.org

The Schwartz Center for Compassionate Healthcare
(Boston, MA)
www.theschwartzcenter.org

Center for Mindfulness in Medicine, Healthcare, and Society
University of Massachusetts Medical Center
(Worcester, MA)
www.umassmed.edu/cfm

Inside Meditation Center
(Cambridge, MA)
www.cambridgeinsight.org

A DISCUSSION GUIDE

A Conversation with Astrid Hendren

Q: How did you choose the words on your list of buzzwords in your first notebook?

A: As a survivor, I wanted to write short stories about things that mattered in my life at that time. I did not want to write specific letters to my girls as if I had died already, but rather, my goal was to provide a guide: a sort of dictionary with topics that might matter at different times in the girls' lives in case I was not there to teach them, and in case I had not told anyone how I felt about those matters.

So when I first put the list of buzzwords together, each word was intended to provoke thought on any given night I would write, but they were random words, chosen to capture the essence of what I wanted to convey in the notebooks.

Q: How did you pick the topic for each letter?

A: I would sit down and pick one word that "jumped out at me," or particularly interested me each night I wrote. Then I would write that word at the top of a blank page in the notebook and I would simply start writing about my thoughts associated with that word. Sometimes it was a poem. Sometimes it was a story that happened in my past. Sometimes it was about my hopes for the girls, my dreams about their future and who they would become, if I could wave that magic wand. I would write about my mistakes, my regrets, my successes, and my worries. I also wrote about the people whom I loved, and who had inspired me. I even wrote about fashion and make-up, and what I thought my kids should know about my values as their mom.

Q: Did you have a particular time you would write?

A: I have always enjoyed writing, and have kept diaries since I was a young girl. Even though I have never taken a writing class, I am the kind of person who is always scribbling on napkins and pulling over on the side of the road to write down a thought or story. However, this project had a very different meaning to me, and from the start, I was very methodical and disciplined in my approach. I would sit down almost every night and write about one word on the list. Sometimes, it would take twenty minutes to complete, sometimes hours. It was a very therapeutic way to reflect and look forward, because it was about the past and the future.

Q: Do you feel this list of buzzwords is complete?

A: No, I think many words can be added to this list of buzzwords and they can be much more personal. Even though I may use the word "Education" to start a letter, this prompt could have several letters with completely different perspective. For example, I have one letter that talks about my own education or lack of education, and another letter called Education talks about how much education plays a role in life and society, yet another letter which is also called Education talks about emotional intelligence and education. So the same buzzwords are used in different letters and have a completely different meaning.

Q: Did you feel you could write honestly or did you worry about writing about controversial topics such as end of life care, etc?

A: It was actually very liberating to write all my thoughts down about what I wanted my girls to know. I was particularly struck by the notion of writing about so many things, which nobody would know about, and therefore would not be able to teach my girls, as I would have. That is not to say that someone else could not do a good job, but writing my deepest thoughts down made me feel immortal. And reassured me that I would have a way to reach my kids in case I died. I think all parents have had conversations with a child about topics or specifics that are not known to anyone else.

Q: Since your children were still so small when you wrote the letters, did you worry how to keep the letters private?

A: I did not really worry about it. I had written with black magic marker on the front of the notebooks: "For the Girls: These books can only be read when you have reached the age of 18, and in case I am not there to tell you this myself. The content is private and for Audrey's and Amy's eyes only. Please respect that this is not intended to be read by anyone else."
I hoped that would take care of it, I was more interested in

getting it down on paper, than protecting it from anyone.

Q: Do you see this as a possible strategy for other people to use in their recovery from medical trauma?

A: I really do. I know I love to write, and not everyone feels that way. However, we now have awesome technology to help you with this kind of project. I can imagine just using the IPhone microphone to tape your thoughts and stories and store them on your computer, like music. I think people would find out how powerful and healing it is to leave that "legend" behind, and to know that your voice will be heard and will matter. As parents, we share the wish to have our children do well, to empower them, and to give them the tools necessary to have a happy and successful future. This exercise is a simple and therapeutic way to feel more control over our own destiny and to still have that impact on our children in case of a tragic event.

Q: Is there anything you would do differently about these letters in hindsight?

A: Yes, I would. Instead of filling two notebooks in one year, I wish I had made it an anniversary tradition to pull down the notebooks from the attic and add to them as the years passed, as I survived and recovered, and my daughters became strong, self sufficient, young women. As I am writing this, I realize that I will do so, and write new letters, and tell them how very proud I am of them and how much I love them, in case I am not here to tell them myself someday.

Q: What were some of your buzzword prompts for your letters to your girls?

A: They were random and in no particular order. The list of buzzwords in my "Red Letters" included:

> Relationships
> Self-image
> Education
> Parenthood
> Marriage
> Attitude
> Drugs and Alcohol
> Hobbies
> Career and work
> Childhood memories
> Fears
> Money
> Humor
> Triggers
> Values
> Love
> Grief
> Fear
> Hope
> Family

Ned Beauman is the author of *Boxer, Beetle*, winner of the Writers' Guild Award for Best Fiction Book and the Goldberg Prize for Outstanding Debut Fiction; *The Teleportation Accident*, which was longlisted for the Booker Prize and won the Encore Award and a Somerset Maugham Award; and the highly acclaimed *Glow* and *Madness is Better than Defeat*. He lives in London.

~

'Scabrously funny and satirical'
Jamie Buxton, *Daily Mail* Books of the Year

'An endlessly inventive, witty and bleak literary thriller set in the not-so-distant future . . . it'll make you laugh and make you think'
Stephen Bush, *Financial Times*

'Full of fun and big ideas, [Beauman's] conceptually tricksy novels crackle with comic zip, alive to the past as well as the present . . . His mischievous intelligence can be felt everywhere'
Anthony Cummins, *Observer*

'Ned Beauman is a speculative genius . . . This book holds all the great pleasures of the best science fiction novels, hyperbole, technical prowess – but with unusual humour and sensitivity to what it feels to live in this moment. Beauman could not be a more versatile writer. I will read anything he writes'
Elvia Wilk

'This novel is well paced and warm-hearted, culminating in an ambitious and memorable ending'
Jessie Lethaby, *Sunday Times* Science Fiction Novel of the Year

'Ned Beauman captures brilliantly the contradictory blend of urgency, paralysis, panic and resignation the climate emergency and its attendant mass extinctions inspire. The book left me hoping – but doubting – that Beauman is a lot less prescient than funny'
Chris Power

Venomous Lumpsucker

Ned Beauman

sceptre

First published in Great Britain in 2022 by Sceptre
An imprint of Hodder & Stoughton
An Hachette UK company

This paperback edition published in 2023

2

Copyright © Ned Beauman 2022

Extract from *Selected Poems* by W.S. Merwin (Bloodaxe Books, 2007) reproduced
with permission of Bloodaxe Books. www.bloodaxebooks.com

A CIP catalogue record for this title is available from the British Library

Paperback ISBN 9781473613577
eBook ISBN 9781473613546

Typeset in Sabon MT Std by Manipal Technologies Limited.

Printed and bound in Great Britain by Clays Ltd, Elcograf S.p.A.

Hodder & Stoughton policy is to use papers that are natural, renewable and
recyclable products and made from wood grown in sustainable forests. The logging
and manufacturing processes are expected to conform to the environmental
regulations of the country of origin.

Hodder & Stoughton Ltd
Carmelite House
50 Victoria Embankment
London EC4Y 0DZ

www.sceptrebooks.co.uk

'Every living thing on earth today – every fish, beetle, mammal, and tree – is the forward point in a flame of life that has remained aglow throughout billions of years . . . a phenomenon that evolved through a fathomless stream of events to become unique and unrepeatable in the universe.'

The Value of Species, Edward L. McCord

'I write as though you could understand
And I could say it
One must always pretend something
Among the dying'

'For a Coming Extinction', W.S. Merwin

Author's Note

This novel is set in the near future. However, to minimise any need for mental arithmetic on the reader's part, sums of money are presented as if the euro has retained its 2022 value with no inflation. This is the sole respect in which the story deviates from how things will actually unfold.

Chapter One

At a primate research institute in Leipzig, a scientist was caught disabling the surveillance cameras inside the enclosure of an orangutan who knew two thousand words of sign language. He had with him a container of prunes, the orangutan's favourite snack, and upon these prunes suspicion soon fell; perhaps the scientist let something slip under questioning, or perhaps he was seen casting nervous glances at the container. So the prunes were examined, and a pill was found hidden in one of them. Tests revealed that the pill was a 4mg dose of the memory-suppressing drug bamaluzole.

In other words, he was planning to roofie the orangutan.

After the story got out, nearly everyone assumed that the scientist's intentions were sexual, and this became gag material for comedians all over the world. But Karin Resaint, who had once seen this scientist taking part in a panel on animal cognition – who remembered a remark he had made about unspeakable loss – understood at once that the scientist didn't want to have sex with the orangutan. He wanted something far more extreme.

*

She was ready to put the last of the fish into the air when Abdi came running out on deck to warn her. He pointed north into the dusk. Some time ago, Resaint had noticed on the horizon what

1

she had taken for an isolated storm cloud, the mist tightening as night fell into a knot of heavier weather. But now that it had drawn closer, and she looked again, she could make out the three tall columns at the base of the cloud, like chimneys venting the surge out of the sea. A spindrifter, sailing in this direction. The first she'd seen in all her time on the Baltic.

Her cargo drone was supposed to fly due north. That would take it right into the spindrifter's path, she realised, and it would be lashed out of the air. The storm around a spindrifter was like no storm in nature. It was prodigious not in strength but in geometry. Guillemots and herring gulls, which were unfazed by the most furious winter tempests, got tossed around like waste paper. It was too alien to their wings. And this drone, which most of the time did OK in high winds, wouldn't even know what hit it.

She still had the drone's flight path up on the screen of her phone, so she turned on the overlay that showed other nearby vessels. Abdi pointed out the spindrifter, which on the map was just an anonymous white dot. She bent the flight path so the drone would keep a nice safe distance off to the east.

'Thanks,' she said, touching him on the arm. She looked again at the spindrifter's course on the map. 'It sort of looks like it's heading straight for us?'

'It won't hit us,' Abdi said. 'But also it won't care about getting really close. You want to be inside for that, definitely.'

In any case, Resaint thought, the *Varuna* was almost the size of an aircraft carrier, so the spindrifter would probably come off worse in a collision. Which was a pity, in some ways, because she enjoyed the thought of the *Varuna* getting rent open. Not while she was on board, maybe, but nevertheless this was a ship that deserved to be sunk. That would be a much more productive use of the spindrifter's evening than dazing a few seabirds.

She murmured to her phone, and the drone's rotors began to whirr. It lifted from the deck, trailing four lengths of cable from its underside, until the cables tautened and its cargo heaved up too: a plastic tank that held ten venomous lumpsuckers swimming around in sixty gallons of seawater. The drone continued to rise until the tank was high enough to clear the railing around the deck, and Resaint felt a sacramental sprinkling on her forehead as water slopped out over the side. Then, accelerating gently, like a stork with an especially precious baby in its sling, the drone set off north over the ocean.

The drone would fly about twenty kilometres to the South Kvarken reefs where venomous lumpsuckers gathered every breeding season, and then dump out the contents of the tank. In theory, after finishing her experiments, Resaint could have just lowered the fish over the side of the *Varuna* and let them find their own way home. They were perfectly capable navigators. But she refused to take the risk. There were so few left. Every one was so precious. Which is why it would have been a particularly shameful mishap if, say, the spindrifter had clobbered the drone so hard that all those fish broke their spines when they hit the water.

'So that's it?' Abdi said. 'You are finished?' He was a maintenance technician who sometimes helped her out with her equipment, and they had become friends in her three months on the *Varuna*. He was twenty-six and she was thirty-two. Every few weeks he went home to Malmö. He had a girlfriend there, a nursing assistant. She sounded OK.

'I just have the rest of the lab to pack up.'

'And you leave tomorrow?' He kept his tone flat, hardly looking at her, which of course was the incontrovertible sign of somebody who definitely had no feelings on the subject one way or another.

'Yes.' At that moment the *Varuna*'s orange floodlights all came on at once, even though the sky wasn't yet dark. On these industrial ships the lighting was always cranked so high at night that from a distance they looked Christmassy.

'Will you miss the fish?' Abdi said. And then: 'Why are you laughing?'

She was laughing because Abdi had used the same brisk tone even for 'Will you miss the fish?' as if that was just another automatic pleasantry. 'Nobody ever asks me that. Yes, I will. But I hope I can see them again soon.' By 'them', she meant the species in general – *Cyclopterus venenatus* – not her experimental subjects in particular. She'd grown fond enough of those that she would be delighted to see them again, but of course she never would. Their strange secondment in the human world was over.

'Really?'

'Yes. I feel like I've barely begun.'

'Wow, OK, so . . .?'

She didn't reply, but she gave him a little tilt of the head. She knew what he was asking and the answer was yes.

Perhaps even the tilt of the head was a mistake. Never discuss your findings before you submit the report. That was the rule in her field. Certainly not with the client, or anybody who works for the client – and least of all when those findings are likely to be disagreeable to that client. That suited her fine, the not talking, because she had never been the kind of person who could only digest each day with a willing listener as her ruminant organ. And on top of that, she had other, non-professional reasons, reasons nobody knew about, for her interest in the venomous lumpsucker, which made her especially cagey about the whole subject. Even with Abdi.

Officially she was here on the *Varuna* to evaluate, on behalf of the Brahmasamudram Mining Company, whether the venomous lumpsucker exceeded a certain threshold of 'intelligence' – a word so scientifically and philosophically embattled that it was almost useless, churned to mud, but that nevertheless had implications for a company who might want to mine a species' breeding ground. And now, because of that tilt of the head, Abdi could guess what her report was going to say. But perhaps he had already. There had been evenings when he couldn't have failed to notice how excited she was about what had happened in her lab that day. No scientist sat down beaming to dinner because they'd found out that a fish was nothing special.

'Do you want to celebrate finishing?' Abdi said.

'Celebrate?'

Abdi hesitated, searching for ideas. There weren't a lot of ways to cut loose on a mining support vessel. Resaint had a bottle of Absolut in her lab, but Abdi was forbidden from drinking by both his religion and the biosensor Brahmasamudram made him wear on his forearm. Then there was karaoke, which was popular on board. But Resaint was barred from karaoke sessions by *her* most deeply held beliefs, in the sense that she believed karaoke ought to be a taboo punishable by stoning. 'Cake?' he said at last. 'We could eat some cake.'

The mess did indeed offer a decent *kladdkaka,* the Swedish sticky chocolate cake. 'I think I'm going to stay out here for a bit longer,' Resaint said. 'It's my last night at sea. I'll see you later, though.'

'I'll get you a PFD.' Meaning a life jacket.

Resaint waved him off. 'I'll be fine.' Technically she was supposed to strap on a hard hat just to come out on deck, even though there was no danger of anything but gull shit falling on her head, but in her case the safety manual was never enforced to the letter.

After Abdi had gone back inside, Resaint stood at the railing looking out to the north, the hood of her anorak raised against the wind. The Baltic was one of the filthiest seas on the planet, full of chicken-farm run-off and birth control hormones and even nerve gas from old munition dumps, but from a vantage like this you could forget all that. The last of the sunset had died out of the mist and the sea and sky were both darkening iron. Her drone had already shrunk beyond sight, but the spindrifter was near enough now that she could make out the ridged shape of its rotors, like three gigantic spinal columns scudding over the ocean, and the red warning lights at their tops, fifty metres above the water. She could feel a change in the air, too, the outer touch of the spindrifter's storm.

The plan, originally, had been for a few thousand spindrifters, scattered all over the planet. A spindrifter's rotors looked like masts but were really more like sails, in the straightforward sense that they propelled the vessel forward by getting in the way of the wind. But because they were always rotating at high speed, they could harness that wind in unstraightforward ways, like a tennis ball backspinning off a racket. And as they rotated, they pumped seawater up into the sky, spraying it through a silicone mesh to create a mist of droplets so tiny that a flu virus would have called it a fine drizzle. The clouds that formed around these droplets were softer than usual, more cashmere than cotton wool, and because of this they were also whiter, which made them reflect more radiation from the sun. So with enough of these spray vessels seeding enough of these clouds, you might be able to hold back the warming of the earth.

There had been a lot of excitement about spindrifters, once. Unfortunately, after a bit of testing, they were found to have certain foibles that hadn't been anticipated by any of the computer models. They whisked up these eldritch low-altitude storms, which were of no concern to anyone but seabirds; but they also seemed to interfere with rainfall patterns, even at quite unaccountable distances away. And rainfall patterns had been brutalised enough already. It wasn't fair to put them through anything else. This time they might really lose it.

After that, the excitement dissipated like a fine-gauge cloud, the optimists turned their hearts to some new prospect, and the armada was never launched. But several different outfits had built those early spindrifters – the competition to save the world being some of the bitterest competition there is – and a couple of them closed up shop without ever getting round to taking their prototypes off the water. So there were still about a dozen spindrifters roving the Baltic. Unmanned, self-navigating, powered by the wind, built from almost incorruptible polymers, these ghost ships would just carry on until a rotor cracked or a circuit shorted, which might take decades.

Such were the new fauna of this poisoned sea. No ringed seals any more, no harbour porpoises, no velvet scoters, no European eels, no angel sharks, and practically no venomous lumpsuckers. But a thriving ecosystem of these faceless pack-beasts: cargo drones and spindrifters and the autonomous mining vehicles that browsed the ocean floor for ferromanganese nodules forty fathoms beneath their mothership the *Varuna*.

By now the spindrifter was less than a kilometre away. The wind in her face was wet and cyclonic and scouring. She zipped her jacket up to her nose and pulled the cord to tighten the hood. Within a couple of minutes the spindrifter would pass the *Varuna*, and, remembering Abdi's warning, she knew she ought to go inside. But something had caught her attention.

At the base of the spindrifter, which skated on two hulls like a catamaran, she could make out a white glimmer. She thought of sea fire, the phosphorescent plankton that sometimes shone from the waves at night. But it wasn't that. The light had an artificial hue. Yet it was flickering like a candle flame, and anyway a spray vessel, crewless, had no need for any lights apart from the warning beacons up on its rotors.

And then Resaint realised she'd already waited too long. The storm had arrived.

The spindrifter didn't create its own wind, but something about the serpentine airflow between its huge rotors, in combination with the salt fog it spewed out above, was a wormhole in the weather, an anomaly which lured in naive little breezes and turned them out as rabid squalls. This jacket could keep you dry in a monsoon but now her skin was soaked down to the small of her back as if the water hadn't leaked in past the cuffs or the hood but had ghosted straight through the nylon. She felt like chewing-gum under a jet wash, a loose bolt in a turbine engine. Even though she was almost sure the force of the wind couldn't suck her over the side, she was scared to let go of the railing. But she was also scared to just wait out here for the spindrifter to pass. So she started to pull herself along the railing towards the stairs. She wished she hadn't turned down that life jacket.

Her foot slipped. One knee hit the deck. The spindrifter's rotors loomed overhead like the columns of some vast temple half hidden in the mist, their shafts tinted orange by the *Varuna*'s floodlights.

She heard a clunk behind her. She looked back. It had been the sound of a door flying open. Abdi was standing in the doorway holding a coil of rope, one end weighted with a steel snap hook. He shouted something – she couldn't hear it over the roar of the storm and the thrum of the rotors – and then threw. His aim was pretty good: the snap hook nearly walloped her in the face. She grabbed it before the wind could drag the rope away.

And yet she waited a moment longer before she pulled herself to safety. Because she needed one last look at the spindrifter as it passed just a few metres away from the *Varuna*. She needed to be sure she had seen what she thought she had seen.

The glow was coming through a window in the spindrifter's helm. This window was masked from inside by a curtain or blind, but one corner of the blind was flapping back and forth, as if the interior of the ship wasn't quite sealed against the wind. That was why the light had fluttered like a moth's wing. And behind the window, visible only in snatches, a human silhouette. Somebody trying to fix the blind back into place.

The spindrifter had a passenger.

*

An hour later, lying in Abdi's bed: 'I thought you had a girlfriend.'

'Yes, but she . . .' He hesitated. 'We have an "open relationship" now. She wanted to try.'

'She wanted to try because you live on a mining support vessel half the year.'

'Yes, exactly.'

'And she's in Malmö.'

'Yes.'

The *Varuna* had a rotating crew that currently numbered eleven men and five women, and sexual relationships on board were forbidden by company policy. Malmö was a city of half a million people. 'Do you ever feel like she got a better deal?' Resaint said.

'It is fine,' he said, not very convincingly. 'I am fine with it.'

She hoped she hadn't spoiled his mood, which had been good even before the sex. After he rescued her, he wasn't cocky about it, but she could tell he was privately elated about his feat of heroism. In hindsight, she hadn't been in any real danger standing at the railing, but if she'd exaggerated it to herself, why shouldn't he exaggerate it to himself too? It was quite sweet. If Abdi ever told anyone about this, he would be able to say he'd reeled her in, literally hook, line and sinker. And so here she was in his cabin, which was redolent in so many ways of her room back in her first year at university: the textureless blond wood, the soft glow of a light fixture with a T-shirt draped over it, the single bed which barely fit two bodies. After smelling that unfortunate lemon hair tonic on him every day for weeks there was something weirdly gratifying about finally seeing the bottle it came in, like meeting a famous person. She hadn't expected this to happen, although admittedly it was consistent with past practice: sleeping with people when circumstances ensured she would never see them again.

'The spindrifters – would they ever have people on board?' She hadn't yet told him about what she'd seen. Somehow it felt like a secret she'd been entrusted to keep.

'No.'

'Never?'

'Some of them, I think they can do rescue. Like if someone's boat is sinking and there is no one else to pick them up. They have little cabins inside so they can take you back to land.'

But why, Resaint thought, would a castaway, presumably desperate to be picked up, black out the windows of their lifeboat?

Later, she was awoken by knocking, just in time to save her from a steam train bearing down on her across a shingle beach. She was surprised to find the two of them had dozed off together on his precipice of a bed. Her whole arm was numb.

'Karin?' The voice calling through the door belonged to Devi, the *Varuna*'s captain. Resaint felt Abdi tense beside her.

'What is it?' No point pretending she wasn't here if Devi already knew.

'Please come out.'

She unfurled her phone. It was four in the morning. For some reason she had no network connection. 'Is it urgent?'

'Yes, it is.'

'All right. I'll be out in a few minutes.' Resaint was pretty sure Devi would want to maintain the polite fiction that nothing illicit had been going on in here. The captain was an extremely fastidious person, which meant she was a stickler where it mattered, but also preferred to leave the animal lives of her crew unacknowledged. Whether Devi had any animal life of her own was of course the subject of exuberant speculation.

'I am very sorry, Karin, but if you do not come out right away I will have to open the door myself.'

The bedmates muttered swear words in chorus, she in German, he in Somali. Hurriedly they dressed, handing clothes back and forth like barter, and then Resaint went to the door and opened it. 'Come with me back to your own cabin, please,' said Devi, who averted her gaze as if Resaint was still naked, clearly so painfully embarrassed about the whole situation that for a moment Resaint almost felt sorry for her. This would have been a lot easier if Resaint had been asleep in her own bed, instead of – for all Devi knew – interrupted in a moment of forbidden ecstasy.

'What's going on?' Resaint said. She'd rebooted her phone but it still couldn't find a signal. 'Has something happened? Is the network down?'

'It's not down for me,' said Abdi. And Devi still wouldn't meet her eye.

It was this, more than anything, that made Resaint suspect that her situation here had taken a nasty turn. 'Did you kick me off the network?' she said. 'What is this?'

Another polite fiction, a deeper one, was essential to Resaint's work here. This was the polite fiction of her independence.

There was a reason Brahmasamudram Mining Company had set her up in a lab on board the *Varuna* when she could perfectly easily have worked from the Swedish coast. It was one of those psychological tactics, tribal rites, that lurked so often inside even the most impersonal transactions of the multinationals she worked for. Like most of her clients, Brahmasamudram wanted her to have it always in the back of her mind that, for the duration of her contract, she belonged to them. She lived in their domain and she worked in their domain and there was nothing beyond that domain but chilly Baltic water.

And yet you weren't supposed to say that out loud. Yes, she was dependent, surveilled, confined, a vassal of the *Varuna* just like every other crew member. But the premise of her work was that she was a scientist making objective judgements, uninfluenced by the client who was paying for her time. And everybody involved benefited from that premise – from her immaculate priestly aura. For Devi to treat her like this – to reveal so blatantly the coercion behind their hospitality – was a sullying not only of her current assignment but of every assignment she had ever taken.

At least Devi seemed as uncomfortable as Resaint was indignant. Clearly this wasn't her choice. Somebody was making her do this. 'Your own cabin,' she said. 'Please.'

Resaint knew she could refuse. Devi was hardly going to drag her out of here by her hair. And yet if she made Abdi's cabin into her last stand, things would get a lot more awkward for Abdi, and she didn't want that. 'If we go back to my cabin, are we going to sort out whatever the fuck is going on here?'

'Yes,' said Devi, relieved to see an opening. 'Yes, we will sort it out. I promise. Someone is coming to talk to you.'

Chapter Two

Earlier that same night, Halyard was in a taxi on his way to dinner when he saw a tumour crash to earth like a meteorite.

They were at the back of the convoy, a minibus and three overflow taxis shuttling everybody from the Mosvatia Bioinformatics headquarters outside Copenhagen to a hotel on the waterfront. He wasn't sure what would have happened to the taxi up ahead if it hadn't swerved off the road at the very last moment. It was an interesting rock-paper-scissors-type question, because the tumour was made of flesh, and flesh was traditionally the loser against car bumpers, but on the other hand he knew you could get killed hitting a deer on the road, and this thing had to weigh at least three times as much as a deer.

His own taxi hadn't swerved, it had just braked – hurling him and his three fellow passengers forward into their seatbelts, and his phone out of his hands and into the footwell – which meant he now had a clear view through the front windscreen. The monstrosity, which had burst apart when it hit the asphalt, now lay there in four ragged chunks, and even those were the size of shipping crates. The sound of impact had been just one sharp drum hit, but somehow also symphonic – deep and wet and ruptive and sproingy all at the same time, really remarkable Foley work on the tumour's part – and yet in terms of textural horror the sound had nothing on the image. The meat was reddish-white, glistening,

12

ruffled and pleated, except in some places where it was wrapped like tenderloin in translucent epimysium, and in others where it had thick black or white fur. Here and there a nub of bone poked through.

For Halyard the experience was startling, yes, but not quite as nightmarish as it might have been if he hadn't known what he was looking at. And he did know, because he'd seen coverage of the last time this had happened, during a conference outside Madrid. What had just landed was a teratoma, meaning a tumour made of germ cells that could resolve themselves into any type of tissue (so there were probably teeth buried in there somewhere, brain matter, even eyeballs, like an anagram of a mammal's body). It had been grown in an unlicensed laboratory somewhere using DNA bootlegged from Chiu Chiu, the 'last' giant panda. And it had been launched from a catapult as a protest against what Halyard did for a living.

Chiu Chiu had died twelve years ago of a fungal respiratory infection in the intensive care unit of the Giant Panda Breeding Research Base in Chengdu. At that time, he was the last giant panda. But he was not the last giant panda for very long afterwards, because plenty of clones followed, nurtured in the wombs of black bears. Still, he would always be the last in an unbroken chain of wet begetting, the last panda who came out of a panda who came out of a panda who – ellipsis here – came out of the very first panda.

In terms of sheer emotional tonnage, Chiu Chiu's death may have been a convulsion unprecedented in the history of the human race, the largest number of people multiplied by the deepest sincerity of feeling. You couldn't usually make generalisations about a nation of 1.4 billion people, but pretty much everybody in China loved Chiu Chiu. In his last days, no hour-to-hour news of his condition was permitted to leak out of the Research Base because of its potentially destabilising effects on the stock market. This mysterious fungal blight, which scoffed at even the tightest quarantines, had already killed hundreds of wild and captive pandas around the world, and when it killed Chiu Chiu too, the

13

Chinese fell into a frenzy of lamentation and self-reproach. They had failed to safeguard their own national animal, and they were tortured by the shame. For days, the streets were crowded with what appeared to be howling ghouls released from the netherworld: these were in fact children who had put on panda make-up in tribute to *ji mo de Chiu Chiu* (lonely Chiu Chiu) but whose uncontrollable weeping had slubbered it down their cheeks. A Beijing journalist who wrote a column with the headline 'Why I do not care about Chiu Chiu' was forced to go into hiding. Yes, there would soon be cloned pandas, but this was the period of the Communist Party's campaign against 'lying goods', and clones were often compared to blood pudding illicitly thickened with formaldehyde.

For the most powerful country in the world, emotion found an outlet in action. During the period of what cynics would later describe as China's great national derangement, 196 other states, acting basically at economic gunpoint, signed up to the newly formed World Commission on Species Extinction. 'There will be no more Chiu Chius,' proclaimed one Chinese official at the WCSE's founding. 'Chiu Chiu will be the endling of endlings. Because we will never let such a tragedy happen again. The giant panda will be the last species ever driven to extinction by human activity.'

Of course, that was not at all what happened. What happened instead was the extinction industry.

And the extinction industry was the target of this protest: specifically Halyard and his colleagues, dozens of them on this junket, not only from his own line of work – he was the Environmental Impact Coordinator (Northern Europe) at the Brahmasamudram Mining Company – but also consultants, contractors and bureaucrats. Over the next hour or so a communiqué would be released online and the police would find a catapult abandoned somewhere nearby. Semiotically, the stunt had more or less the same structure as those old protests – from before the 2°C warming era, in hindsight so gentle, so forbearing, so quaint – where they would throw fake blood on people to convey 'Your

14

hands are stained with blood.' But in this case they were throwing Chiu Chiu on people to convey 'Your hands are stained with Chiu Chiu.' As Halyard understood it, the activists weren't saying that he and his colleagues were somehow culpable in Chiu Chiu's demise twelve years ago – nobody but a few history-scrambling paranoids believed that – they were saying that he and his colleagues were culpable in the ongoing extinction crisis, of which Saint Chiu Chiu was the great avatar.

Well, that was a complicated issue.

But there was one sense in which the people in this convoy indisputably did have their hands stained with Chiu Chiu, so to speak. They owed all their affluence to that adorable and poignant bear. They lived in the world Chiu Chiu had made with his death. There was a Chinese creation myth in which human beings came into existence as mites feeding ravenously upon the god Pan Gu's hairy corpse, and as Halyard watched a woman climb out of the taxi on the shoulder up ahead, wincing and rubbing her neck as she walked over to the meat in the road, he imagined her, him, all of them, swarming over it until there was nothing left but those nonsense bones.

*

Indeed they did feast on that tumour, but only in the sense it gave everybody something to talk about while they waited for dinner. The actual hors d'oeuvre, which was served an hour late because of all the commotion, was veal brain carpaccio. And Halyard was famished by then, which made it all the more frustrating that the carpaccio was almost impossible to eat. The meat, which had been cut to a width of 100 micrometres, shrivelled away to nothing the instant you touched it with your fork. It was like trying to eat the surface tension off a glass of water.

Really, the carpaccio was a biotechnological stunt, much like the tumour. Earlier, at the Mosvatia Bioinformatics headquarters, the invitees had watched a presentation about how the brain of a critically endangered animal could be sliced up by a vibrating diamond blade to lay bare its every synapse for electron microscope scanning, and now their reward for sitting through the pitch was meat prepared with that same apparatus. Back at its day job in the laboratory, the diamond blade would shave off wisps of just ten nanometres, so this much heavier carpaccio gauge was supposed to be a compromise between the full capabilities of the machine and the practical demands of catering. But the compromise had been ill-judged, and everyone else around him also seemed to be having trouble, including the vegans with their heirloom beetroot version (although not including his colleague, Ismayilov, who hadn't even touched his carpaccio and was looking a bit withdrawn). In the end Halyard just resorted to sucking the carpaccio directly off his plate, and even then he could taste the lemon juice and the black pepper but he could not taste the veal brains, except perhaps as a faint neural clamminess at the back of his throat. He had specifically refrained from taking his usual dose of Inzidernil this morning, in anticipation of enjoying a good meal, and now this flop.

'What the fuck was the point of the presentation?' he said to Ismayilov, pouring himself another glass of wine. 'Who are they trying to impress? OK, we all have to pretend for the public that we really honestly think scanning an animal's brain and putting it in a computer is as good as keeping it alive, but there's no reason to bullshit each other behind closed doors. Nobody cares about most of these species. Nobody cares about the rusty pipistrelle or the legless skink. Even the activists don't care about them – not individually. So once the poor little fucker gets scanned, that's it. That's the end. It's just going to sit there in the database forever like some mouldy old library book that nobody will ever read. It's pointless. They might as well just wipe the data after a week to save on server space, it's not like anyone would ever know the difference.'

In response, Ismayilov began to cry.

Halyard was taken aback. He must have said something tactless. Was it possible that Ismayilov, perhaps for some obscure ethnic or ancestral reason, was deeply invested in the fate of the rusty pipistrelle or the legless skink?

16

Then he thought of Ismayilov's wife, who had died of multiple myeloma last year, and he formed a strong hunch about what had so upset Ismayilov.

Ismayilov had never said anything about having his wife's brain scanned when she died, but then again Ismayilov hadn't gone into detail about any aspect of his widowing; Halyard (thirty-eight years old, Australian with some Thai from his grandmother) and Ismayilov (forty-five-ish, Azerbaijani) were friendly but not close. Halyard could picture it: Ismayilov holding his wife's hand as she slipped away, and then, before he felt remotely ready to leave her, getting hustled out of the room so that her brain could be flooded with preservatives, surgically extracted, washed, chilled, encased in gelatin, and sliced up (like carpaccio) for the scanning microscope. It was much the same process that they'd seen in the presentation just now, except the aims were different. When you scanned the brain of a human being, it was because you hoped that one day you might be able to revive that human being in some new incorruptible form. But when you scanned the brain of a rusty pipistrelle or a legless skink, it was only because, after the whole species went extinct, the continuing existence of the scan would make it easier to argue in a legal or regulatory context that the species was in some sense *not yet lost*.

The former was an act of love, the latter an act of arse-covering, but to Halyard they were both equally pointless. Both seemed to imagine a future of untroubled leisure and plenty, an infinite Sunday morning, when humanity would have worked its way so far down its to-do list that it really had nothing better to do than resurrect millions of not particularly rich or famous or talented people from decades past, or commemorate some vanished reptile of no greater distinction by recreating it in the laboratory. It sounded nice. But it was not at all the way things were going.

Nevertheless, if Ismayilov had indeed got his dead wife transcribed, Halyard could see why he might not want to think about all that. 'Of course, it's completely different with people,' Halyard said in a breezy tone, as if he hadn't noticed Ismayilov was crying. 'Every human life is precious, so if you scan a human brain, it's

17

very easy to imagine a time, probably in the near future, because the technology only has to advance a little bit, maybe five or ten years, probably closer to five, when we're bringing people back as just a totally routine thing.' He studied Ismayilov – who was jerking his napkin around his face in a motion evidently designed to wipe his eyes and nose while making it look as if he was only wiping his mouth – for signs that he was on the right track. 'It's really the next best thing to immortality,' he went on, 'especially if—' His phone tingled. 'Oh, sorry, Mergen, just a sec.'

The call was from Devi, the captain of a Brahmasamudram support vessel called the *Varuna*. 'I wanted to give you an update on the evaluation,' Devi said.

'When's she submitting?'

'I don't know,' Devi said. 'Soon. But it sounds like she's going to re-certify the lumpsucker as intelligent.'

'You've got to be kidding.'

'That's what I've heard.'

'From – what's her name? The Swiss woman?'

'Resaint. No, not from her. From one of my guys who heard it from her.'

'Well, the fish is still doing fine, yes?' *Cyclopterus venenatus* was a bumpy, greyish fish, about five inches long fully grown. It had a toadlike face with bulging eyes and a fat upper lip; looking at it, you felt that if it were a human being it would sweat from the forehead all the time and yet have a shockingly cold handshake.

'Yes. We haven't gone anywhere near that sector.'

'Good. Because we're going to have to take another look at this whole thing. We may need to take her off it. Thanks for letting me know.' Halyard hung up. 'Can you believe that?' he said to Ismayilov. 'Apparently she's going to re-certify. She must think that fish is some kind of Einstein. Have you seen it? It doesn't even look clever by fish standards. It looks stupid *for a fish*.' Still hungry, and unsure when the main course was coming, he noticed that Ismayilov hadn't touched his carpaccio. 'Do you mind if I have that, if you're not going to?' Ismayilov didn't make any objection, so Halyard reached over and took the plate. As he was slurping up the film of grey matter, he inadvertently made eye contact with Ismayilov, and he wondered if Ismayilov was still thinking about his wife's brain. That took away a little bit of his gusto.

'Fifty nanometres,' Ismayilov said in a strangled voice.

'Sorry?'

Tears began to run down Ismayilov's cheeks again. 'We spent so much on her cancer treatment. Even though nothing ever worked. We took out loans. By the time it was over I didn't have enough to pay for a Korean preservation team like I wanted. So I hired some Italians. They sectioned her brain in fifty-nanometre ribbons. They said that was the standard. Now I come here and I hear about ten nanometres for the legless skink. Ten nanometres maximum for an accurate connectome scan. The skink gets ten, my wife gets fifty.' Ismayilov made a gesture as if he held between his fingers not a delicate skim of carpaccio but rather a fat clumsy slice of back bacon. He screwed up his whole face in despair. 'I will never be able to bring her back.'

Halyard made a mental note never to mention to Ismayilov the recent story about the Hainan black crested gibbon. 'Oh, Mergen, don't worry about it. I bet fifty-nanometre sections are totally OK. Maybe you miss the odd detail but you still get everything that matters. Obviously these guys want to sell us on ten because that way they can charge more, but – sorry, it's Devi from the *Varuna* again, one sec. Devi?'

'There's a problem with the fish,' said Devi on the phone.

'You mean apart from the re-certification?'

'Yes. It looks as if . . .'

'What?'

'It looks as if we've already mined the sector where it lives.'

'But you weren't going anywhere near that sector?'

'Yes, we weren't supposed to be,' Devi said, 'but just now, after I called you, I checked again to be absolutely sure, and it looks as if the AMVs got to it.'

'When?'

'Five days ago.'

'How the fuck could that happen?'

'I don't know.'

The *Varuna* was the home base for eight AMVs, autonomous mining vehicles, which mined ferromanganese nodules from the bottom of the Baltic. Each AMV was twenty metres long, weighed a thousand tons, and looked like a siege weapon out of *Mad Max*. At the front they had huge, spiky cutting heads to plough through the continental shelf, and at the back they had ladle chains to scoop up the nodules thus liberated. Powered by hydrogen fuel cells, they grazed the seafloor like cattle on a hillside, deciding for themselves where to go next. Of course, limits could be set in advance, and in this case the AMVs were supposed to have kept their distance from the home of the endangered fish. But something must have gone wrong. Devi sounded mortified, but it almost certainly wasn't her fault: a team back in Mumbai were in charge of programming the AMVs, and the crew of the *Varuna* were basically just grease monkeys.

'Are there are any fish left down there?' Halyard said.

'I don't know.'

Halyard's job entailed dealing with a lot of threatened species, which often was like being the overnight manager of some grand hotel full of neurotic dowagers and sickly princelings. In this case, the warming of the Baltic had pushed the venomous lumpsuckers north towards more commodious waters, but above a certain latitude there was a lack of suitably bouldery reefs, and as a result their acceptable habitat had been reduced to one little stretch of the Swedish coast. So it was quite possible that Brahmasamudram's AMVs had just eradicated the species in one fell swoop. 'Fuck! Well, keep it quiet, OK?' Halyard said. 'Until we know exactly where we are.'

'OK.'

'I hope that's all the bad news for today. Don't call me back in ten minutes and tell me the AMVs have crawled up on shore and eaten a fishing village.'

'I can assure you that won't happen,' Devi replied without levity. Halyard was about to tell her he'd been joking but then he remembered that last year a Malaysian company's rogue AMV

20

actually had demolished a number of Bajau refugee stilt-houses off the coast of Borneo.

'Um, all right. Good.' He hung up. 'So first we find out she's going to re-certify,' he said to Ismayilov, 'and now we find out we've already rubbed out the fish she's re-certifying.'

He felt a hand on his shoulder. 'Sounds like trouble!' He looked up, and suppressed a grimace, because it was Barry Smawl. Smawl was the kind of guy who thought of himself as a gossip broker, a listener to vibrations, an oracle of the martini bar – 'Call Barry Smawl, he'll tell you what's really going on, provided you give him something juicy in return!' – except that in reality the only gossip Smawl ever had was gossip that absolutely everyone else in the business had known for weeks or months or sometimes literally years. And yet Smawl couldn't quite be dismissed as a nonentity, because he was a senior policy specialist at Kohlmann Treborg Nham, and within the extinction industry anybody who worked at Kohlmann Treborg Nham had a golden glow of status to them, simply for belonging to the company that, more than any other, had given that industry its shape, had staked out its habitat.

In the aftermath of Chiu Chiu's death, tens of thousands of lobbyists from around the world had swarmed on Chengdu. But lobbying in the PRC was a real test of mettle – this wasn't Brussels, where any moron could get a draft regulation amended. And it was Kohlmann Treborg Nham who had proven themselves the masterminds, the grand strategists. In those heady days of 'The giant panda will be the last species ever driven to extinction by human activity,' the Chinese government had been helped to understand a number of important things. They had been helped to understand that, although of course everyone would be thrilled if Chiu Chiu could be the endling of endlings, that just wasn't possible, short of the human race committing mass suicide like some of the radical greens wanted. For the sake of growth and prosperity – indeed, merely for the sake of eight billion people continuing to get up every morning – it was necessary for some minimum number of other species to be lost each year. Take the rusty pipistrelle, for instance, Africa's smallest bat. The little bastard might not look like much of an adversary, but nonetheless it was, in some very real sense, us or them. And once that was granted, the Chinese government had also been helped to understand that a free market solution, responsive to stakeholders of all kinds, would be the fairest and most efficient way forward.

Hence extinction credits.

Today, if you were a company like Brahmasamudram Mining and you proposed to wipe a species from the face of the earth, you basically just had to hand in a voucher to do it. The name for this voucher was an extinction credit. An extinction credit could buy you bulldozing rights to any species on earth – except when the species was certified as 'intelligent' by experts in animal cognition like the Swiss woman on the *Varuna*. In that case, you had to expend not just one but *thirteen* extinction credits, a figure which had no superstitious or metaphysical significance, but rather was the result, like every other detail of this framework, of wranglings at the birth of the World Commission on Species Extinction. Everyone agreed that to lose an intelligent species was the gravest loss of all, and so, although such extinctions could not be prohibited outright – that would not be a nimble free market solution – they should be very sternly disincentivised.

Every year, a certain number of extinction credits were allocated at no charge by the WCSE, while others were auctioned off, and afterwards they could be bought and sold on the open market. The idea was that the supply of credits would be gradually ratcheted down, so the price would creep up until they were pretty much unaffordable, and people would simply have to use their ingenuity to avoid driving species to extinction.

Unfortunately for the endangered species of the world, on the night of the Mosvatia Bioinformatics dinner the price of an extinction credit stood at just €38,432.

This was the lobbyists' most magnificent project, the stuff of war stories and founding myths, of after-dinner speeches and self-published memoirs. Kohlmann Treborg Nham and their comrades had succeeded in riddling the WCSE framework with so many allowances, indulgences, exceptions and delays that the intended scarcity of extinction credits had never actually come to pass. Extinction credits were plentiful and cheap. You could almost call them *democratic*. In the context of an undersea mining operation, €38,432 was nothing. For that matter, in the context of building a reasonably nice gazebo – supposing your proposed gazebo site was, by bad luck, the last remaining habitat of some endangered shrew – €38,432 was nothing. Even the €499,616 that Brahmasamudram might have to pay for the certified-intelligent venomous lumpsucker because of the mining vehicle's error – thirteen extinction credits at €38,432 each – would barely register as a line item. And because the 197 member countries of the WCSE had mostly subsumed their own laws into the WCSE's framework, there were, in many parts of the world, fewer barriers now to eradicating an endangered species than there had been at any time since laws of this kind were first enacted in the mid-twentieth century. This was Chiu Chiu's legacy. Open season on the almost extinct, and veal brain carpaccio for the extinction industry. If you had asked one of those protestors why they had taken the trouble to reincarnate Chiu Chiu as a two-ton neoplasmic dumpling and launch him out of a catapult at Halyard and his friends, that was probably more or less how they would have answered.

'I was on my way past and I thought I'd say hello to the survivors!' said Smawl, who had left the Hermit Kingdom as a little boy but still had his parents' accent. For some reason he'd recently taken to wearing wide-cut suits, trouser cuffs pooling over his shoes, of the kind that had been fashionable five years ago for people fifteen years younger than him.

'Actually, I was in the car behind,' Halyard said. 'And Mergen didn't even see it. He was on the minibus.'

'Still – close shave. So what's this fish?'

'Ugly little fucker, with a nasty bite.'

'No great loss, it sounds like.'

'Status isn't confirmed yet,' Halyard said, because he didn't feel like gratifying Smawl with even this inconsequential scoop. 'But, yeah, I don't see this one getting a lot of mourners at the funeral.'

'My wife's family are devout Muslims,' Ismayilov piped up, staring glumly at his water glass, 'and they believed it was haram to cut up her brain. We argued about it while she was dying, and I won, but afterwards they refused to let me mourn with them.'

Smawl looked a bit startled. As far as Halyard knew, he had never even met Ismayilov before. 'What did you think of the presentation?' he said.

Halyard shrugged.

'You'd think they really had it all worked out!' Smawl said. 'And, you know, officially I believe them! When our guys are in front of the WCSE, sure, it's not even a question. Connectome scanning is a mature technology.' Smawl looked around as if to make sure none of their hosts were listening. 'But did you hear about the Hainan black crested gibbon?'

Halyard realised he couldn't let Smawl go any further in front of Ismayilov. 'Yeah, I heard about that. But look—'

'I did not hear about it,' Ismayilov said. 'What is the Hainan black crested gibbon?'

'It doesn't matter.' Halyard shook his head at Smawl and made a cut-it motion across his throat, not even caring if Ismayilov saw. 'I actually thought the presentation was quite impressive—'

But Smawl was too excited that Ismayilov didn't know about the Hainan black crested gibbon. 'The Hainan black crested gibbon is EX' – meaning extinct – 'but they have a ten-nanometre scan, so this lab in Shenzhen, they ran a test where they modelled the entire brain on a computer in close to real time and hooked it up to a robot body – all the inputs and outputs – so they essentially had this dead monkey running around in the lab. *Zzzt-zzzt-zzzt*,' he added, making robot motions.

'They reincarnated it,' Ismayilov said.

Smawl nodded. Halyard pointed vigorously in a random direction. 'Hey, Barry, isn't that—'

'What happened?' Ismayilov said.

'At first, nothing. Robot wasn't moving. Then they tweaked a few of the parameters, and apparently this robot started *ripping its own limbs off*.'

'What?' Ismayilov said.

'Yeah, and I don't know whether it was an existential horror type thing for the monkey or just a cock-up with the modelling, but either way, the idea that they're anywhere close to the point where you can run one of these scans and bring an animal consciousness back just ready to go—'

With a howl of anguish, Ismayilov slammed his fist on the table so hard that his starter fork jumped into his lap. All around them people turned to look. Quickly Halyard got up and went round to Ismayilov's side of the table. 'Why don't we go outside for some fresh air?' he said.

Ismayilov carried on mewling but consented to being helped out of his chair. 'This monkey,' Ismayilov said as Halyard guided him towards the exit, past the waiters bringing in the main course – 'this monkey – this monkey gets ten nanometres, and even then – even then—'

'The scanning is fine, the modelling isn't as good yet,' Halyard said. 'That's all there is to it. If the modelling was already where it needed to be, we'd bring your wife back tomorrow. We just have to wait a bit. Like I said, Mergen, a few more years—'

'But what if they bring her back and she wakes up in her new body and she – she—'

Halyard patted Ismayilov on the back. 'Look, by the time they get round to your wife, they will have long since ironed out all that stuff. I mean, it's not like she's going to be . . .' He stopped himself – he had been about to say 'top of the list'. He swerved off in a different direction. 'The mere fact that the robot monkey was even capable of ripping its own limbs off – of forming the intention and then accurately going through with it – that shows they're making pretty remarkable progress over there. They must have solved a whole range of embodiment problems. So in a way it's . . . good news? It's a milestone.' Ismayilov was savagely wringing his hands as if he were trying to crack off a few metacarpals himself.

Outside, the two of them walked over to the promenade and sat down side by side on a bench overlooking the canal. Across the water, the glassy new developments took vague architectural inspiration from the surviving eighteenth-century goods warehouses in their midst, which only made the older buildings look somehow sullen, as if they suspected they were being mocked. Halyard couldn't help feeling some regret that he'd left the banquet hall, because he was still extremely hungry after one and a half spectral portions of veal brain, but as a colleague and sort-of-friend he felt it was his duty to stay out here with Ismayilov for as long as he was needed. So he would leave it to the Azerbaijani to give an indication that he had composed himself again and they could go back inside, an indication that Halyard expected within the next five or ten minutes, well within the availability window for the main course.

But after thirty-five minutes of sitting there in complete silence, Halyard was not only hungrier than ever but also in desperate need of a piss, and when he glanced sideways, Ismayilov had an expression as if he was still thinking about his dead wife, the unendurable cruelty of existence etc. What if Ismayilov was trapped in some kind of . . . mind loop? They could be here indefinitely. 'Do you want to go back in?' Halyard said.

Ismayilov shook his head.

Halyard hesitated. 'Well, do you mind if I just pop in for a sec?'

After he was finished in the toilets, Halyard made for the banquet hall, but he was too late: the waiters were already clearing away the sorbet bowls from the dessert course. So instead he went into the adjoining bar and scanned a bar menu. 'I'll have three bowls of olives,' he said to the barman, 'but just put them all in one big bowl for convenience, and . . . I'm with the Mosvatia dinner – is there a tab?'

'Yes.'

As it happened, Halyard was more flush with cash now than he'd ever been in his life, but he couldn't yet use any of it for traceable everyday spending – least of all very public extravagances – so he was falling back on old habits. 'I'll have a large glass of Komagatake 30 year,' he said, just on the off chance it worked. 'One ice cube.'

'That would not be included on the tab, sir.'

'Make it two glasses.' Smawl had materialised beside him. 'These are on KTN,' Smawl added with a smile, presumably having no idea that a large glass of Komagatake 30 year at Copenhagen hotel prices would cost somewhere between three and four hundred euros. Halyard knew he ought to say no, because he'd been planning to carry his nightcap back outside to the mourning bench, whereas this would oblige him to stay here with Smawl, in itself no enticing prospect, but he just couldn't resist the idea of Kohlmann Treborg Nham – those smug patricians – paying for his Komagatake. Knowing he could afford it himself made it more appealing, not less; this way nobody could call him a parasite. He decided he would suck down the cosmically expensive whisky as fast as he could and then rejoin Ismayilov afterwards.

Their drinks arrived and Halyard took a sip. It was transporting, like a pure distillate of low autumn sun and your dog rooting through dead leaves – his day off from Inzidernil hadn't been wasted after all. And what made it even better was the knowledge that the distillery had been destroyed in the Mount Shogikashira mudslide, so the supply of this whisky could never be replenished. Rushing it was out of the question, and he reassured himself that it wouldn't make any difference if he was gone for an extra ten minutes. Ismayilov probably wouldn't even notice.

About an hour and a half later, Smawl leaned in close. They were both sitting at the marble-topped bar, the last lingerers from the Mosvatia dinner. 'Do you want to know what I heard?' Smawl said. 'I have this on extremely good authority.'

Halyard waited. Smawl stared back at him. He realised Smawl wanted a response. 'Sure,' he said. 'Fine.'

'You've got to keep this to yourself.'

'OK.'

'It's big. Big stuff! But I have it on extremely good authority.'

Halyard waited.

'This,' Smawl said, 'is potentially going to change everything.'

Halyard ate what might have been his ninetieth olive. 'What is?'

Smawl leaned in even closer. 'There's a rumour they're going to vote yes on the biobank thing this year. They're really going to do it.'

Halyard made involuntary fists of frustration. He only just managed to stop himself from shouting at Smawl. 'For Christ's sake,' he wanted to say, '*everyone* in the industry already knows that. *Everyone*. That is not a "rumour", that is acknowledged fact, to the point that I recently committed a medium-sized financial crime that was specifically premised upon it. You didn't have to lean in and make me wait, you fucking heap of mildew.' But he thought about the three large glasses of Komagatake he'd put on Smawl's tab, and looked away.

'The biobank thing' was a radical change in the WCSE criteria for the extinction of a species, which, if pushed through, would be one more triumph for Kohlmann Treborg Nham. The reform under consideration was as follows: even if a species didn't have a single living individual left on earth, it should still not be considered extinct, as long as it had been the subject of what was called 'multimodal preservation'. This meant DNA sequences; microbiota profiles; MRI scans of the body; connectome scans of the brain; recordings of behaviour in the wild; and descriptions of habitat and diet. Nose to tail, you might say. All this would be uploaded to servers under the custodianship of the world's various biobanks, inviolable reliquaries much like the one where Ismayilov kept his dear wife.

What had prepared the ground for this reform was a growing sense that a physical body breathing its last was not the same thing as The End. That was too crude a marker. The End could come before and it could come after.

It could come before because a species was not just a set of bodies. It was a set of habits, relationships, territories, entanglements. Imagine a species of crab that knows how to gently massage a symbiotic anemone so that the anemone will release its hold on the crab's old shell and accompany the crab to a new one – except that all the anemones have long since shrivelled away. Imagine a species of turtle that for millions of years has been

28

returning to the same beaches to breed – except that the beaches are now a waterfront reclamation project. Imagine a species of frog that can gossip back and forth with frogs in other trees – except that in practice the language is as dead as Cornish because none of them can ever find anybody else to talk to. All of these species would be missing some enormous part of themselves – 'reduced to slavery,' as Comte de Buffon put it, 'or treated as rebels and dispersed by force, their societies have vanished, their industry has become barren, their arts have disappeared.' Even if they survived – even if they could be perpetuated indefinitely in laboratories and zoos – their extinction would already be in progress. Like a neurodegenerative disease, extinction was a slow hollowing, not a sharp cut. The death of the last holdout was in some sense a mere formality.

And yet The End could come after the last breath, too, perhaps aeons after, because of connectome scanning technology. The scanning of human beings, though not yet widespread, was at the stage of being a familiar plot point in soap operas about the rich. Nobody had yet tried to bring a dead person back, or at least nobody had yet admitted to trying – the auto-dismembering gibbon was the field's noblest accomplishment so far. But even if the technology was still dubious, its metaphysical premises were now widely accepted. And if a connectome scan of a loved one meant they were not truly gone, didn't a connectome scan of an animal therefore mean that they were not truly extinct? After all, even if you never got round to *Jurassic Park*ing them from DNA, you could still raise them any time you wanted like a spirit at a séance, simulating their inner life on a computer down to the very last neuron.

So on one hand you might have an animal which still had a handful of extant specimens, scooped from their habitat just before it was razed, now fed and watered in enclosures like tribesmen exhibited in some nineteenth-century world's fair after the obliteration of their culture. Death in life. And on the other hand you might have an animal which at present happened to have a living population of zero – yet if any scientist were ever curious about it, she could not only draw on an all-encompassing record of its physiology and behaviour, she could then test her theories on a virtual specimen in a virtual environment, a simulation which perfectly preserved the memory of all those habits, relationships, territories and entanglements from before they unravelled. Life in death. Which of these animals was really more extinct?

OK, fine, probably the population-zero animal. That one was more extinct. Everyone still more or less agreed on that. Nevertheless, this worldwide shift in attitudes, this fuzzing of the line that marked The End, was enough of a pretext for the WCSE to loosen its criteria after only eleven years, without it seeming too obviously like a concession to outside pressures, an insult to Chiu Chiu's memory.

Once ratified by the WCSE, the reform would save a lot of money for companies like Brahmasamudram Mining, who would merely need to arrange for the multimodal taxidermy of a species like the venomous lumpsucker, instead of either tiptoeing around its habitat or expending the extinction credits necessary for its legal disposal. It would make a lot of money for companies like Mosvatia Bioinformatics, whose quivering diamond blades would be much in demand. And Kohlmann Treborg Nham, of course, was cosy with all sides.

Frankly, Halyard felt they ought to be keeping Komagatake 30 year in these biobanks, instead of DNA samples of the legless skink. Some of these facilities advertised themselves as being secure against 'doomsday events'. After a doomsday event, which one of those would people actually want?

'And you know who—' Catching the bartender's eye, Smawl signalled for a fourth round. 'You know who—'

Halyard stopped him. 'No, not for me – I'm sitting outside with Ismayilov,' he said, admittedly in contradiction to the apparent physical facts. 'Got to get back to the poor bastard.' With something less than balletic grace he dismounted his bar stool.

Smawl finally got it out: 'You know who really stands to take a haircut if it happens?'

Don't fall for this, Halyard told himself. For God's sake don't fall for this twice in a row. There wasn't a ten-nanometre wisp of a chance that Smawl actually had any information that wasn't already a matter of public record.

And yet he couldn't help feeling curious. There was something about the lascivious spin Smawl had put on 'who really stands to take a haircut'. As if he weren't just talking about some dolt from the office who'd invested his retirement fund. As if he were talking about somebody major, somebody global, one of the mega-carnivores in the extinction ecosystem. And anybody like that – anybody who'd made a big bet against the reforms, anybody whose misplaced confidence had propped up the price of extinction credits prior to its inevitable slide – had made Halyard's medium-sized financial crime even more profitable. Suppose he happened to meet them one day and he could shake their hand knowing he'd beaten them at their own game . . .

He wanted to know.

Already cursing himself for his gullibility, Halyard sat down again. 'Fine. Tell me.'

But by now Smawl had got down from his own stool. 'I thought you had to shoot off?'

'Just tell me. OK? Come on. Just tell me.' He gestured at the bartender. 'One last round. On him still.' He turned back to Smawl. 'Just bloody tell me.'

That was the last thing he remembered.

*

'Sir, you may wish to wake up. Sir, you may wish to wake up.' When anyone else was listening his scullion was neutral and genderless, but in private it had the posh, breathy voice of a twenty-four-year-old girl with an expensive education. Halyard found himself at home, in bed, at once lingeringly drunk and incipiently hungover. It was close to 4 a.m. His scullion was configured to wake him only when it had extremely important news.

And so Halyard knew without being told that Ismayilov had thrown himself into the Nyhavn Canal.

31

His head felt like it had been lobbed from a catapult on to a motorway, but on this subject his thoughts were absolutely clear. Not once in the time he was drinking with Smawl had it even crossed his mind that Ismayilov might hurt himself, otherwise he (surely?) would have gone straight outside to check that Ismayilov was all right. But now he was as certain as if he'd watched it happen. That look on Ismayilov's face, as if when he wondered what there could possibly be left to live for, the world before him was as blank and answerless as the surface of the canal.

'Is he dead?' Halyard said.

'Is who dead, sir?'

'Is Ismayilov dead?'

'I have no reason to believe Mr Ismayilov is dead, sir.'

'So they fished him out in time?'

'I'm sorry, sir, I don't understand the question.'

'Can you just . . . Where is Ismayilov?'

'I don't have any information about where Mr Ismayilov is currently, sir. Would you like me to ask Mr Ismayilov's scullion for his whereabouts?'

Halyard realised he must have been wrong. This was about something else. He felt, illogically, quite annoyed at Ismayilov, as if the Azerbaijani had raised an irresponsible false alarm. 'Why did you wake me up, then?'

'Some major events, relevant to your interests, have taken place in the past hour.'

Halyard reached for the glass of water on the bedside table. His mouth was so dry the liquid practically hissed when it made contact with his tongue. He became aware that he was still wearing his suit trousers. 'Where?' This had better be worth it, he thought.

'Lausanne, Spitsbergen, Cape Town, Mexico City—'

'Show me,' said Halyard. He knew there was a connection between those four places but at this time of night he couldn't quite bring it to consciousness.

But then the wall opposite his bed started playing a digest his scullion had generated. Halyard watched at first with incomprehension, and then disbelief, and then horror. After a minute or so, he shouted, 'Call Devi! Call Devi! Wake her up!'

'Yes, sir.'

After Halyard's first attempt to sit up in bed had to be humiliatingly aborted due to poor preparation, his second just about made it over the hump. He waited, mumbling 'Shit, shit, shit, shit, shit,' under his breath, until at last he heard Devi say 'Hello?'

'Have you seen the news?' he said.

The *Varuna* was in the same time zone as Copenhagen, so it was the middle of the night there too. 'No. What happened?'

'The evaluator – whatever the fuck her name is—'

'Resaint.'

'Cut her off. You need to cut her off completely. Don't let her back in her lab. Kick her off the network. No communications in or out, and no talking to anyone else on board. If you could lock her in a bloody cupboard that would be – I mean, I know you can't literally do that, but her overall situation needs to as closely as possible resemble being locked in a cupboard, all right? Cut her off and keep her cut off until I get there. I mean it, Devi.'

'You're coming here?'

'Yes. I'm coming to talk to her.'

Chapter Three

A knock at the door. 'Karin? May we come in?'

A boyfriend of Resaint's had once joked, not entirely fondly, that she would be happiest in some kind of high-security lock-up, one hour of human contact a day and otherwise left to her own devices. And OK, fine, maybe she would have been better equipped for it than the average person, but that didn't mean she enjoyed her time under house arrest on the *Varuna*.

First of all, apart from a few safety manuals, there was no paper reading material on the entire ship. Meaning that, because her phone was still disconnected from the *Varuna*'s network, she was limited in her entertainment to whatever happened to be saved on the hard drive. Which was nothing – or almost nothing. A few months ago she'd downloaded a new statistical analysis tool, which came with a practice data-set, a study of the effect of West Nile infection on the feed-ing behaviour of the common house mosquito *Culex pipiens*. Cruelly, when she searched her phone, it turned out that this dataset was the one and only file available to her. So as the hours passed she grudgingly became an expert in it. Just her and these mosquitoes, trapped in a room together, except she was the one hovering and delving, losing interest and then cir-cling back, because the only alternative was staring out of the window at the morning fog.

Second, she didn't even have peace and quiet. Because every so often, at unpredictable intervals, like water torture, Devi would knock on the door to ask if she was all right. What the point of this was, she didn't know, except that Devi probably felt so guilty about the whole situation that she couldn't help herself. Each time Resaint answered yes in a frostier tone, but that only seemed to bring Devi back sooner.

When the captain knocked on the door around noon, however, Resaint knew it wasn't just another periodic check-in. Twenty minutes ago she'd heard the thrum of a VTOL flying towards the *Varuna* and settling on to the helideck.

She got up. 'Yes, you can come in.'

Devi opened the door. 'Karin, this is Mark Halyard,' she said, gesturing to the guy who stood beside her, late thirties, grey suit. 'Environmental Impact Coordinator for Northern Europe.'

'Hi,' he said. 'I'm really sorry about this.'

'So it wasn't your idea?'

Halyard hesitated. 'I suppose what I mean is, I'm really sorry that it was necessary.' He nodded into the cabin as if he wanted to come inside. 'Can we sit down and have a chat?'

'No. I've already been stuck in here for eight hours. I'm not going to talk to you about anything until at the very least I get some fresh air.'

Her demand was met. Outside, the fog had thinned and the sky was the palest a blue could be while still having any colour at all. No spindrifters on the horizon this time, but from belowdecks she could hear the deep chuttering of ferromanganese nodules being unloaded from one of the *Varuna*'s autonomous mining vehicles, like a worker ant regurgitating food into the mouth of its queen. Devi gave Resaint one last apologetic look before shutting the door, leaving her alone with Halyard on the same upper deck from which she'd launched her cargo drone the day before.

'I promise everything will be back to normal in no time,' Halyard said. 'I just need to talk to you about your report.' In the daylight he was a bit haggard-looking, as if he hadn't really slept.

'I haven't submitted it yet.'

'Right, I know.'

'We can talk about the format of the report if you like. Obviously you're not suggesting we talk about the content.'

'Yeah, no, of course not, but . . . Look, the word is you're going to be re-certifying.'

'"The word is"?' she repeated.

'Yeah.'

Resaint sighed. Last night, she'd intimated to Abdi that she was going to re-certify the venomous lumpsucker as intelligent, and he must have told Devi, and Devi must have told Halyard. She was pissed off at Abdi for gossiping, but she didn't see any malice in it: he couldn't possibly have anticipated such a psychotic overreaction from the Brahmasamudram corporate hierarchy.

'So I just came down here to find out if . . . I mean, I realise we can't talk about the actual content of the report, but just in terms of current status, is it final, or is there, you know, a bit of room for give and take there?'

'Give and take?' Resaint said.

'Looking at it not just in terms of this job on its own, but holistically in terms of your overall ongoing relationship with Brahmasamudram.'

'Sorry?'

He gazed at her, warmly, meaningfully, expectantly, as if trying to coax from her an understanding that might be right on the cusp. But when she showed, on the contrary, no sign of meeting him halfway, he went on. 'I mean, we really value having you involved, Devi says you've been great, so I don't think it's too early to start thinking about the next assignment. Whether that's around here, or somewhere else entirely. Pretty much wherever you like. We have sites all over the world. We're going to be expanding our zinc operation near Arequipa and I've heard it's gorgeous down there – the cold nights used to keep people away but they don't really get those any more and now it's like the new Brazilian Riviera, apparently. Nice change from Sweden. Or I don't know how you feel about all the travel, so if you'd rather have a break from that, maybe it's more along the lines of a consulting contract in my department? For as long as you want. Twice the money for half the work, that's what they always say about outside consultants, right? Just reconsider this report. I would never ask you to *lie*' – smiling as if that was almost a comical notion – 'but it's a matter of interpretation, isn't it, this stuff? The science. Maybe this fish isn't such a bloody mastermind after all. That's all I'm saying.'

Resaint stared at this oblivious dickhead. Nobody who had even an inkling of what the venomous lumpsucker meant to her would have tried to buy her off like this. But he didn't know. How could he? 'So all this fuss is because you don't want me to re-certify?' she said. 'You put me in lockdown just so I wouldn't be able to submit my report?' It didn't make any sense to her. The intelligence certification of one species shouldn't have meant anything to a company of Brahmasamudram's scale, or at least not enough that they would be willing to nuke the protocols like this. Eventually they would have to let her off the *Varuna*, and when they did she would tell the WCSE what had happened, and a full investigation might very well follow. Whatever potential costs were associated with the venomous lumpsucker, they couldn't possibly justify the fallout. It was like committing a murder to cover up a parking ticket. 'I'm afraid you wasted your time,' she said. 'Brahmasamudram can expect my report by the end of tomorrow.' She turned to leave.

'No, wait,' Halyard said. 'OK. Just wait. Forget the report for a second. How many fish do you still have in your lab?'

'None. I sent the last of them back last night.'

'And how would you get hold of those fish again?'

'Why would I do that?' she said.

'But just imagine you needed to for some reason.'

'They're not tagged. I'd have to send drones back to the reefs to look for them.'

'The South Kvarken reefs? That's, um . . . that would be the critical location?'

'Yes.'

'OK, how about DNA?' Halyard said. 'Do you have samples in your lab?'

'I sterilised most of the equipment yesterday. There's nothing stored there any longer. But I uploaded all the bioinformatic data I collected to GenBase. If you want DNA sequences, they're all there.'

'But say we wanted to clone this fish and we couldn't use Gen-Base, are you really telling me you don't have a few . . . a few loose scales lying around – or anything else, you know, right at the back of the freezer—'

'What are these questions? Why would you want to clone them? What has any of this got to do with anything?' While she waited for Halyard to answer, she noticed that he was playing with the cuff of his left shirt sleeve, slipping the button in and out of the buttonhole over and over again. For the first time she understood that behind his smile he was rigid with anxiety. And so she realised what must have happened – a realisation like the first news of a friend's death, too horrible to take in all at once.

'You've done it already, haven't you?' she said. 'You've mined the reefs. You didn't even wait for me to submit the report.'

*

Growing up, Resaint had never been a lover of animals. Her ex-boyfriend, the same one who thought she'd be happy in prison, had once called her a sociopath for her total indifference to the antics of his Maine Coons. She would have laughed at the suggestion that one day she might end up devoting herself to the zoological. But then again, nobody ended up in a job like Resaint's except by accident.

This was because the qualification that you might think would be most relevant – some kind of postgraduate training in animal cognition – was in fact regarded as a *dis*qualification. The fear was that people who'd specialised in animals from the start, who'd spent years in laboratories with ravens and pigs and cuttlefish, might be too infatuated, too liable to see intelligence in them via the pathetic fallacy, like dog owners who gaze into the vacant lolling faces of their pets and then confidently expound on the sophisticated, practically Aristotelian reasoning process they imagine to be going on within. The corporations and governments paying for these tests did not want testers who were secretly on the animals' side.

But on the other hand, the WCSE insisted on testers who at least had the right sort of conceptual grounding, who understood how you might poke and prod at an unfamiliar mind to decide whether or not it was intelligent. Which left a pretty narrow path into the field, because other than animals there weren't a lot of unfamiliar minds available for examination. One guy Resaint knew had studied children who were too severely autistic to communicate in any recognisable way but nevertheless gave oblique evidence of rich inner lives; another had published some work speculating on how one might bridge a similar gulf with extraterrestrials. But otherwise it nearly always meant artificial intelligence. Resaint's masters thesis at ETH Zurich had been on 'Unlimited associative learning as a sufficient condition for minimal consciousness in artificial systems.'

At the end of her masters, she was in the middle of applying for a Machine Learning Residency at Antichain when it emerged that Antichain predictive analytics tools were being used to run detention camps in Assam and Kashmir. And then Ferenc Barka, Antichain's founder, gave his notorious interview at Davos where he defended the contract, arguing that 'when a community is able to function more efficiently, that's good for everybody who lives there.'

A couple of her friends from ETH already had jobs at Antichain lined up, and one of them loudly announced he was going to pull out. Which was quite a stand to take. After all, it wasn't only that they'd been offered such sought-after jobs, it was that they'd been offered them in such a straightforward way, right out of graduate school, with no additional rigmarole. Famously, Barka loved people who shortcut the selection process with an inventive demonstration of how desperately they wanted to work for him – some sort of elaborate hack or prank or tribute – and over the years this preference of his had filtered down to every level of the company, so that even though the whole point of it was to highlight maverick thinkers, it had become almost ritualised, with various third-party consultants offering to help you come up with a semi-original gimmick. If you could avoid all that, skip straight to your five-figure signing bonus without having to worry about how you were going to squeeze a chuckle out of the jaded kings – well, that was tough to pass up, no matter what Barka had said at Davos.

Sure enough, the friend of hers who'd talked endlessly about pulling out never followed through, and the other one just avoided the subject altogether.

But Resaint, who'd got as far as the last round of assessments for the Residency, did withdraw. Frankly, she was relieved to have an unimpeachable excuse. What everyone said about these research jobs was that you had to give two hundred per cent of yourself, go in every morning ready to juice your brain like an orange. Her friends seemed excited by the idea in some masochistic way, but not Resaint. She resented it, even before the news about the detention camps. She didn't want to be property.

Instead she ended up in Berlin, working at a series of short-lived product development jobs. Here, too, she observed an almost libidinal desire to relinquish autonomy, except this time in the context of various silly, infantilising 'innovations', each product solving some non-problem – 'No more browsing for hours while your dinner gets cold: let *us* decide what movie you'd enjoy tonight, based on your hormonal and metabolic indicators!' – like a prosthesis fitted over a perfectly healthy limb so it could shrivel from disuse inside the plastic casing. When she'd done her masters, she'd believed that artificial intelligence was about computer minds ascending into personhood, but this was more about human minds decaying out of it. The upside, in theory, was that nobody possibly could take this work so seriously that they would expect her to dedicate every fibre of her being to it; except the unbelievable reality was that they *did*. Even worse, these consumer-facing start-ups had a much higher proportion of smooth, well-adjusted people than a company like Antichain, and one big thing about the socially normal was that they loved their social

40

norms. Whereas Resaint couldn't stand the politics, the niceties, the meetings where she had to spangle her expression and tone of voice with false enthusiasm just so people didn't think she was a bitch.

Then at a wedding she met a woman who worked as a WCSE-licensed species intelligence evaluator. You mostly work alone, the woman told her, and you travel a lot. Often, these are places that nobody else chooses to go; often, they cease to exist shortly after the assignment ends. So they feel almost private, personal, these fetid marshes that will soon be drained, these scrubby hills that will soon be levelled. The pay is worse than tech pay, but still not too bad, because there aren't that many people who know how to do it. And you don't have to love animals, but you will soon come to find their minds intriguing. After all, every feature of every animal is a solution to a technical problem. Examining an animal mind is like examining a missile guidance system or weather-predicting computer designed in some old totalitarian state: it's primitive, janky, hobbled by extraneous constraints, and yet at the same time it is the most resourceful and inventive technology you have ever seen, still more advanced in certain esoteric ways than anything that has come since.

That was how, like everybody else in her field, Resaint ended up there by accident. She found a job with an ecological consultancy who were prepared to subsidise her retraining. There, she mastered the Herzing intelligence metrics: encephalisation quotient, communication signal complexity, individual complexity, social complexity and interspecies interactions. She practised the laboratory tests used to measure them. And she absorbed – with the proper distance – the dissents and counterpoints. ('If you really can't see intelligence in the ability of a shrub to recover from having ninety-five per cent of its mass consumed by goats, maybe *you're* the vegetable.')

She stayed with the consultancy for four years and then struck out on her own. The venomous lumpsucker was her fourteenth assignment since then, and even before she started it was by far the strangest.

Back in 2015, a Japanese ichthyologist called Kazu Horikawa had come to Sweden to study certain Baltic fish. She had no institutional affiliation, having recently been sacked from her post at Nagasaki University. (Resaint had made what enquiries she could into Horikawa's life, but the only hint she had about this period was a curt response from a retired colleague of Horikawa's mentioning 'some disturbing actions'.) After two years in Sweden, Horikawa produced a paper titled 'Social strategic behaviour of the venomous lumpsucker'. But this paper was rejected by all the major journals: Horikawa was, after all, a lone researcher making wild claims in patchy English. Finally the paper found a home in *Open Fish Science*, an online-only publication with a small audience, and thereafter it was never once cited, perhaps never even read. Horikawa returned to Nagasaki, published nothing else, and later died during an outbreak of mutant COVID-24.

However, at the birth of the World Commission on Species Extinction, when the WCSE's registry of species was first compiled, decades of scientific journals were trawled for data. If a species had been documented as exhibiting behaviour that met the WCSE criteria for intelligence, that species was officially certified as intelligent until proven otherwise. Even a single paper was enough to ennoble a species in this way, as long as it had been published in a legitimate peer-reviewed journal in the past forty years. The WCSE had deigned to include *Open Fish Science* in the trawl, and so the extraordinary claims of 'Social strategic behaviour of the venomous lumpsucker' were recognised at last. Except, even then, nobody paid any attention.

Nobody, until the Brahmasamudram Mining Company began dragging the Gulf of Bothnia for ferromanganese nodules. They had hired Resaint expecting her to find that the venomous lumpsucker was not in fact intelligent and Horikawa had just been a lonely crackpot. This would relieve any twinges of concern about the very real possibility that the venomous lumpsucker might be purged in the course of the mining operation. Brahmasamudram would not be breaking their own policy forbidding the eradication of intelligent species – always bad for PR – and they would only have to submit one extinction credit to the WCSE instead of thirteen. Which, with extinction credits at €38,000, was hardly a spectacular dividend, but nonetheless enough of a saving that Resaint's three months on the *Varuna* would pay for itself. Resaint, too, started off assuming that the Horikawa/WCSE/lumpsucker situation was like when a government finally digitises hundreds of years of old rural land claims and in one of those old rural land claims it says that the tall oak tree by the river owns six acres of grazing land, or something folkloric like that, and this ends up in the database amongst everything else. The irrational vacuumed up along with the rational.

But she now knew Horikawa had been right all along. The venomous lumpsucker was one of the most intelligent creatures on the planet.

*

'There was a problem,' Halyard said. 'A problem with the software. The AMVs mined a sector they weren't supposed to mine. Devi's still looking into it.'

'When did this happen?'

'A few days ago.'

Resaint felt her stomach turn. Until last night she'd had almost a dozen lumpsuckers safe in her laboratory. But she'd unknowingly sent them back to a home that no longer existed. 'Do you realise what you've done?' she said.

'Yeah, I know, it's a real cock-up.'

'There is no other species on Earth like the venomous lumpsucker. And you've destroyed them.' She couldn't say any more because she was worried her voice would break.

And yet the strange thing was, Halyard looked as if he was almost as upset himself. The longer she watched him, the more certain she felt: he wasn't here because he wanted to put out a fire for his employers, he was here because he was desperate on some very personal level.

Maybe he was barely holding on to his job, maybe he was on his final warning at Brahmasamudram and he thought the venomous lumpsucker could be the end of his career. But that theory did not explain the recklessness with which he was operating here. Just how bad did things have to get before your best option was imprisoning the people who worked for you? And then he'd barely even tried to feel her out before he started tossing around his consultancy contracts and trips to Peru. All this on top of recruiting Devi as his accomplice, even though breaking rules made Devi so uncomfortable that she was probably longing to escape in a lifeboat.

Still less did that theory, patience running low at the office, explain the sheer agony she saw in him now. His tic with his shirt cuff had got even worse, so that by this stage it looked like he was vigorously fucking the button-hole with the button.

'Either you tell me the truth,' Resaint said, 'or this conversation is over. The venomous lumpsucker is very important to me. Why is it so important to you?'

For such a long time after this he seemed to be in stasis, fidgeting, with a glassy sleepless stare, so that if she'd known him better she might have shaken him. But then at last his shoulders went slack. 'OK,' he said. 'I've got myself into some fairly serious trouble. And you're the only person who can get me out of it.'

Chapter Four

Halyard had missed his first chance to make a lot of money without doing any work. He knew about the off-label use of Inzidernil before just about anybody, and he could have bought stock in Inzidernil's maker, Henan Pharmaceutical Group. But he didn't have anything to invest, so he just had to sit there and watch as HPG's stock price tripled in a few weeks as word spread about the drug.

Inzidernil had been part of the first wave of pharmaceutical drugs designed from the bottom up by AI. What it was officially supposed to do, Halyard kept forgetting – something endocrinal. The point was the side effects. Two years ago, a friend of Halyard's had given him a bottle containing thirty tablets of this medication Halyard had never heard of. 'The next time you know you're going to have a really depressing food day, take one of these first thing in the morning.' This friend was the same as Halyard: to them, almost every day was a really depressing food day.

Halyard's parents had both cared deeply about food, and by the time he was a teenager he had become just like them, voracious, forensic, worshipful towards good meals and caustic towards bad ones, decadent in the sense of pursuing sensual pleasure with great seriousness and conviction. About the Halyards even a Chinese family would have said, 'God, these people never shut up about food.' He didn't get much pocket money but his parents had taught him and his sister Frances that you didn't necessarily have to spend a lot to eat well: Honey Gold mangoes cost four dollars apiece and his family had nicknamed them Groaners because you couldn't help making noises when you ate one. Still, he looked forward to growing up and getting a bourgeois job so he could spend the rest of his life gorging himself on whatever he most loved.

And then he watched as all of it disappeared.

In Ontario, the heat dried up the sap in the maple trees; in Kenya, it wilted the coffee plants and invigorated their pests; in Champagne, it broke down the acid in the grapes; in Kentucky, it cooked the bourbon in its barrels. In Campania, the mozzarella buffaloes stopped lactating for a week after every bout of strange weather; in Iberia, a fungus hollowed out the oak trees that were supposed to drop the acorns that fed the pigs; off the coast of Tasmania, the oysters' shells dissolved in the corrosive seas; and off the coast of South Australia, the bluefin tuna starved because there were no smaller fish left to prey upon. Even Halyard's beloved Honey Golds shrivelled away because there wasn't enough water in Queensland to cultivate them.

And it wasn't just delicacies that suffered. Staples, too. Halyard's grandparents had often said that fruit and vegetables didn't taste quite as good as they used to. But if flavour had been very gradually leaking out of produce for decades, the last of it flushed away with a terrible suddenness as Halyard entered adulthood. Potatoes, carrots, beets and apples were distinguishable only by colour, not by taste. Aubergines were spongy, kale was bitter, honey was as thin and tasteless as egg white. It was as if fecund Mother Earth had been replaced overnight by one of those food service companies who mostly do internment camps. There were attempts to compensate – genetic engineering, sealed biodomes, AI farmers that nurtured every sprout and youngling with the care an anxious parent gives an only child – but as was the general trend of things, even the boldest advances in technology could not keep up with the rate of collapse.

Eating well was still possible. It was just extraordinarily expensive. The wealthy of the world were all competing for an ever-shrinking ration of food and drink that actually tasted of something. And for Halyard, it became an obsession. Like everybody, his memories of youthful meals were wreathed in a glow of nostalgia, except that this wasn't the nostalgia of people who falsely believed their mothers had been good cooks, it was a nostalgia corroborated in its melancholy by the certain knowledge that the past really was a lot better. Nearly every meal he ate was a disappointment to him, an insult, a torture. He just didn't seem to be able to accustom himself to it like other people could, and he sometimes felt like a climate change refugee, displaced from everything he'd grown up with (although he soon learned this was not a sentiment you should express publicly). Yes, the world was losing a lot of other things, in fires and floods and pandemics and riots and wars, more important things, even Halyard could see they were objectively more important – but they just didn't matter to him the same way. After all, he couldn't eat pandas, or glaciers, or Jakarta. When the Buddhists taught that craving is suffering, they were absolutely right. I would pay anything, he sometimes said to himself, *anything*, for just one piece of good sushi.

And, disastrously, he meant it.

By the time his friend slipped him the bottle of Inzidernil, Halyard had made a decent career for himself in the field of environmental planning for the extractive industries, but he had no assets, no savings, nothing but debts, because every cent he earned went straight down his throat. He'd had the misfortune to fall in with a very bad crowd: serious gourmands, Olympian high-rollers, all of them rich, some of them dynastically so. And for a long time he'd tried to keep up with them, because somehow he'd convinced himself it was vital to do so. The best meal of his entire life was an omakase at Sushi Ashina in Tokyo, prepared before his eyes by the legendary Goro Yoshida just weeks before his retirement. Where Yoshida sourced his fish was a closely guarded secret, but that night Halyard ate tuna, salmon, mackerel, scallops, red clams, gizzard shad, freshwater eel, everything you couldn't get any more, everything he used to eat with his parents when they took him to Masuya in Sydney for his birthday, except here it was elevated to another plane entirely.

It cost 300,000 yen, or about 2,500 euros. Not including drinks.

But of course real life wasn't Sushi Ashina. Real life wasn't even a Mosvatia Bioinformatics presentation or any of the other top-tier junkets where you could at least drink a bit of decent wine (quite a lot of it if you had Halyard's expertise in wringing out a corporate tab). Real life was airports and worksites, conference centres and mining support vessels. Real life was depressing food days. And so, one morning when he knew he was facing one of those – three meals that would take as much from him psychologically as they put into him physically, three meals that for social and professional reasons he would be obliged to sit there and eat instead of just dodging the whole issue with a nutrient shake – he swallowed an Inzidernil.

And after that he just didn't care.

The Inzidernil didn't stop him tasting what he was eating. And it didn't fool him into thinking that what he was eating was delicious. Rather, it took away his evaluative response. He no longer felt any disappointment or resentment or grief. He no longer compared the meal against his memory of what it should have tasted like. It just didn't bother him.

Whatever part of the brain it was that turned all animals into foodies – that had evolved so that an animal would relish a sugar-rich berry or an iron-rich liver and reject an unripe gourd or an indigestible stem – that part of his brain fell silent. All his discernment, his snobbery, went with it. What he was eating was neither bad nor good, except in the limited sense that he had been hungry before and now he was full. Presumably this was what eating was like for those robotic people who had never learned to care about food in the first place; and what it was like, also, for the most enlightened Buddhists, who according to the fourteenth Dalai Lama could savour shit and piss as if they were the finest food and wine. Such were the side effects of Inzidernil, completely unintended by Henan Pharmaceutical Group.

Halyard wanted a lifetime supply of Inzidernil. And lots of other people would too, enough to keep HPG's pill factories extremely busy. Halyard understood this right away, even if he wasn't prescient enough to guess the other markets Inzidernil would penetrate a few years later (as it would turn out, even its off-label uses had off-label uses). The problem was, he'd already spent everything he had on exalted *nigiri*, which meant he had no way of buying HPG stock before word got out. So he went to Terence, his closest friend among the rich gourmands, the only one he'd ever had real conversations with that didn't consist entirely of ranking meals, and explained the blissful relief of Inzidernil, hoping Terence might be willing to stake him the money. Terence wasn't afraid of a spicy investment opportunity: he was backing one of the laboratory start-ups on Surface Wave, the new biotech city floating in the Gulf of Finland.

But Terence didn't get it. Terence ate mediocre food sometimes, but only when he was too apathetic to organise anything better. Because of his inherited billions, it was always on some level a choice – he was never truly trapped with it, the way normal people were. And so Halyard just couldn't make him understand why Inzidernil was such a boon. Also, a guy Terence knew from university had gone to work at Henan Pharmaceutical Group, and that guy was a complete moron, which to Terence was a very important data point. He could not be persuaded to underwrite Halyard's investment – even though Halyard had once seen him spend twelve thousand euros on a bottle of Bordeaux.

*

By the time Halyard saw his second opportunity to make a lot of money without doing any work, he had been brooding on the Inzidernil episode for some time, and also he was in quite a lot of credit card debt. The debt made him so anxious that for a while he developed an addiction to those videos of people mixing oil paints together (the kind that he had found soothing as a teenager, back when they were still made by real human beings mixing real paint – but of course now they were entirely generated

49

by computers, which optimised them until they were narcotic, brain-imprisoning). This time, he wasn't going to let a windfall slip through his fingers.

Just like he found out about the off-label uses of Inzidernil before just about anybody, he found out about the imminent reforms at the WCSE before just about anybody. And although his job took him all over northern Europe and sometimes further afield, although he spent hours in the hotel bars where expense accounts loosened tongues until they practically fell off, although he was an international superspreader of extinction industry gossip, it was for none of these reasons that he found out. Rather, it happened by sheer coincidence. In what promised to be the first instance in his entire life of an extravagant meal actually paying for itself many times over, he happened to overhear a conversation in a restaurant.

It was at a place in Oslo known for serving some of the most exquisite produce to be found in Europe, which is to say produce that matched what his mother might have picked up from Eveleigh Farmers Market on any given Saturday when he was a child. Halyard's dining partner cancelled at the last minute, but he didn't want to waste the reservation, so he sat alone at the horseshoe-shaped dining counter. Within eavesdropping distance across the horseshoe were a man and a woman who, he gradually realised, were high-ranking executives at Kohlmann Treborg Nham. As the twelve-course meal proceeded – tomatoes, or chickpeas, or cabbage, served almost unadorned – it became clear that the executives were feeling ebulliently satisfied with themselves. They had just slotted into place the last of the pieces necessary to secure the reforms that KTM had long been pushing for. The big prize. A change in the very definition of extinction, so that a species would not legally be considered extinct by the WCSE, even if it had a living population of zero, as long as enough relics of it were preserved in biobanks around the world.

No doubt the food was great, but Halyard ate mechanically, all his attention in his ears instead of his mouth. At that time, extinction credits were at around €67,000. Halyard knew that portents of the reforms would depress that price, as the rumour trickled out of Kohlmann Treborg Nham and through the wider extinction industry until it reached investors, analysts, reporters and eventually even people like Barry Smawl. And once the reform was an irrevocable fact, the price would collapse completely. After all, nobody would bother buying extinction credits if it was so cheap and easy to 'save' a species from extinction. However low companies like Mosvatia Bioinformatics could push the cost of multimodal preservation – which could be done in bulk for especially biodiverse habitats, automated like a factory line – that would be the ceiling for the price of credits. Halyard could see the price falling into the mid-four-figures, perhaps even lower.

When you know for certain that an asset is going to drop in price, you can short that asset. Meaning you borrow some of it; sell what you borrowed; wait until the price falls; buy it back; return it to whomever you borrowed it from; and pocket the difference.

The problem was, this normally required a broker. And no broker would take Halyard's business. Any time he tried to open an account that would allow for short sales, the broker would run a background check on him, and although he tried dozens of different brokers, he was rejected every single time. He had no criminal record, no bankruptcies. But these background-check algorithms were like Saint Peter at the gates of heaven, combing through pretty much all the data on Mark Halyard that had ever been recorded anywhere. And, unanimously, they decided he just wasn't worth the hassle. They were under no obligation to explain their reasoning, so he never knew what he'd done to disgrace himself.

Fortunately, however, if you really wanted to sell some extinction credits you didn't own, there was another way you could do it. You could be Environmental Impact Coordinator (Northern Europe) at Brahmasamudram Mining.

When Brahmasamudram finalised the plans to begin mining the Gulf of Bothnia for ferromanganese nodules, Halyard was called upon to secure thirteen extinction credits using his department's budget, thirteen being the maximum number that might be required if the venomous lumpsucker did in fact get eradicated and its intelligence certification hadn't in fact been reversed. Credits were at €67,000. But he knew that, by the time they were needed, the WCSE reforms would already be a reality, and the price would have fallen below half that. So he could short these extinction credits all by himself. This time there would be no Terence to turn him down, and no background-check algorithm either.

He could discreetly borrow the credits from his own department; sell off all thirteen at €67,000 each, directing the €871,000 gross to a crypto account; wait a few months until the price tumbled; buy back thirteen extinction credits for much less than €871,000; return those to Brahmasamudram, who would never know the difference; and spend the profits on some combination of debt service and dazzling gluttony.

Yes, in one sense he would be proving the background check algorithms right, by committing a financial crime. But in another sense he would be proving them wrong, by making a lot of money that they could have had a piece of if they hadn't been such supercilious pricks.

Around the time Halyard was formulating this plan, something happened at Brahmasamudram that just for a moment shook his resolve. The Junior Finance Director back in Mumbai, a guy called Pratury, was found to have been fabricating billings. The gossip was that he had a mistress who liked couture dresses from Seoul. Pratury hadn't even been running his racket for that long before Brahmasamudram's accounting software detected patterns associated with embezzlement, and he was well liked within the company, so it was assumed that he would just be removed as quietly as possible. But then the board of directors shocked everybody by ordering that he should be prosecuted to the fullest extent of the law. And after Pratury was arrested, the magistrate denied him bail, saying he was a flight risk because he had so many relatives in Dubai. So he was sitting in a jail cell.

One of the terrors of this era, to people like Halyard, was the suddenness with which life could become *physical*. Imagine that, because of your economic position, you are safe and serene and almost untethered to the earth. Your body is nothing, really: it's just the part of you that gets tired at the gym, the part of you that will be shucked into a furnace after your connectome is uploaded. And then, overnight, your body becomes primary again, because your home is flooded or burned or buried or confiscated, and you are plunged into a life of physical degradation, physical constraint, physical danger.

The past decade had demonstrated that this could happen to anyone, absolutely anyone, even people who seemed far above it all five minutes earlier. If it hadn't happened to you, you were grateful for your good fortune. And so the thought of recklessly inviting it upon yourself, this grim entrapment in the body, when you really didn't have to, when you were doing fine, when you weren't in the path of the hurricane – well, Pratury in his prison uniform looked like a real dope. Halyard didn't want to be one too.

But he reassured himself that his scheme was quite different from Pratury's, because he wasn't stealing anything. In a sense he would just be acting as a sort of informal investment manager for Brahmasamudram, taking their idle assets out for some bracing exercise. When it was all over, the company would be left entirely whole – that was the genius of it.

The only way it could go wrong would be if the price of extinction credits rose, rather than fell. And that was impossible.

'Some major events, relevant to your interests, have taken place in the past hour.' The scullion waking him from a Komagatake coma. His confusion, thinking it was about Ismayilov. And then the breaking news on the wall opposite his bed.

Six attacks, one at each of the six major biobanks: Lausanne, Spitsbergen, Cape Town, Mexico City, Taizhou, and Yokohama.

At each biobank, a computer worm took control. First, the worm broadcast a fake chemical hazard alert to herd all the staff away from the cold storage areas. Then it locked the doors, switched off the freezers, and cranked the facility's heating system until those freezers turned into ovens.

53

In Lausanne and Cape Town, where the biobank's staff managed to regain control within a couple of hours, the attack stopped there. In Spitsbergen and Yokohama, where they did not regain control – and in Taizhou and Mexico City, where they regained control but then lost it again – the attack proceeded to a second phase: blasting the automated cleaning hoses until they flooded the entire facility and then boiling the water like an enormous kettle. But this was gratuitous: the destruction at Lausanne and Cape Town was later found to be almost as thorough from the superheated air alone. Millions upon millions of frozen tissue samples cooked into useless snot.

There was a single human casualty: a technician in Taizhou who re-entered the cold storage area, against the orders of her superiors, when it appeared the attack was over. Distraught, she couldn't wait any longer to survey the damage, and she was boiled to death after the worm reasserted its dominance.

And yet, as staggering as this was, it was only half of what was happening. The other half was still barely understood by the time the attacks on the biobanks became world news.

Even though the biobanks still lavished a lot of floor space and man hours on frozen tissue samples, to many biologists these were now as archaic as wax cylinders or punch cards. These days you could send a digital file over to your enzymatic printer and in a few hours it would synthesise a DNA strand on a microplate; no need to mess around with anything swabbed out of an animal when you could just download the genome from GenBase. So on that way of thinking, if the worm had only deep-cleaned the freezers, not much would have been lost. The biobanks would still have had all the fruits of multimodal preservation: DNA sequences, connectome scans of the brain, MRI scans of the body, and so forth. And although the biobanks were the administrators, the librarians, of that data, the data was not, of course, physically stored in the biobanks: it was distributed between cloud servers all over the planet.

The worm attacked those too.

It hacked into thousands of different cloud servers simultaneously, and deleted every file ever uploaded by the biobanks.

Experts later said this should not have been possible; they discussed it with awe, like scientists confronted with some transgression against the basic laws of physics. But the worm was extraordinarily adaptable and devious, and so it wrought this dark miracle. This was technology that could have crippled nations, won wars, and here it was being used to erase videos of the legless skink.

And not just the legless skink. Also the velvet scoter. The Hainan black crested gibbon. The angel shark. The rusty pipistrelle. The Stone Mountain fairy shrimp. The variable cuckoo bumblebee. The marbled gecko. The Alagoas tyrannulet. The thicklip pupfish. The hoary-throated spinetail. The white-chested white-eye. The Cozumel thrasher. The spine-fingered tree frog. The Zempoaltepec deer mouse. The cracking pearlymussel. The Papaloapan chub. The dromedary naiad. The warrior pigtoe. And about nineteen thousand other species that had been preserved in the biobanks since their extinction in the wild. All gone.

In some cases, this still didn't really matter. For instance, the worm rubbed out everything the biobanks held, physically and digitally, on the giant panda. But that was hardly going to erase pandas from history. For decades before their temporary extinction, pandas had been documented about as thoroughly as anything on earth, plus now there were actual cloned pandas lumbering around.

Consider, however, *Gulella warinyangus*. This was a species of tiny land snail found only in northern Ghana. *Gulella warinyangus* was first discovered when biologists attempted to count the population of another, very similar snail, *Gulella atewana*, on behalf of a company who intended to build a solar panel array right on top of *atewana*'s habitat. In other words, *Gulella warinyangus* was never studied in any context other than the bureaucracy of its certain extinction. There were no nature documentaries about *warinyangus*, no scientific papers, no pickled specimens in museums, no sports mascots in its image, no plush toys for children, no folktales in which it outwitted or was outwitted by some other animal. The only record of *warinyangus* was in those biobanks, its multimodal preservation funded by a WCSE grant. And after the attacks, even that was gone. It was named only so it could be destroyed; it was destroyed; and now only the name was left, like some minor figure in a medieval chronicle with an editor's footnote saying 'About this person nothing else is known.' It might as well never have existed.

Admittedly, in this sense *Gulella warinyangus* was no different from innumerable other species that had plummeted into the blackness of time, that had lived and died without the human race ever noticing. Indeed, the overwhelming majority of species that had ever evolved on earth had gone extinct before the human race first awoke. A species rotting in an unmarked grave could not in itself be considered a tragedy unless the entire history of life was to be considered a tragedy. But these were nineteen thousand species whose extinction human beings had carried out knowingly, almost nonchalantly, on the basis that their existence was only really being suspended, and in the future they could be restored to life, or if not literally restored to life at least studied, understood, paid the proper tribute. We had pawned those animals, intending to buy them back one day when things were a bit less stretched, and now the pawn shop had burned to the ground with all the animals inside.

But of course when Halyard watched the news in horror, it wasn't because he cared so much about *Gulella warinyangus*.

*

The WCSE reforms were dead. That was obvious. Nobody could seriously suggest changing the definition of extinction, putting biobanks at the centre of everything, when biobanks had turned out to be about as eternal and inviolable as a wet cardboard box. For a while now, the smart money had been on the reforms passing – not just the smart money, in fact, but also the money of average intelligence and the money of below-average intelligence and even the kind of money where you find yourself wondering about the industrial pollutants this money might have been exposed to as a baby. This expectation had been like a weight pressing down on the price of extinction credits. Halyard had sold Brahmasamudram's thirteen credits when they were still at €67,000 each, and then watched with satisfaction as the rumour spread and the price fell. But now, with the reforms an impossibility, the weight had been snatched away, and the price would not just revert but rebound.

Halyard's scullion woke him after the news of all six attacks was verified by multiple sources, but by that time the algorithms who bought and sold extinction credits on the Asian exchanges had already been trading on it for a geologic age in algorithm years: the first garbled report had come out of Mexico City, then a similar one out of Yokohama, and that second one was enough for the algorithms to anticipate some sort of trend.

Right away they started scooping up credits, bidding each other higher and higher. Pretty soon they were joined by the short sellers, who now urgently needed to cover their short positions so they wouldn't take too much of a loss. The buying frenzy fed the short squeeze and the short squeeze fed the buying frenzy. And that was just the hedge funds and speculators. The people who actually did things with credits, the states and corporations and state-owned corporations who very much relied on having the legal right to eradicate a few dozen species every year, were only just beginning to react. Nobody knew how high the price could spike, so everyone was suddenly desperate to be holding some credits to make sure they wouldn't get totally fucked.

And what was emerging was that the market was a lot tighter than anyone would have expected. For the past several months, extinction credits had exuded this stink of decline, so you would have thought there would now be a lot of credits sloshing around, just waiting to be bought up. But there weren't. In fact – and all this was playing out in a few heartbeats of a variable cuckoo bumblebee (RIP) – there was practically nothing out there.

Almost as if someone had cornered the market in extinction credits before the attacks took place.

Halyard had once gone with four colleagues to visit a potential monazite mining site in the badlands of southern Spain. When they arrived at the site, a sun-blasted former olive grove miles from anywhere, it was announced that the car that was carrying all the drinking water had suffered some minor technical problem and would not arrive for about another forty-five minutes. Instantly Halyard, who had not been thirsty ten seconds earlier, was the thirstiest he had ever been in his entire life. He guzzled every last drop of the mostly empty bottle of water he happened to have with him and then began to consider how he would kill the other four if it came to it.

This reaction, which Halyard felt a bit sheepish about afterwards, was basically what proliferated through the extinction credits market after it became clear that there weren't enough credits to go around. Even the algorithms were hyperventilating. By the time Halyard rushed out of his flat in Copenhagen so he could catch an early-morning flight to Stockholm and then a high-speed train to Sundsvall and then a VTOL to the *Varuna*, the price of a single extinction credit had risen from €38,432 to €287,057.

*

He didn't confess it all at once, out on the deck. Instead, he tried to evoke a feeling of entrepreneurial spirit and noble failure. 'Have you ever read that book *Free Climbers*?' he asked Resaint. She had not. 'It's about people who take risks in business. Sometimes you make a risky bet,' he went on, 'and if it pays off, people celebrate you, but if you make the same bet, and your luck is bad, and it *doesn't* pay off, you get treated literally like a criminal. That's the situation I'm in. I made a decision at work that I really believed in, and now it could have personal consequences for me. Basically what I mean is, I could go to jail.'

Just saying that word out loud – 'jail' – filled him with the same strangling dread he'd felt as he digested the news of the attacks. And he knew it was reckless to admit even this much to a person he didn't know.

But he hadn't been prepared for this conversation to be so hard. Most of the biologists he dealt with knew their place. They had their pride, yes, intellectual and professional, but also they understood that they were working for Brahmasamudram, and they wanted more work in the future. He had never asked a biologist to reverse their conclusions before, but it had always felt as if he could if he really needed to. As the VTOL was flying towards the *Varuna*, and he thought about Resaint spending three months on this sparsely crewed mining ship in the middle of the Baltic fog, living in the same conditions as the roughnecks except for a slightly less claustrophobic cabin, it had seemed obvious that she would accept his offer to liberate her from jobs like this. (Also, he'd looked up pictures of her on the way here: she was attractive, with a nice smile in one of the pictures, and in hindsight maybe that had made him assume unconsciously that she would be easy to get along with, charitable about the mistakes he'd made . . . And therefore the negotiations would run smoothly.)

But when he admitted to her that the AMVs had already mined the venomous lumpsucker's breeding ground – much sooner than he'd meant to admit it, but somehow she seemed already to know – she gazed at him with a fury that made him feel peeled and chilled and sectioned like a brain bound for the scanning microscope. It soon became clear that she could not, in fact, be bribed, and although he'd been prepared to threaten her, or at least make some threat-like observations – 'I know everyone in this industry who can hire you for these assignments, and I hope you realise we talk to each other about who worked out well and who didn't' – that felt just as futile. Plus, Devi had already told him that she wasn't willing to hold Resaint in her cabin any longer, which left Halyard with no more cards to play. Everything was going wrong.

Except maybe, if he was at least partially honest with her about his predicament, explained enough so that she could see how trapped he felt . . . He could think of moments in his past where that tactic had worked surprisingly well. People could be very forgiving. Women could be very forgiving. (But he hadn't told her anything about the attacks on the biobanks, and *that*, at least, she hadn't guessed. If she felt so strongly about the venomous lumpsucker, how would she feel about the erasure of another nineteen thousand species? He'd told her only that the price of extinction credits had gone up.)

'When Devi tells Brahmasamudram that the fish is EX,' he explained, 'if it's still certified as intelligent, then Brahmasamudram are going to want me to submit thirteen extinction credits to the WCSE. Thirteen credits we bought months in advance in order to insulate ourselves against any market volatility. And like I said, you don't want to hear all the boring details, but those credits aren't going to be available, because basically I took a risk for the good of the company. Whereas if you help me – if you submit a report saying that the weird Japanese lady was wrong—'

'Horikawa.'

'—saying Horikawa was wrong and the venomous lumpsucker isn't intelligent – that way, we only need to submit one credit to the WCSE.' And he could pay for that one credit out of the €870,000 he still had from the sale. It would sting, but he could pay for it.

'What about the other twelve?' Resaint said. He knew she'd grown up in Germanophone Switzerland, but she spoke English with almost no accent. 'Brahmasamudram will think they still have those. Eventually they'll want to use them for something else.'

'Yeah, but that won't be for months. That'll give me time to sort all this out. That's all I need – time.' Maybe the price would go back down. Or if it didn't, he'd find a way to cover it up. He'd made it look as if the credits got stolen by hackers. Or as if there had been some operational blunder and the credits had never been bought in the first place. 'At worst I'll get fired. I won't go to jail. And if I do get fired,' he hastened to add, 'I'll already have made everything nice and cosy for you at Brahmasamudram. You know, the consultancy thing. A real modelling contract, I promise.'

'A "modelling contract"?'

'It's an expression – one of those jobs where you get paid an outrageous amount of money just to turn up and look serious.'

'I've told you. The venomous lumpsucker is highly intelligent. I'm not going to submit a report pretending it's not.'

'Please. Karin. It's my only hope.' He searched her face for any indication of mercy.

She shrugged. 'I don't care.'

Feeling suddenly that he needed to lean on something, Halyard turned away from her and walked to the railing.

Yes, he would be prosecuted in Denmark, which was famous for its humane criminal justice system. But that didn't mean he would end up serving a six-month sentence in one of those open prisons that were about as punitive as a celebrity ashram. He would be subject to the environmental fraud laws. These laws were designed to make sure that if, say, you lied to the government about the emissions from your cement factory, you would be prosecuted as an especially wicked sort of criminal. Give a lot of kids severe asthma, and you couldn't expect to be treated any better than the sicko who'd choked a few with his bare hands, just because you'd taken a more roundabout route to the same result. Halyard had not in any way befouled the environment. His crime was entirely abstract. These laws were surely not intended for situations like his. Nevertheless, they had been written broadly enough to foil even the most serpentine manoeuvres by corporate lawyers, which meant that with Brahmasamudram's cooperation the Danes would probably be able to charge him with 'profiting from a fraudulent act involving the misrepresentation of the status of an environmental regulatory instrument', or something like that.

He hadn't given this any thought when he was planning his extinction credits sale, not even when he heard the news about Pratury. But this morning, following a little bit of research, he had begun to realise the danger he was in. If he was convicted under the environmental fraud laws, he would serve a long sentence in a closed prison, which would be just like a prison anywhere else. And he'd heard that these days the people you met inside were not fondly disposed towards environmental crimes, not the guards and not the other prisoners either. It was never good to be the culpable human face of an ongoing mega-tragedy affecting every living being. All it would take was one guy on your wing who'd lost his village to a flood or his grandma to a heatwave back in his home country and you really would be on the shit-list next to that child murderer. And they wouldn't care about the details. 'It was just a bet on the price of a financial asset!' he imagined himself screaming in terror. 'Please – surely you can understand – I'm not a bad person, I just saw an opportunity in the markets!'

And then there was the food. Year after year of slop, and no Inzidernil. Something else he'd heard about prison life was that the food wore you down as much as anything else. Precisely because most people on the outside couldn't understand that – 'It's just lunch, what does it matter?' – the food was often the vehicle of particular sadism by the authorities, sadism that would have been too conspicuous in any other form.

For a moment he imagined throwing himself into the water like Ismayilov (oh, except Ismayilov hadn't thrown himself into the water – he kept forgetting). But he'd probably just land on one of the lower decks. From here you could look down on them, the labyrinths of spare machinery and cable reels and other unidentifiable forms swaddled in translucent tarps. Somehow the sight calmed him a little bit, his anxiety soaking up into the purposeful density of it all.

He turned back to Resaint. 'What if they aren't extinct?'

She just looked at him.

'If the venomous lumpsuckers aren't extinct,' he went on, 'then it makes no difference what you say in your report – Brahmasamudram won't need to submit any credits to the WCSE. Then I'm OK. At least in the short term.'

'They are extinct,' she said. 'Effectively. There were so few left down there even before this. South Kvarken was their last habitat. That's why you people sent me here in the first place. Yes, there may a few survivors after what you did to the reefs. And there are the ten I sent back there last night. But now they'll scatter. And the Gulf of Bothnia is not a koi pond. There will be no easy way to find even a single one of them without hundreds of drones and some blind luck. And no breeding ground means no breeding season, which means no more baby fish. So it's over. If you want to bring them back from extinction, you'll have to clone them with the DNA sequences I sent to GenBase. That's all that's left of them now, and it's not even much of a gene pool. As for who's going to pay for that – who's going to pay for an artificial habitat, because you'd need an artificial habitat, they can't live indefinitely in a tank . . .'

He couldn't stop himself from cringing at the mention of GenBase, which had been managed in collaboration between the Spitsbergen and Yokohama biobanks and was now just a vast howling blank. 'What about Sanctuary North?'

Resaint frowned. 'Why would anyone pay to keep venomous lumpsuckers at Sanctuary North?'

'Don't they do stuff for other fish? Other fish like having them around?'

'Yes, but from what I've heard, Sanctuary North is not exactly meticulous about—'

'But they might have a population of their own. It's the right kind of biome.'

'I suppose.'

'Let's go there and see,' Halyard said.

Resaint looked at him in disbelief. 'What?'

'It's only, like, five hundred k's from here. We could just go over there and take a look. We might get lucky.'

'You had me locked in my cabin for eight hours and now you want me to travel to Estonia with you?'

'Look, we both really want to find this fish. And we still might. I have a Brahmasamudram expense account, and I know Pavel at Sanctuary North, and I know pretty much everyone else in the industry as well. Anywhere this fish could still be hiding, I can get us there, I can get us in, OK? But you – you are actually acquainted with the fish itself. That's pretty bloody crucial too. I won't be able to do this alone, and neither will you. But . . .' He bounced his hand back and forth between them as if to say 'You and me together . . .'

Resaint turned and walked away.

Halyard watched, paralysed, as she shut the door behind her, leaving him alone on the deck.

He took out his phone. Maybe something would have happened in the last half an hour. Maybe the Chinese would have revealed that they'd been secretly running a seventh major biobank in the tunnels under the Yueliang Gong moonbase, and there would have been an enormous embarrassed counter-reaction in the markets, and the price of an extinction credit would have dropped below ten thousand euros, and now he would make even more money from his scheme.

But he knew that his scullion would have interrupted if anything like that had happened. And in fact the latest news only confirmed the disaster. Now that the experts had had a few hours to take stock, they were even more despondent. Nothing could be salvaged from the great library's ashes. Halyard knew he needed to take some urgent and possibly drastic steps relating to his own situation, but he wanted more than anything to put all that off for just a few more seconds, so he asked his scullion for a digest of the latest speculation about who might have been behind the attacks.

But then he remembered that he'd never broken the news of the attacks to Resaint. And Devi had warned him that she was going to restore Resaint's access to the internet. He rushed to the door.

If Resaint found out the wrong way – without preamble, without cushioning – he didn't know how she might react. Those protestors had lobbed the mega-tumour at the Mosvatia convoy precisely because guys like him, extinction industry suits, were a useful target for a lot of inchoate rage about the extinction crisis. (Of course, that was a very immature way of thinking, because in reality the extinction crisis was the result of complicated structural issues, but you couldn't shoot meat at a complicated structural issue, and these were people who'd lost the ability to express their emotions in any other way.) If Resaint read about the attacks on her phone, and she became crazed by grief when she learned that everything was gone, not just the last trace of the venomous lumpsucker but the fairy shrimp and the velvet scoter and all the rest, and he was still fresh in her mind as the representative of everything that was wrong with the world, he would be her first target when she lashed out. And he'd been stupid enough to invite her into a confidence with which she could do him enormous damage simply by talking to Devi or anyone else at Brahmasamudram.

He dashed through the *Varuna*'s interior. His scullion gave him the route back to Resaint's cabin, and yet somehow, even though he thought he was following its instructions, he still managed to lose himself in the ship's featureless beige passages, which were like a maze you'd design if you specifically wanted to evoke the experience of wandering bewildered in a dream.

Until at last he was hammering on the door. 'Karin? Are you in there? Please – I need to talk to you again. Karin?'

The door opened. She stood there looking at him without expression.

'Maybe you already know,' he said, 'but if not, I just want to prepare you for—'

'I saw the news,' she said.

'You don't seem . . . ' He stopped himself from saying 'crazed with grief'.

She turned away from him and went to her chest of drawers. One of the drawers was already open, and a backpack sat on the bed. He realised he must have interrupted her in the middle of packing. 'I want to go to Sanctuary North,' she said, rolling up a T-shirt. 'So if you can get me there, fine.'

Halyard was taken aback.

'It's astonishing, isn't it?' she said. 'The thoroughness. Those nineteen thousand species – we've watched ourselves destroy them *twice* now. Even locusts can't do that – locusts can't destroy one thing twice.'

'Um—'

'I don't know if I feel numb or if I genuinely just don't care. I never really gave a shit about the biobanks. I never believed we were going to bring any of those species back, except maybe a few of the cuddly ones. It was always just an empty ritual.'

'Well, I'm with you there. But maybe the loss of all that – you know, not having a fallback any more – maybe that will make us work harder to save what we still have. Maybe that's the silver lining.'

She looked at him sceptically. 'Do you really think that?'

'No,' he admitted.

Chapter Five

Halyard saw them first. The VTOL was cruising at 1200 metres over the ocean, and Resaint, on the left, was looking out over the archipelagian shores of Finland, dozens of little pine-covered skerries broken across the water as if the coastline was dissolving into atoms, but Halyard, on the right, was looking west over the gulf, and he tapped her arm to get her attention. 'What the fuck are those?' She turned her head, and her breath caught when she saw them.

The spindrifters migrating.

She could make out five of them, colossal white tridents poking up out of the sea, familial in design but not quite identical. Their catamaran hulls left double wakes and their scalloped rotors left triple contrails, neat stripes painted on the water and messy stripes painted on the air. In fact, the VTOL must have been breathing the spindrifters' exhaust for some time before it caught up with them, because they were moving on roughly the same heading: south, towards the Sea of Åland, same as the one that had passed by the *Varuna* last night, almost as if that one had been scouting the route for the rest of the pod. She thought again of the human figure she'd seen trying to cover the window.

'They're spindrifters,' she said.

'I know that, but why are they all going in the same direction?' Halyard said. 'I thought nobody was controlling them any more. I thought they just . . . mooched around.'

'I have absolutely no idea.'

'Bloody weird.'

He was right: there was something eerie about how purposeful they looked. She uncrumpled her phone and called up the map of nearby vessels on the Baltic. There she discovered two more that weren't yet in sight. Seven spindrifters on a spring run with their miniature storms.

*

Just before they left the *Varuna*, she'd come out of the toilets and found Abdi standing there.

'I'm really sorry,' he said.

'You said something to Devi about my assessment.'

'I wasn't trying to, like . . . *inform* on you. I was just talking to her and I mentioned something. I didn't think it would matter.'

'It shouldn't have mattered.'

'But I shouldn't have said anything.'

Resaint shrugged, meaning she didn't hold it against him.

'Did you hear about the biobanks?' Abdi said, in a tone suggesting that, like Halyard, he was expecting her to be grieving them.

'Yes, I did.'

'Crazy, right?'

She nodded. 'I've got to go.'

Abdi hesitated. 'I'll miss you,' he said, then immediately turned and hurried away.

She would at least have given him a hug.

*

They were on a train in the Talsinki tunnel, fifty metres below the Baltic instead of 1200 metres above it, when Halyard said to her, 'So tell me about the venomous lumpsucker, then. Why is it so special?'

She gave him a sceptical look. They sat facing each other, and the train window mirrored them against the blackness of the tunnel, an emergency light blipping past every few seconds.

'I'm not going to try and argue you out of it again,' he said. 'I promise.'

'Then why are you asking?' The beginning of the journey had been awkward – although awkwardness had always been a concept that obsessed other people a hell of a lot more than it did her – because they didn't know each other at all, there was nothing but mistrust between them, and yet there they were sitting side by side in the little two-person cabin of the VTOL, which pitched back forty-five degrees during ascent, reclining its passengers in their seats and giving any conversation an incongruous pillow-talk quality. Following the purgative honesty of his confession to her on the deck, he'd soon regained his inhibitions, as if coming down from a drug. His occasional attempts at small talk were like a guy trying to distract his girlfriend from brooding on something he'd done to her. But then there was the excitement of the spindrifters, and after that he seemed more at ease, as if when he looked at her he was no longer thinking exclusively about her capacity to ruin him.

'I'm asking,' Halyard said, 'because this fish is my entire life now. And, to be clear, I love fish, but they don't make sushi out of this one, which means I don't know shit about it. I certainly don't know why it's worth thirteen credits. And when I look at pictures – I mean, not to judge a book by its cover, you wouldn't guess, would you?'

'And you wouldn't guess that Mexican prairie dogs have the most advanced vocal language of any non-human species on earth. But they do. Nature distributes intelligence in entirely unpredictable ways.' She didn't especially want to talk to him about this, but on the other hand she felt he ought to understand the damage Brahmasamudram had done. So she put down her phone and made a start. 'In evolutionary terms,' she said, 'the reason the venomous lumpsucker needs to be so intelligent is that it works for a lot of different clients. And we all know that sometimes dealing with your clients can be a lot more hassle than the job you're ostensibly there to do for them.'

Halyard gave her a look of mock contrition.

The venomous lumpsucker, Resaint explained, was a cleaner fish, meaning it survived by nibbling parasites and algae and dead skin off other fish. These other fish needed the lumpsuckers as much as the lumpsuckers needed them: deprived of their regular spa treatment, a trout or a porbeagle would soon find itself absolutely encrusted with dross. In a single day a single venomous lumpsucker could attend to over a thousand clients, and from each of them it could remove over a thousand blood-sucking parasites. Truly a model of expertise and professionalism.

But that wasn't even the half of it. Because sometimes a lumpsucker would floss the teeth of a creature many times larger than itself, a shark or an eel who could shut its jaws and swallow the little scavenger any time the whim took it. So a prospective client would have to build up a relationship of trust with the lumpsucker, tentatively, gradually, over the course of hundreds of visits. And the lumpsucker had a detailed mental database of all its clients, keeping track of how often it had groomed each one and when they were next entitled to a session.

This much the venomous lumpsucker had in common with cleaner fish all over the world, from the neon gobies of the Caribbean to the hornet cichlids of Lake Malawi. All of the cleverest fish species on the planet were cleaner fish, because maintaining a client database demanded such extraordinary mental powers, and indeed the first fish ever observed to recognise itself in a mirror – one of the canonical tests of self-awareness – had been a bluestreak cleaner wrasse. (When Resaint, during her retraining, had read about the stubborn disbelief with which such discoveries were always greeted, it all felt pretty familiar. The guys who had once proclaimed 'Nobody will ever find an animal in the wild who can do X – only humans are capable of that!' spoke in the same voice as the guys who had once proclaimed 'Nobody will ever be able to program a computer to do Y – only humans are capable of that!')

But what Kazu Horikawa had discovered – and what Resaint had confirmed in her recent experiments – was that the venomous lumpsucker had certain peculiarities unlike any of its cousins.

When a client abused a lumpsucker's trust by gobbling it up during a cleaning – which did occasionally happen – nearby lumpsuckers sometimes exacted punishment. They might swarm the culprit and nip it to death, their bites no longer merely exfoliant but deep enough now to squirt venom into the bloodstream. Several lumpsuckers working together could paralyse and kill a much larger fish. Over millions of years of coevolution, this had taught the lumpsuckers' client species to be wary of desecrating the relationship, just as they knew better than to eat a sea slug whose garish colours advertised that it would poison them.

But the lumpsuckers didn't always punish a bad client. Sometimes, they just let things slide. Horikawa had a theory about this, and it was this theory that had most contributed to her difficulties in placing 'Social strategic behaviour of the venomous lumpsucker' with any respectable journal. Resaint herself had thought it sounded absurd the first time she read it.

Horikawa, in the discussion section of her paper, compared the venomous lumpsucker to the *kkangpae* street gangs of Seoul during the Japanese occupation of Korea between 1910 and 1945. In an autobiography dictated to the Japanese author Isaburo Tsuchiya by an illiterate *kkangpae* hoodlum known only as Sung-ki, Sung-ki explained how his gang dealt with the colonial branch of the Japanese *yakuza*. The *yakuza* employed the *kkangpae* as low-level distributors of contraband goods, but they also seemed to feel they could swindle and murder the *kkangpae* with impunity, and whenever that happened the *kkangpae* had to decide whether to take revenge against the man responsible.

'When we were making a lot of money, we struck back, because we felt like we had nothing to fear,' Sung-ki recounted. 'And when we were very weak, we struck back, because we felt like it might be our last chance. But when we were neither very weak nor very strong, we did not always strike back: at such times everyone just wanted stability in our dealings with the Japanese, and if there's one less man to split the takings with, sometimes you don't mind too much, even though you know you ought to honour his spirit.' This, Horikawa believed, was precisely the MO of the venomous

71

lumpsuckers when they were deciding whether to punish a bad client.

Horikawa had deduced all this by observing the lumpsuckers in their natural habitat, the rocky reefs off the coast of Sweden. But she had hoped one day to verify the behaviour in a controlled setting. Conversely, Resaint had based her report entirely on experiments she'd run in her laboratory on board the *Varuna*. But she hoped one day to study the lumpsuckers under the sea – or had hoped to, until the news about the genocidal mining vehicle. Horikawa's work had required endless dedication and patience, and sometimes Resaint wished she could go back in time and donate to Horikawa some of the technologies that had made it possible to complete the Brahmasamudram assignment in only three months. For instance, in order to simulate good and bad clients, she had placed a dozen robot cod in the tanks with the lumpsuckers. Their elastomer skins were rubbed down with a bacterial paste, engineered to order for her by a company in Suzhou, that not only gave off a realistic fish odour but also extruded microfibrils tasting just like algae and mucus. They could swallow up a lumpsucker, appearing to have eaten it, and then release it unharmed once the experiment was over.

Later in his autobiography, Sung-ki related an episode when a *wakashu* – a low-ranking *yakuza* soldier – raped a *kkangpae* courier's girlfriend and then shot the courier dead in the confrontation that followed. 'At that time we were doing very well from our own gambling rooms, and we didn't care much about annoying the Japanese, so we all agreed to kill this man. But then we found out he had gone back to Japan because of some other matter. So that night a few of us waited near Mogyo Bridge until we saw a Japanese man walking past on his own. We beat him and then stabbed him to death. We never found out who he was.'

Strangely, this too had a parallel among the lumpsuckers. Horikawa found that when the lumpsuckers were ready to take retribution but the client in question had already vanished, they would swarm another individual of the same species and kill that one instead. In evolutionary terms, this was hard to explain. If you are hoping to 'teach' another species not to attack you, you have nothing to gain by punishing a scapegoat. You are trying to cull the transgressor from the gene pool: it is perverse to cull the one who *did not* attack you.

And it was here that Horikawa skidded at high speed off the path of acceptable science. She argued that lumpsuckers were like the *kkangpae*: when their revenge didn't have a pragmatic goal, it instead had an emotional or ritual function. They would sooner attack the wrong fish than just do nothing. The apparent irrationality of this behaviour was what proved the lumpsuckers were more cognitively advanced than any other fish: only a very advanced species would be capable of something so useless.

'So the reason these fish mean so much to you,' Halyard said, 'is because they're vindictive like a Korean street tough?'

'It's not *just* because they're vindictive that I think they're intelligent. It's also because they maintain a mental database of thousands of different clients. They perform better than chimps on certain logic puzzles. They can solve a maze on their first attempt and still remember the route several weeks later. They recognise themselves in a mirror. They become visibly depressed when separated from their mates. But yes, my belief that they may be a really singular species has a lot to do with their apparently irrational behaviour.'

'I don't believe you.'

'I can show you the data.'

'No, I mean I don't believe it's only that,' Halyard said. 'I'm sorry but there's something about the way you talk about it. You get this expression on your face. You're not telling me everything.'

'You can talk. I'm supposed to believe *you're* telling *me* everything? I'm supposed to believe those thirteen extinction credits are missing because you made some kind of adventurous business decision?'

'So you admit it? There's more?'

She looked away from him, into the Estonian sunlight dawning in the tunnel.

When Stepanek met them at the gates of Sanctuary North, he was wearing what Resaint took at first to be some sort of hooded monk's robe in fuzzy brown fabric. Then she saw that he had a tail dangling from his rear. He carried two large packages sealed in clear vinyl covers.

'Why are you wearing that?' Halyard said.

'It's an otter costume.' To demonstrate, Stepanek flipped his hood up over his head. It had ears, eyes and a nose. He held out the packages. 'I have one for each of you as well.'

Resaint shut her eyes and inhaled. For more than seven hours they'd been travelling inside various different containers: the VTOL to Turku, a train to Tallinn, another train to Tartu, and then a taxi out of the city and past the rapeseed fields until the rapeseed gave way to clover and then the clover to wild grass and then at last they were in the forest. So it was wonderful now to breath in the peaty air coming off the marshes, even if Sanctuary North's tall steel fence, which curved off into the trees as far as you could see in both directions, obliterated any real feeling of wilderness. It was about an hour before sundown, and the birches groaned in the breeze like a castle's worth of creaky old doors being opened and shut.

Halyard looked at Stepanek's costume. 'Thanks a lot, but I'm fine, actually.'

'I need you to put these on before you come inside,' Stepanek said with a smile.

'Why?'

'If a black-footed otter pup comes into contact with human beings while it is growing up, and develops positive associations with them, the pup will find it much harder to reintegrate into the wild population. This is just what the experts tell me – I'm more of a systems guy myself.'

'You're worried some baby otters might see us?' Halyard said.

'Yes.'

'Are there are a lot of them running around in there?'

'We don't know for sure. But, yes, it is possible that you will unexpectedly come across a black-footed otter pup during your visit.'

'OK, if I do, I'll just make sure I don't give it a chance to develop any positive associations. I'll treat it with the utmost coldness, I promise, Pavel.'

'I'm afraid we can't take any chances,' Stepanek said, pressing one of the packages upon Resaint and the other upon Halyard. 'We have to make sure the pups are growing up in a world of other otters, not a world of human beings. After all, we would hate to mess up the future of even a single pup. The breeding programme is just not quite where we want it to be right now,' he added, his tone suggesting this was a matter of no great concern, and therefore the otter costumes should under no circumstances be interpreted as any kind of desperate measure or last resort.

There was a brittle quality to his cheerfulness which reminded Resaint of some of the bosses she'd had while she was still working in product development. At that level, it was an absolute taboo to show stress; any problem or setback was trivial and uninteresting at worst, stimulating and instructive at best. Once Resaint had asked one of them how she managed to stay so calm when an unwelcome development in a patent lawsuit had left them with six weeks to disassemble their own code and rebuild it almost from scratch. Yoga and ginseng tea, the boss told her, but later Resaint found out she wore a patch on her upper arm containing a neuropeptide originally designed to stop disaster survivors from going catatonic during an evacuation.

Resaint unzipped the plastic cover of her costume. Halyard wrinkled his nose. 'That smells terrible.'

'Yes, we spray all the costumes with otter urine,' Stepanek said. Halyard took this in. 'Is everything OK in there, Stepanek?'

Stepanek smiled even wider. 'Oh, yes. Yes, yes, yes, yes. Absolutely OK. Yes. You've just come at sort of a crazy time, you know?'

'Don't you want to know why we're here?' Resaint said.

Stepanek nodded as if he was excited to find out.

'We're looking for a species called the venomous lumpsucker.'

Stepanek took his phone out of a pouch in his costume. 'Tell me again?'

'Venomous lumpsucker. *Cyclopterus venenatus*.'

Stepanek murmured to his phone. After a moment he looked up at Resaint. 'Yes, we have those here,' he said.

Chapter Six

Sanctuary North was an ark and an Eden. Occupying about forty-five square kilometres on the western shore of Lake Peipus, and administered by a company called Delta Ecological Services, it was the result of a partial privatisation of Estonia's Peipsiveere Nature Reserve. Up until the history-making death of Chiu Chiu the panda, Delta had specialised in the protection and restoration of wetlands and waterways for companies trying to meet the demands of the EU Water Framework Directive. But in the early days of World Commission on Species Extinction, when people were earnestly predicting that the price of a single extinction credit would soon be thrusting towards seven figures, Delta saw a whole new business model, a business model so bold and innovative it made the words 'EU Water Framework Directive' sound almost boring in comparison.

For every species you drove to extinction, you had to submit a credit to the WCSE. But, conversely, for every species you saved that would otherwise have perished, the WCSE would toss you a credit in recognition. So Delta's idea was to build nature reserves where they could house dozens of different endangered species all in one place, allowing for tremendous economies of scale. The WCSE would ply them with credits to reward their work, and so long as their overhead per species was less than the price of a credit, they would have a profitable business, selling off those off-sets to the planet-wreckers who desperately needed them.

This, after all, was half the point of extinction credits as a market mechanism: that the job of saving species would be efficiently allocated to whomever could perform it most cheaply, achieving the same result at a minimum cost to the world economy. Brahmasamudram might pulverise a lot of animals, but it wouldn't make any sense for them to atone for it by building a lot of reserves. That wasn't what they were good at. Instead, by buying credits on the open market, they could indirectly pay Delta to do it.

For a while Delta's pitch seemed quite promising. Fat with new investment, Delta approached the government of Estonia (along with a number of other governments from Honduras to Myanmar) and offered to take over part of the Peipsiveere Nature Reserve. The area's priceless ecological endowments would be stewarded to the highest possible standard at no further cost to the Environment Ministry, and if certain profitability goals were met, Delta would pay generous royalties back to the treasury. Estonia had never been blessed with any great mineral riches, but this would be as good as a mining concession, digging up millions of euros' worth of extinction credits. And the country happened to be going through a budget crisis at the time. So Delta negotiated a thirty-year lease, put up a fence, and set about landscaping this new enclave so that it could support emigrés from all kinds of different northern European habitats.

This was why Halyard had wanted to come to Sanctuary North. Delta had scooped out artificial lakes full of cold, brackish water, complete with concrete reefs at the bottom, to welcome aquatic species from the Baltic and the Caspian. So there could be a lovely home here for the venomous lumpsuckers. And Stepanek had been warmly disposed towards Halyard ever since Halyard got him a booking for his wedding anniversary at a Somali tasting counter in Helsinki where you couldn't eat dinner for any amount of money unless you knew someone who knew someone. So he felt Stepanek could hardly turn him down if he asked for a favour in person.

Sure enough, here they were, in a compact jeep with toothy swamp tyres, Halyard in the back seat and the other two in the front, speeding along a dirt track towards the lakes.

'Do you wear these costumes every single day?' Halyard said, adjusting his tail beneath him.

'Oh, no, we just took them out of storage this morning,' Stepanek said. 'Like I said, it's a weird day for you to be here. This is definitely a period of transition. I was going to say I didn't have time to see you but then Halyard mentioned you were an animal behaviour person,' glancing at Resaint, 'and we could really use one of those right now!'

'You must have plenty of behaviourists on staff,' Resaint said.

'Actually we've had some trouble with retention in that area.'

The sunset flickered orange between the trees as they rounded a curve. 'What do you mean by period of transition?' Halyard said.

'Because of the price spike. Nobody saw that coming! You know it's close to four hundred now?' Meaning that a single extinction credit sold for nearly €400,000. 'Remarkable, no?'

'But what difference does—'

A brown shape flashed in front of the jeep, which braked suddenly, jerking all three of them forward in their seats. For an instant Halyard thought they'd almost hit a bear – not a cannonball of panda cells this time but an actual functional bear – but then he realised it was just another human being in an otter costume sprinting past. In one hand the otter had carried a tranquilliser gun, recognisable as such because of its long skinny barrel like a ski pole with a shoulder stock.

'What was that?'

'That was Pekka. He normally works in compliance. He may have sighted a Bavarian pine vole. Do you know anything about Bavarian pine voles? We are finding them quite evasive.'

'You don't know where your animals are?' Resaint said. Her voice had taken on an edge that Halyard had already begun to recognise and fear, its power somehow undiminished by the otter costume she had on.

79

The question was a reasonable one. Sanctuary North could function only because it was a panopticon. When you mixed together dozens of species who were mostly strangers to one another, carnage was certain to result, and the only way to mitigate that carnage was continual intervention from above. So inside Sanctuary North cameras and sensors tracked every animal, feeding enough data into the Antichain predictive analytics software to maintain an exquisitely delicate balance. Cull a few of species A so it won't overwhelm species B. Breed a few more of species X so it can pollinate the trees that feed species Y. With each nudge and tweak, the entropic doomsday of this pocket world was postponed for a few more minutes, the same way Newton thought the only thing saving the universe from collapse was the ceaseless plate-spinning of God's 'amending hand'.

This was why Sanctuary North was run by a guy who (like Resaint) had a background in technology as opposed to ecology. These days Delta liked to present themselves as a data business as much as a digging-out-ponds-and-bottle-feeding-endangered-squirrels business.

'So, what you have to understand is, when credits got down into the thirties, that really changed the maths for us,' Stepanek said. 'At that point it's very difficult to make sure your overhead for each species doesn't exceed what you get back from each credit. Fortunately we were able to find savings in a lot of different places.'

'Like what?'

'Well, you wouldn't believe how much maintenance the surveillance grid needs. In terms of cameras alone, we have over two thousand. Sometimes I think looking after the cameras is harder than looking after the animals!'

'So you've just been letting them go offline?' Resaint said.

'Right now we're not as 360 degrees as we'd like.'

'This is why you don't know where your otters are.'

'It just means we have to be a little more hands-on with our tracking until we get the surveillance grid back up to full strength. Like you saw with Pekka just now. That can be good, though. Hands-on is very grounding.'

'What's that smell?' Halyard said.

'I told you, it's otter urine.'

'No, it's not that.' It was a vinegary, industrial smell on the breeze.

'Oh, yes, you're right. We are quite close now.' Stepanek rummaged in one of the pockets of his costume. 'These pockets are quite authentic! Some real otter species have skin folds in which they store their favourite rocks. Can you believe that?'

'Yes,' said Resaint.

'I'm sorry, of course you can, you are an animal person. But it was new to me. Like I said, I'm more of a systems guy. But you learn so many interesting things about animals in this job!' He passed a filter mask to Resaint, the flimsy single-layer type, and reached back to pass a second to Halyard. 'I strongly suggest you wear these.'

'Why?'

But at that moment the jeep crested a ridge and the view opened out across the marsh flats. About a hundred metres off the side of the road, Halyard could see an incursion upon the landscape: jumbled ranks of what looked like steel barrels – a few hundred at least, bright blue against the muddy ground – and parked near the barrels a truck with a grapple loader mounted on the back, and standing around the truck a few more human-sized otters.

One of the otters came rushing over waving its arms, this time deliberately trying to intercept the jeep instead of skeltering into its path by accident. Stepanek told the jeep to stop. Here the smell was so powerful it raked at your sinuses, and Resaint and Halyard had both put on their filter masks.

'This is a fucking disaster!' shouted the otter, a female, when she reached the jeep.

'What's the problem?' said Stepanek.

'First of all, the truck is stuck. We should never have driven it out here in the first place.'

'We've had lots of trucks out here.'

'That was in winter. The ground was hard. But now the truck is really bogged down. Why didn't we get something with treads?'

'I don't know – talk to Pekka.'

'Also, the barrels are leaking.'

'We knew that already.'

'We thought it was just a few of them. But it's at least half. That's why the smell is so fucking strong.' And indeed Halyard's filter mask didn't help at all. Stale otter urine was like orange blossom compared to this.

'Why so many?'

'Ask the Russians. Ask your friends from the fucking Lyudinovo Special Economic Zone!'

'We need to seal them before we move them.'

'Yes, obviously, but how? And we don't even know where we're moving them yet!'

'I'm sure we can find a great solution, but right now I need to take my friends over to Lake Seven. I'll be back soon.' Stepanek gave the frantic otter a little wave.

'No, Pavel—'

But the rest was lost as the jeep accelerated away.

'What's in those barrels?' Resaint said.

'Is this even the right kind of mask?' Halyard said.

'So, like I said, when credits bottomed out, that really changed the maths for us,' Stepanek explained, 'and we did some, you know, maybe in hindsight it might look like short-term thinking, but I have personally always seen it as long-term thinking, because it was about securing a future for Sanctuary North by diversifying our income streams. Of course, as of last night, the maths has changed again, and now it's time to get back to our core mission.'

'How much of the reserve is contaminated?'

'Well, there wasn't supposed to be any impact on the ecosystem at all. Obviously we were not expecting this issue with the containers. But as you just saw, we are in the process of moving everything out, and after that I think things should revert back to normal quite fast, because we've built a really robust ecosystem here. Also, Delta have been experts in wetlands restoration for a long time before we started our own nature reserves, so if this wetland does need a little bit of, you know, polishing, we can get that done, no problem.'

There had been rumours in the industry that Delta was floundering, but Halyard had not had any idea that Sanctuary North had gone quite so far south. At any rate, he understood why they were panicking today. Each time Delta pocketed a credit from the WCSE as a reward for adopting a species, they were taking on a risk: if the last of that species later died out in Sanctuary North as a result of Delta's negligence, the WCSE would demand to be refunded the credit. And with extinction credits at €38,432, if they'd fumbled the black-footed otter or the Bavarian pine vole, it wouldn't have mattered much. But with extinction credits suddenly at ten times that, those liabilities would fast become crippling.

As a condition of entry to Sanctuary North, Halyard and Resaint had downloaded non-disclosure packages on to their phones. These were not of the most slavish kind, where your own scullion was instructed to monitor your conversations in order to alert the other party to any future breaches of confidence, but they did, of course, disable the phones' authentication chips, meaning that any audio or video you might surreptitiously record would be worthless because there would be no way to prove it was real. Hence Stepanek was speaking pretty freely, and Halyard had an urge to ask him straight out just how much trouble he was in. But on the other hand, maybe Stepanek was speaking *too* freely, because Resaint was looking at him like she wanted to drown him in the marsh.

Regardless, it made Halyard feel a lot better to know he wasn't the only one racing to avert a terrible exposure. All over Europe, all over the world, there would be others whose grifts, gambles and shortcuts were now burning up in the merciless light of the €400,000 extinction credit.

They came to the necklace of little lakes, some natural and some artificial, that lay along the shore of the much larger Lake Peipus. They were arriving just at the time in the dusk when the mirror image of the sky in the calm of the waters was sharpened to its greatest perfection, no longer compromised by a sun whose dazzle could not be realistically rendered. The rotten-egg smell that rose out of the mud did not eclipse the searing tang from those barrels although at least the otter piss was basically muscled out by the other two. 'Here is Lake Seven,' said Stepanek as the jeep parked itself. 'Hydrologically it is just like the Gulf of Bothnia, very deep, with reefs and everything! And when we first populated it we brought in a colony of venomous lumpsuckers to support the other fish.' Halyard gazed out at the lake: was this to be his deliverance? 'Would you like to take a look?' Stepanek asked Resaint.

'Why?' said Resaint. 'I won't be able to see any fish from the shore.'

'Yes, of course, but actually the reason I wanted to bring you out here in person was that I'd love to get your professional opinion on the lake. Lately it has not been operating at full capacity, ecologically speaking, but we hope to get things back on track very soon. I hoped you could give us an idea of how much work we have ahead of us.'

Resaint gestured at the far shore, where a bank of hydrological machinery stood part-submerged in the water. 'You must be getting data from your regulators.'

'You remember what I was saying about the cameras – well, this is a similar story.'

'Then you need a marine ecologist with a case full of instruments. I work on animal intelligence.'

'Sure, yes, we had some really great marine ecologists, but again, retention has been an issue. We are in touch with everyone who left to see if they will come back, but until then . . . I don't need hard numbers, just first impressions.'

Resaint shot Halyard an expression meaning 'Do I really have to do this?', and he looked back at her apologetically. She opened the door of the jeep, got out, and began picking her way through the marsh grass towards the shore of the lake.

When he was alone with Stepanek, Halyard said, 'Are you looking at any legal issues with those barrels?' He privately hoped

84

the answer was yes. Estonia held corporate executives personally liable for environmental crimes, and if Stepanek was also facing potential jail time that would be very comforting.

'No, not at all,' said Stepanek breezily. 'Our agreement with the government gives us certain blanket exemptions – you know, so our operation can be agile. We cleared everything with our lawyers in advance. Also, you know where it comes from? The factory in Lyudinovo makes antifouling resins for – have you heard about reverse electrodialysis energy capture? Very promising green tech – so it's absolutely an environmental positive, but the problem is there aren't a lot of places they can go with this stuff any more, it's not nearly as straightforward to just ship it to Africa as it would have been even five or ten years ago, so they paid us a terrific rate. It was the right move at the time, even if not everyone was happy about it. And honestly I thought it would just be temporary until ZymoD could clean it up for us.'

ZymoD were a Japanese biotech company developing a genetically modified peat moss that could digest even the vilest industrial pollutants, leaving behind only a harmless compost to be vacuumed up. For as long as Halyard could remember they had been saying they were about a year from bringing a product to market. But according to rumour, towards the end of a long night of karaoke during a conference, one of their scientists had admitted that they were at a dead end in their research and they had no idea whether what they'd promised was even possible. 'No, the real problem,' Stepanek continued, 'is that there are a number of species in those lakes – well, you know, back when credits were at forty . . .' He waggled his hands like a laid-back juggler who didn't mind dropping a few balls. 'But with credits at four hundred . . .'

Halyard nodded. ZymoD, conversely, would no doubt be celebrating the price spike, because habitat remediation would suddenly become an urgent topic again. It might even buy them one more round of investment before the other shoe dropped. Every death sentence today would be balanced by a reprieve somewhere else.

Resaint appeared at the open door of the jeep. 'That was quick,' said Halyard.

'The lake is dead,' said Resaint.

'I'm sorry?' said Stepanek.

'Whatever's in those barrels, it must have seeped into the water table. The lake is poisoned. There's nothing left. No fish, no insects, not even plankton.'

'So definitely no lumpsuckers?' said Halyard.

Resaint ignored him. 'You told me the lake "has not been operating at full capacity"?' she said to Stepanek, in the tone that scorched your ears like the air scorched your nose. 'It's toxic. It stinks of chemicals. Nothing could live in there. A child could see that.'

Stepanek shrugged. 'Like I said, I'm more of a systems guy.'

*

A few years ago, Halyard had attended two days of Hostile Environment Training at a hotel in Vienna. (The Baltic states were not exactly a hostile environment, but it was at least conceivable that he might get summoned to one of the dicier Brahmasamudram sites in eastern Ukraine or the South Caucasus, supposing another Environmental Impact Coordinator was unavailable. In any case, he never turned down an awayday.) A bar crawl down Reindorfgasse the night before meant that he more or less dozed through the first morning of the course, and the only thing that really roused his attention was the instructor talking about how to strike up a rapport with your captor if you got kidnapped.

'You want them to see you as a human being, not a sack of potatoes,' the instructor said. 'So try to talk to them. Find something simple that you have in common. Family, for instance. Sports. Hobbies.'

It reminded Halyard of a conversation he had once had with his mother, in his university holidays, not long after his sister Frances' death, when he was volunteering as part of the clean-up of the Hawkesbury River floods. He had complained to her that he didn't like any of the other volunteers, and she had told him that you could be friends with anyone if you just came up with something to talk about.

It's one thing when your loving mother gives you garbage advice with no connection to reality, but you don't expect to have to go all the way to Vienna and pay eight hundred euros a day for it. (Well, Brahmasamudram were paying, but still.) Impulsively, perhaps with a sense that it would compensate for his conspicuous inattentiveness if he asked a question, Halyard put up his hand. 'But what if you really don't have anything in common with the guy?'

'You'll find something.'

'But what if he's a prick? Or what if he's just boring?'

Everyone laughed as if Halyard had been making a joke, and the instructor moved on. But it had been a genuine question, and Halyard felt embarrassed afterwards. The next day he didn't even turn up for the session. Which meant he was entirely ill-equipped for what happened on the way back from Sanctuary North.

And not only because he could have used a few hours of Hostile Environment Training just for sharing a taxi with Resaint when she was in a dark mood. They were both sitting up front but neither of them said a word as it bore them back to Tartu. It was ten o'clock at night and Halyard was weighing up what to do next. He hadn't been serious when he thought about throwing himself off the *Varuna*. But he was serious, now, when he thought about disappearing in some other way. He still had time before Brahmasamudram found out about the missing extinction credits. Except how *could* he disappear? Disappearing was something people did in the old days, when there were a lot more gaps in the world. Now you were always under surveillance wherever you went – what a hellish time to be alive. Anyway, it would mean never seeing his parents again, or his family's old arthritic dog . . .

And then, suddenly, darkness. All the lights in the taxi cut out, and so did the engine. It rolled to a halt.

'What the fuck?' Halyard said.

There was a tap on the window beside him, which was open an inch or so. He looked up and saw that something was being pointed at him through the gap. Just what manner of object this was, it took him, stupidly, a moment to understand, even though it had much more of a classic kind of shape than that spindly tranquilliser gun they'd seen the otter toting earlier. He'd only ever seen one like this in real life once before, at a motorway service station in Latvia, his car pulling out past two guys arguing outside the toilets, one waving a pistol in the other's face. Even that had given him a squirt of adrenaline that stayed with him for miles, but actually to have one aimed at him made Halyard feel as awake as he'd ever felt in his life.

'Jesus Christ. Call the police. Call the police.' But neither his phone nor the taxi seemed to hear.

'Get out of the car,' said the guy with the gun.

Resaint had taken out her own phone but the screen was blank. Terrified, Halyard slapped the dashboard in a hopeless attempt to get a response out of the taxi.

'I'm not a rapist or a serial killer or anything like that,' the guy said. 'I'm not going to touch you with my hands.' He spoke English with what sounded like a local accent. 'This is an act of conscience. Just get out of the car, or I'll shoot you both.'

Halyard's instinct was to do nothing the guy said, but then Resaint pulled the manual release to open the door on her side. If he'd been a better student of Hostile Environment Training, he might have felt qualified to settle the question. Instead, he just did as Resaint did. They both got out of the taxi. As Halyard stood, a light came on, shining right in his eyes. The gunman was wearing a headlamp on his forehead, the kind you'd take camping, and the glare of it kept Halyard from making out the guy's face, so he only observed that the guy was wearing laceless hiking trainers whose zesty purple-and-yellow colour palette felt a bit flippant in the circumstances. He was short, skinny, restless in his posture.

'What did you do to the car?' Resaint said.

'Start walking that way,' the guy said, pointing into the trees at the side of the road.

Halyard already regretted getting out of the taxi. When it disappeared from the network, an alert would have been triggered.

Probably some little drone was already on its way to check what had happened. These days you were always under surveillance wherever you went – what a heavenly time to be alive. 'No,' he said. 'No fucking way.'

The guy took a step forward and stuck the gun right in Halyard's face. Halyard felt his bowels simmer.

He turned away from the gun and started walking, Resaint at his side. In the darkness the headlamp's beam threw their shadows on to the ground ahead of them like real-time projections of where their bodies would fall. It had been a mild spring day but it was cold now.

'What are your jobs?' the guy said when there were some trees between them and the road. This was an apple orchard, Halyard realised, at present so exuberantly vernal that it was like spelunking through a cave system of white blossom.

'What did you say?'

'What are your jobs? Who do you work for?'

'I'm the Environmental Impact Coordinator for Northern Europe at Brahmasamudram Mining.'

'I evaluate species intelligence for a number of different clients.' Resaint sounded remarkably calm.

The guy gave a huff of amusement, like this was just what you'd expect. 'The game continues.'

'What game?' Halyard said. The gun made him so conscious of his movements that he found himself walking with a stiff puppety gait, the same way that if you point a camera at a novice actor they will suddenly forget how to open a door or drink from a cup.

'I knew you'd be coming.' Which didn't seem possible to Halyard, because he hadn't even known himself until lunchtime today. 'I knew as soon as I saw the reports about the "hack".' The guy put a sarcastic spin on that last word. 'You're here to start the next phase.'

Halyard didn't know what this was supposed to mean, but nonetheless it sounded promisingly like an opening. 'No, mate, there's obviously some kind of misunderstanding here. We're just here about a fish. At Sanctuary North, in the lakes, they were supposed to have this fish—'

'Bullshit. There are no fish there.' Which was true. But that had been news even to Stepanek less than an hour ago. 'Sanctuary North is nothing but a chemical waste dump. We traced the shipments from Russia.' By this point the guy was starting to sound pretty much omniscient – except then he added, 'Sanctuary North is a sham just like the biobanks.'

'Hold on, the biobanks are not a sham,' said Halyard, still clinging to the possibility that he could find the weak link in the chain of reasoning that had directed this gun to his back.

'Yes, they are. I know that. I'm not stupid, OK?'

'There were thousands and thousands of species in them before the hacks.'

'No, there weren't. They've always been empty. That's what this "hack" stuff was for. To reset the lie so it matches up with reality. "Oh no, everything got wiped! We lost it all!" Of course they never had it in the first place. Now the next phase starts, and everyone has to be briefed, everyone has to know their part. That's why you came to Sanctuary North. To deliver the instructions. To continue the game.' Another derisive huff. 'The extinction industry has never saved a single species. It's just a performance, a fiction. It's about extracting subsidies and kickbacks, year after year. That's all. The price of credits goes up, you make money. The price of credits goes down, you make money. The suits always win and the animals always lose. A hundred thousand extinctions a year and you're just making it easier for them.'

The problem here was that Halyard couldn't dispute the guy's overall analysis, which was quite astute, so he would sound pedantic trying to dispute the guy's factual premises, which were deluded. Still, at least now he had a sense of who they might be dealing with.

'Yesterday, I was in another taxi, and somebody threw a tumour at us, a big one made of cloned Chiu Chiu cells,' he said. 'The people who did that, I'm guessing you're comrades-in-arms?'

'I stand in solidarity with anyone, anywhere in the world, who takes direct action against your industry. We had an action of our own planned. A major action. But then Rasmus, last night, he saw the news about the "hacks", he wanted to talk to the rest of us right away. He was too tired, maybe, or too excited . . . He forgot to observe the security protocols. KAPO have been looking for us ever since we posted the manifesto. So as soon as Rasmus started sending messages in an unencrypted channel . . .'

KAPO was the Estonian internal security service. 'You're on the run?' Halyard said, wondering if their common interest in evading justice could be the subject around which they nurtured a rapport.

'They already have Rasmus but Martin was supposed to meet me here. I said to him, "The action can't happen now, there isn't time, but we can still do *something* before they find us. We can still make our voices heard. We can still speak up for the animals." Keep walking please,' he added, because Halyard had stopped.

The reason Halyard had stopped was that he knew for certain now where all this was leading and he couldn't let it play out any longer. He turned around to face the guy. 'You're totally right, OK? The extinction industry is not always good for the animals. And, yes, I'm just another extinction industry cunt. But like I said, the reason we are here is to find this fish, the venomous lumpsucker. And *she*' – gesturing at Resaint – 'is not just another extinction industry cunt. This fish and its huge Korean brain are everything to her. She knows more about it than anyone else on the planet and she wants it to not be extinct, just as much as you want all the other animals to not be extinct. Karin, tell him.'

'Is that true?' the guy said. 'You're not one of them?'

Resaint shrugged. 'I've worked for Brahmasamudram, Cromer, Zhejiang-Lacebark. I've never turned down an assignment and I've never certified a species as intelligent. I've done nothing to help.'

Halyard stared at her in bafflement. It was as if she didn't understand that their lives were in danger. 'But you were going to certify this fish. You were willing to ruin your relationship with the company just to protect it.'

'Yes, but nevertheless I was part of the apparatus that legitimised its extinction.'

'Karin, he is planning to kill us. That's what people like this mean when they talk about "making their voices heard".' The guy was hearing all this, obviously, but Halyard didn't know what else to do. 'We have to help him understand that we are not what he thinks we are.'

'I'm exactly who he thinks I am. I can't comment on you. I've only known you for half a day.'

So Halyard was the only sane one out of the three of them. 'At least wait until – did you say Martin?' he said. 'Wait until Martin gets here. Don't do anything crazy without him.'

'Martin was supposed to be here hours ago. I think they've already got him. They'll probably be here soon.' The guy bent his knees in a little curtsy of anguish. 'I don't want to kill you. I don't want to kill anyone. We weren't going to kill anyone in the action. But I have to speak up for the animals.' For the first time the guy lowered the gun, holding it sideways in front of him as if to study its workmanship. 'Maybe – I mean, maybe I should just . . .' He turned the barrel towards himself, the black metal glinting in the beam of the headlamp. 'It would still be an act of conscience. It would still make news if I did it before KAPO could get me.'

'No!' Halyard shouted. He was surprised to find that he felt almost as panicked at the prospect of watching this guy shoot himself as he did at the prospect of getting shot. 'No, you don't need to do that either. You don't need to kill *anyone* today. Karin, come on, tell him.'

'Do what you have to,' Resaint said. Halyard glanced at her, appalled. When he looked back, the guy had the gun held to his own temple.

Halyard took a step forward. The guy snapped the barrel back towards Halyard.

But then his free hand flew to his neck, as if a mosquito had stung him. And Halyard saw that something was sticking out of the guy that hadn't been sticking out of him a moment ago.

He couldn't make out what it was until the guy pulled it out of his neck and held it up to the light. It was a thin syringe with a red tuft on one end. A tranquilliser dart.

'They're here!' the guy exclaimed. He raised the gun and started firing into the apple blossom, the beam of his headlamp swinging wildly as he searched for a target. And then a six-foot otter loomed out of the darkness and hit the guy over the head with a branch.

*

It turned out that in the course of Stepanek's vigorous cost-cutting there had been a few bodges involving Sanctuary North's IT systems. And for reasons that nobody had yet been able to unpick, these bodges had interfered with the installation of certain software updates. Only after Halyard and Resaint had left did somebody point out to Stepanek that the non-disclosure packages the two of them had obligingly downloaded were several months out of date, meaning they might not be watertight either technologically or legally.

It wasn't that Stepanek didn't trust Halyard – and it wasn't that his bosses didn't allow him a lot of leeway down here – but to invite a couple of outsiders in, show them around the reserve when it was still rather déshabillé, and then let them leave without even the basic safeguards in place: that was out of the question. So Stepanek called Halyard, and when Halyard's scullion responded that Halyard's phone was off, Stepanek jumped in the jeep in the hope of catching them up and sorting it all out. On the road back to Tartu, he came upon the empty taxi. Fearing right away that something was up – the reserve was the target of regular threats from activists – he strapped on his smart goggles and tracked them into the orchard like a couple of Bavarian pine voles.

'That was a bloody incredible shot, Pavel,' Halyard said after-wards, astonished by Stepanek's show of competence in this whole matter. His ears were still ringing from the gunshots.

'Actually, the goggles did the aiming for me,' Stepanek said, tapping the pair around his neck. 'Very cool technology! But what I do not understand is why the dart didn't work. I thought he would just fall over.'

'Ketamine in the bloodstream takes several minutes to get to the brain,' Resaint said.

'Oh.'

In any case, Resaint added, a dose intended for a small mam-mal would have, at most, a recreational effect on a human being.

'Well, look, the important thing,' Halyard said, his admiration ebbing only slightly, 'is that the branch you hit him with didn't take several minutes to get to the brain.'

Together they carried the unconscious terrorist to the jeep so that Stepanek could lock him inside. Strapped to his hip they found a second weapon, this one looking a bit like a hairdryer with a flared mouth and a cumbersome battery pack – the Czech-made microwave gun he'd used to fry all the circuits in the taxi. Halyard and Resaint were also down two phones and a smart-watch, which meant there wasn't much Stepanek could do just yet about the non-disclosure packages. They were supposed to wait at the orchard for the police to arrive, but Stepanek said that after what they'd been through they ought to rest. He would handle it all tonight and they could give their statements tomorrow.

Halyard, embracing him, promised that one day he'd fly him out to Tokyo for dinner at Sushi Ashina. He said this sincerely, putting out of his mind the fact that he'd probably never eat *chutoro* again.

*

Back in Tartu, they checked into a hotel near the river. There was some hassle at the start because their nuked phones couldn't sup-ply their vax passports, so in theory they weren't allowed to set foot in the hotel, but eventually a desk clerk helped them connect to their scullions so they could straighten everything out and order new phones. Upstairs, as they were going into their adjacent rooms, Resaint said, 'Meet you in the bar in ten minutes?'

'No thanks,' Halyard said.

'I need a drink after that. Don't you?'

Since the orchard he'd pretty much frozen her out, hardly speaking to her or looking at her beyond what was absolutely necessary, but now he wondered if she'd even noticed. At last his post-adrenal shakiness found outlet in anger. 'Yes, of course I need a drink. I need a million bloody drinks. I need a Lake Peipus of very good whisky. I just don't want to have a drink with *you*.'

She looked back at him as if she wasn't quite sure what he meant.

'Karin, he was going to kill us.' Just saying it called the dread back down upon him. 'And I gave you a chance to defend us. I teed you up. And you didn't. It was like you didn't care. And then he was going to kill himself. And I tried to stop him, like any normal person would have. And you said . . . Jesus fucking Christ – "Do what you have to." I'm not standing here saying I'm Mr Number One King of Ethics, but, seriously, what the fuck is wrong with you?'

In the end, they did go downstairs. And she told him.

Chapter Seven

At first, Resaint had found it easy not to care about extinction, because the arguments against it were so feeble.

Yes, we were losing tens of thousands of species a year. But what was seldom mentioned in the news stories about extinction, illustrated with adorable fennecs and resplendent macaws, was that vertebrates made up only about eighty thousand of the millions of species on earth. So if you picked a doomed species at random, it almost definitely wouldn't be a species people genuinely cared for, like a bear or a waterfowl, or even a species people had some faint curiosity about, like a frog or an eel. Far more likely it would be some total nonentity.

After all, the vast majority of animals on earth were extremely parochial parasites. Almost every species visible to the naked eye had at least one parasite that was specific to that species and could survive nowhere but its body; often it had several such dependants and sub-dependants ('. . . and little fleas have lesser fleas, and so on ad infinitum'). Nobody gave a shit about any of those. You could tell because, when the WCSE had resolved early on to exempt all such microscopic parasites from its purview, essentially rendering them nonpersons, not even the most radical greens had so much as muttered in protest. They had about as much value in their own right as a proprietary cable for some discontinued smartphone.

Even if you took the hangers-on out of the equation, it was still insects who constituted the bulk of the many millions. And although some of them might have slightly bolder careers than the monoxenous parasites, in practice they were still as distant from human apprehension as any species that died out with the dinosaurs. Nobody had ever set eyes on most of the endangered bugs, not even the naturalists whose job it was to compile the catalogues. Therefore nobody could pretend to miss them. They were 'precious' only in the abstract. New ones evolved, and old ones went extinct; this churn had been going on since the Ordovician period. To wring your hands over it would be absurd. And the tiny fraction of species that were genuinely mourned were certain to have DNA on file, which meant that at any time they could be resurrected like the giant panda. (As she sat in the hotel restaurant recalling these old attitudes, Halyard nodded as if they sounded pretty sensible to him.)

There were some technical arguments for why the extinction of some fameless critter might be a bad thing, but these always felt rather strained. For instance, every species played some role in its ecosystem, so in theory its removal could have an unpredictable ripple effect. But most of the time there would be dozens of other species who were almost indistinguishable from it and would be quite happy to fill its shoes; after all, how could there be several million types of insect if most of them weren't basically just trivial variations on each other? The truth was, most biodiversity was redundant. And in any case, at a time when the air was turning hot and bitter, when the rain was claggy with microplastics and endocrine disrupters, when the entire planet seemed angry and nauseous, it was difficult to care that much about how the loss of some aphid might perturb the food web of the subtropical hollow in which it had lived, or even how the loss of a hundred different aphids might perturb the food webs of a hundred different subtropical hollows. Our ecosystems had bigger things to worry about.

Sometimes it was noted that these bugs might take unsuspected treasures with them to the grave. If the Brazilian hornet *Polybia paulista* had gone extinct before we'd studied it, how could we have isolated the compound in its venom that dissolved tumours? Or if the Ecuadorian cockroach *Lucihormetica luckae* had met such a fate, how could we have copied the asymmetric micro-structures in the luminescent spots on its back to improve the efficiency of our LEDs? But most of the time, when people made these arguments, you could tell their hearts weren't really in it. The biodiversity enthusiasts were trying to talk to capitalists in the language of capitalism, but they knew as well as the capitalists did that it just wasn't a strong pitch. Only a tiny minority of species had anything unique and packageable to offer. After all, if the rainforest was really 'nature's medicine cabinet', oozing with new penicillins and improved morphines, then the big pharmaceutical companies would have been buying up Brazil for a thousand euros an acre. But in fact none of them had ever bothered. So either they didn't like making money, or they understood that, actually, nature didn't pay for itself. The most exciting discoveries were now being made by algorithms working millions of times faster than evolution could. We didn't need to infringe on Mother Earth's intellectual property any longer.

And Resaint felt the same way about the crustaceans and the molluscs and the amphibians as she did about the insects. The lizards, too, and the fish and even most of the birds. If they hadn't mattered to anyone when they were alive, they couldn't matter to anyone when they were dead; and anyway, there were still so many left, and evolution was always making new ones.

The only partial exception to Resaint's indifference was in the realm of her own livelihood: intelligent species. She could at least respect the argument that the loss of one of those was a terrible loss. Any complex mind very different from our own will parse the universe in ways that we can't. As Darwin once wrote, 'He who understands baboon would do more towards metaphysics than Locke.' Back when primatologists first started teaching sign language to chimpanzees, that seemed to be the closest any human being could come to communicating with aliens.

And yet Resaint couldn't help but notice that, even after decades of research into the minds of apes and crows and octopuses, there had still been very little in the way of philosophical revelations. Yes, we recognised a lot more animals as thinkers, and we knew a lot more about their thinking. As that woman at the wedding had promised, Resaint found the science engaging, which was fortunate because otherwise her job would have been a slog. But the hope that these little brains would have anything profound to teach us now seemed as specious as any proverb about wisdom coming out of the mouths of babes. The truth was, most of the time, talking to a chimpanzee was more like talking to a child than it was like talking to an alien; which is to say, it was like talking to a very stupid adult. That was all.

This was how she felt while she was studying to become a species intelligence evaluator, and continued to feel for her first four years of assignments. But then she met *Adelognathus marginatum*.

She had gone to western Ukraine to study a critically endangered bird, the Ruthenian tawny bunting *Emberiza campestris*. An agricultural company called Kalynove AgroProduct, which owned about 1.2 million hectares of sunflower fields, the largest such holding in the country, was proposing to replace its entire crop with a new strain genetically modified to resist pests. The buntings, whose population was already very diminished, relied on these pests as their main source of food, and a computer model of the ecosystem projected about an eighty per cent chance that the newly pristine sunflowers would starve them into extinction. Also probably finished off would be a rare parasitoid wasp called *Adelognathus marginatum*. The buntings were similar enough to some highly intelligent passerines that an evaluation was felt to be necessary – perhaps they were secret tool-users – but she would have no business with the wasps, which had a mere forty thousand neurons in their heads (compared to a million in even a cockroach or a honey bee).

And yet it was the wasps that caught her attention, because they shared with several other parasitoid wasp species a particularly devious method of self-perpetuation.

Marginatum would look around for a small stripy spider called *Metapanamomops bohemicus* (like *marginatum*, *bohemicus* had no common name in any language). It would sting the spider, temporarily paralysing it, and then drill an egg into its abdomen. After about an hour, the spider would regain control of its limbs and go on about its business. Over the next few weeks, the wasp larva would grow from the egg, feeding on the spider's blood like an ectopic pregnancy. And then, when the larva was almost ready to pupate, the spider would build a web. But this web would not have its usual meticulous pattern, spiralling inward around a couple of dozen spokes to weave a mesh as tight as a tennis racket. Instead, the web would be a primitive-looking thing of just four thick cables, an X suspended between the sunflower stalks with extra strands duct-taped around the intersection. Once the spider had finished this web, the larva would poison the spider, disembark from its abdomen, and suck out its juices. Then it would waggle over to the centre of the web and build the cocoon in which it would grow its wings.

The point of all this was to furnish the wasp larva with a cradle where it could complete its metamorphosis. A standard spiderweb was strong enough to catch flies, but not strong enough to stand up to strong winds, heavy rain, or marauding ants – so it was no use to the larva. However, *Metapanamomops bohemicus* also knew how to weave a much sturdier web when it needed a comfortable place to shed its exoskeleton. So the larva's trick was to release ecdysteroid hormones into the spider's bloodstream, fooling the spider into thinking it was about to moult, so that it would supply a web that better met the larva's needs.

As if this wasn't humiliation enough, *marginatum* also ran an additional scam on *Metapanamomops bohemicus* – a scam that had been scientifically described for the first time only a few years earlier, and was, as far as anyone knew, unique among the parasitoid wasps. If you watched the larva dragging itself out of the spider's abdomen, you would notice that it was wearing a sort of birth caul around half of its body. This, too, the spider had inadvertently provided for it. At the start of the whole cycle, when the wasp jammed its egg into the spider, sirens would go off in the spider's immune system. It would begin forming a layer of white blood cells called a granuloma around the invader, an abscess intended to wall it off from the rest of the spider's insides. Under normal circumstances, the process would finish once this granuloma was of a serviceable thickness, but here, too, the wasp larva released a treacherous hormone, this one disorienting the spider's immune response so that it just kept slapping on more and more coats of paint. Later on, once the spider was dead and the larva was ready to start on its cocoon, it would hold on to this granuloma, which was perfectly fitted to its body, and use it as an inner lining, allowing the cocoon to be finished much faster. In other words, it twisted what was supposed to be a defensive measure into another gift for itself.

One evening Resaint watched a video of an *Adelognathus marginatum* larva climbing out of a *Metapanamomops bohemicus* carcass with the granuloma around its shoulders. It was one of those videos from invertebrate reality where the physics look wrong, so it feels like you must be watching the footage backwards or upside down – the larva that strained for escape but didn't pop out until exactly the moment when it seemed to have gone slack; the granuloma that looked gummy and soft but still tore right through the spider's cuticle – and you feel compelled to play it over and over again because you can never quite assimilate its strangeness.

The next day, on a call with one of Kalynove's population biologists, she mentioned the video. 'Have you watched it?'

'No.'

'You should. They're a pretty interesting species.'

The population biologist gave a little shrug. 'Probably gone soon.' And then she moved on.

Probably gone soon. Resaint had never felt grief in the course of her work before, but those words stayed with her like a papercut that won't stop bleeding. There was something about the biologist's casualness that threw it into relief: *marginatum*'s breeding cycle had played out hundreds of millions of times a year for ninety million years, but one day soon, somewhere in a field in western Ukraine, there would be a final performance, and then never again.

Yet the reason she found this so hard to accept was not because of the improbability that it could all just peter out after a quadrillion rounds, but because of the improbability that it should ever have happened in the first place.

Evolution was a monstrous maker, a blind heedless thing inching along in no particular direction, the whole disaster fuelled by spilled blood and wasted effort, Amazon rivers of both. All of it was premised on random mutation, which was like editing a novel by simply copying it out again and again in the hope that the typos you made would not just spare the meaning but actually render new insight. What could be more absurd? And yet this clusterfuck had yielded *Adelognathus marginatum*, which could mind-control a spider with counterfeit hormones in order to swipe its best handiwork for the larva that has just drunk its lifeforce like a smoothie. Somehow, inert matter had organised itself into something so convoluted and delicate and whimsical and cruel. If, somewhere in space, a scattering of asteroid fragments happened to drift into the shape of a perfect tetrahedron a thousand kilometres wide, it would be no greater miracle.

Resaint thought about the number of wasps that had to die for *marginatum* to evolve its abilities; the number of different metabolites that various larvae must have dribbled into various spiders before they found just the right molecule to hijack *bohemicus*; the number of false starts, wrong turns, near misses, interesting follies; the number of times the code was cracked a million years early but the wasp in question got eaten by a tawny bunting before it could breed. All of this happening without intention or direction, just a tumbling and jittering in darkness until form emerged; a story told in numbers that boggled any human reckoning, until, by human carelessness, those numbers were at last reduced to a more familiar scale, a thousand, a hundred, five, four, three, two, one, zero.

OK, so what was new? It wasn't as if this was the first time she'd watched a video of a critically endangered species showing off a clever talent, nor were the principles of evolutionary biology some kind of revelation to her. So why, over the days that followed, did she feel like *Adelognathus marginatum* had laid an egg in her brain?

Even now, she had no answer to this. Her turnaround was as abrupt as it was unexpected. Perhaps it was only a question of timing, and any species that came along at just that moment would have had the same effect. Or perhaps it was because *marginatum* and its dark arts were almost unobserved, even by *marginatum* itself, and that clarified things for her.

In hindsight, of all the beliefs that had to be overturned to make Resaint's epiphany possible, the most fundamental, the most axiomatic, was that a tragedy could only be a tragedy if it hurt somebody. In other words, if something happened in the universe, and it didn't impinge on the conscious experience of any living being, human or non-human, real or potential, then that was not a moral matter.

Well, if that was true, the extinction of the *Adelognathus marginatum* was an absolutely meaningless event. 'What is it like to be a golden-headed langur swinging through the forest? What is its unique and ineffable experience of life? Can we bear to erase that from existence?' Sentimental questions like that could not be asked about *Adelognathus marginatum* and its forty thousand neurons. 'What is it like to be a parasitic wasp larva injecting hormones into the bloodstream of your host?' It was like nothing. *Marginatum* was basically a mechanical process, like a virus or weed. Save *marginatum*? For whose sake? In whose interests? *Marginatum* had no interests, was void of sake.

'But think of how much future generations of nature lovers will be missing out on!' No. A meeting of *marginatum*'s global fan club – a few biologists who'd studied its behaviour; Resaint herself – could probably fit in a small hotel room, and those numbers were hardly likely to swell as the years went by. On the contrary, parasitic wasps were so repugnant to the soul that they had become a classic argument against creationism: 'I cannot persuade myself,' wrote Darwin in 1860, 'that a beneficent and omnipotent God could have designedly created the Ichneumonidae with the express intention of their feeding within the living bodies of Caterpillars.' Nobody made remarks like that about pandas. Nobody ever said to Chiu Chiu, 'You prove there is no God who loves us.'

And yet, despite all that, it was self-evident to Resaint that *Adelognathus marginatum* had some sort of inherent value. How could this brilliant, intricate, hilarious thing – the fluke result of an unrepeatable process, the legacy of some dizzying number of past individuals, all of them, in hindsight, striving unconsciously towards a single invention – not be valuable in itself? What did it matter if anyone appreciated it, if it did any good for anyone? The more Resaint thought about it, the more any conception of value that did not include *Adelognathus marginatum* seemed nonsensical. A tragedy could only be a tragedy if it hurt somebody? Now she saw that was obviously false. Imagine that nobody had ever discovered *Adelognathus marginatum*, so it had no cult at all. In that case an erasure could not have hurt anybody, it would not have impinged on the conscious experience of any living being real or potential. Yet it would still have been a terrible loss to the universe. The absence, in this case, of the weaker arguments against extinction – wouldn't we be sad to lose this cute little fellow? – made space for Resaint to feel the truth of this far graver argument.

It was at this time that she had the first intimations of what she later called the Black Hole. The name was appropriate even at this early stage, because in the same way that astronomers often come at their discoveries sideways, deducing that some cosmic body must exist even though they don't yet have telescopes big enough to observe it directly, Resaint felt a prickle of awareness regarding her own Black Hole, an early sense of something in the numbers, long before she was capable of looking squarely at its darkness. For many people, the conversion from moral apathy to moral commitment requires some sort of vivid first-hand experience: meeting a survivor, visiting a slum. Peculiar, maybe, that for Resaint it involved watching a video of a wasp grub shimmying out of a spider husk, but then she had never really been a person whose deeper feelings were called forth by straightforward means.

The statistics about species dying out were not news to her, any more than the science of species coming into being; she worked, after all, in the extinction industry. Ten thousand species a year, about a hundred times the rate that would be expected in the absence of human activity. (Those were estimates, arrived at by multiplying other estimates; like the Drake Equation for the number of other intelligent civilisations in the Milky Way, it was really just a mille-feuille of unknowns, although now that biologists could census the forests and oceans with little drones, there was more and more reason to think the truth might lie somewhere in that range. The figure the guy with the gun would later quote to her – a hundred thousand extinctions a year – was at the very highest end of what was considered plausible.)

The statistics were not news to her, but the force of them was. To go from caring about this not at all to caring about it more than anything was like being turned inside out. Ten thousand *marginatums*. Probably gone soon. The Kalynove biologist's casualness on that phone call came to represent for her the general casualness with which this great bonfire was allowed to burn. Yes, she was at the centre of a vast and elaborate bureaucracy theoretically intended to prevent extinction, but that bureaucracy's wilful uselessness only emphasised the point. What gripped her at this point was not grief or rage but puzzlement and incredulity. A single extinction was an unspeakable tragedy; and many thousands of them were happening a year; and nobody was really doing anything about it, *including her*. Those three things could not be true simultaneously, any more than A=B and B=C and A≠C could all be true simultaneously. It didn't make logical sense. The Black Hole was beginning to reveal itself to her, but in the same way that an astronomer might disbelieve her own numbers at first, she kept feeling like there had to be some kind of mistake.

She watched videos of some of the more remarkable species that had recently vanished: the Christmas frigatebird, which relentlessly hassled other birds until they puked from sheer exasperation, and then ate the vomit; the oyster mussel, which snapped its shell shut to trap a fish inside, and then released larvae which attached themselves to the captured fish with little hooks; the Japanese crested ibis, which secreted a kind of tar from its throat, and then dabbed the tar on its face like eyeshadow to attract a mate; the aye-aye, which tapped a tree up and down the trunk until it made out the sound of a hollow place, and then gnawed through the bark so it could pull out the grubs inside with its extraordinarily long third finger. In each case, as with *marginatum*, Resaint felt awed by how evolution had not only wound its way towards this weird, snaggly, marginal way of life – so many options and you choose *this one*? – but held on to it, continued to sharpen and perfect it, until it was no longer marginal but was in fact a triumph, a raison d'etre for a whole species. An astonishing story, now ended.

She began her experiments on the Ruthenian tawny bunting, in a laboratory Kalynove had rigged up for her in one of their farm buildings about forty kilometres outside Khmelnytskyi. As the weeks passed, her captive experimental subjects grew to trust her, but every time one of the buntings ate out of her hand, she found herself thinking, 'You shouldn't be doing this. You should hate me. You should be pecking out my eyes, because I am your doom.'

Maybe that sounded dramatic, but she believed it. If you imagined concentric circles of culpability in the bunting's extinction, at the very centre would be the Kalynove executives who pushed through the plan to switch to the new strain of GM sunflowers even after the population models had warned that it would lead to extinctions; next would be the whole apparatus of Kalynove employees and contractors and investors who made its operations possible; a few circles beyond that would be everyone who had ever eaten a meal cooked in sunflower oil made in one of Kalynove's crushing plants; and beyond that would be everyone whose carbon footprint and resource consumption had contributed to the rapid climate change and habitat loss that left the bunting population in such a precarious state to begin with. She was not a Kalynove executive, but she was in all those other circles. Indeed, almost every human being in the developed world was in that outermost circle (a fact the WCSE framework made no attempt to capture, despite some fringe proposals early on). That was why the buntings should have raged at her. But they didn't blame her for what she'd done, the same way you can chain up a dog and starve it to death and even as its organs fail it won't love you any less. Animals were like very stupid adults. They didn't know any better.

At night, in her company apartment in Khmelnytskyi, she thought about the Black Hole. Ten thousand *marginatum*s a year. If evolution gave her a sense of the sublime – so many billions of animals over so many millions of years, just to devise one species – then the extinction crisis did too. She called it the Black Hole not just because it was like a vast leak into which so much was irretrievably disappearing, but even more so because in moral terms it was a cosmic singularity, a region of infinite horror. The Black Hole warped spacetime around it: in comparison, any other moral question seemed irrelevant, vanishingly small. The Black Hole was shrouded by its own enormity: you couldn't properly examine it because it just swallowed up your regard in its blackness. It was a breach like no other breach that had ever preceded it, a breach that could not be measured on any existing scale. The diversity of life on earth was (as far as anyone knew) the most majestic thing in the universe, and human beings were (as far as anyone knew) the only living things with the capacity to appreciate that majesty, and yet human beings were also the ones who were stamping that majesty out, not deliberately but carelessly, incidentally, leaving nothing behind but a few scans and samples that nobody would ever look at.

If every man and woman on the planet were tortured to death, she was beginning to feel, it would not be a sufficient penance.

In 1997, in the far east of Russia, a hunter called Vladimir Markov had been killed outside his cabin by a Siberian tiger.

Nobody knew for certain what had happened, but it was believed that Markov might have shot and wounded the tiger after the tiger came to feed on the carcass of a boar Markov had downed. The tiger escaped, and some time later it found its way to Markov's cabin. Markov was out, so the tiger chewed up everything it could find with Markov's scent on it: his latrine, his beehives, even his saucepan and axe. When Markov finally returned home, the tiger ripped him to shreds. It was not so fanciful to suggest that the tiger was taking premeditated revenge on Markov; certainly the locals, who understood these animals better than anyone, believed as much.

But of course the tiger didn't know that its species had been winnowed by poaching and deforestation from a population of seventy-five thousand at the beginning of the twentieth century to a remnant of just a few hundred. Its vengeance was short-term and personal, but it could have had a much grander scope, if only the tiger had realised the perfectly good reasons it had to loathe *Homo sapiens* on behalf of its own diminished race. This idea came to obsess Resaint. She tasted in it the possibility of a burden lifted, a debt redeemed. It wasn't really that she *wanted* it; rather, it felt like the only permissible outcome. Humans deserved a terrible punishment for their crime; but this punishment ought to be enacted by that crime's victims; and that enaction could be meaningful only if those victims recognised it for it was. She knew it was a bit sloppy to talk about victims at all, when the whole premise of her conversion had been that there did not need to be an injured party for an extinction to be wrong. The last thing she wanted was to become one of those people who worshipped Chiu Chiu like a martyred saint. But if the Black Hole was to have any terrestrial champion, it had to be the animals themselves.

For humans to begin paying in blood even an infinitesimal fraction of their debt, you would need to find a species that had been driven by humans to the brink of extinction, that actually *understood as much*, and that wanted to take revenge.

Chapter Eight

'This thing about wanting to get eaten by the tiger,' Halyard said. 'Are you sure it's not just that you want to fuck the tiger?'

The hotel, it turned out, didn't have a bar as such, only a restaurant that was theoretically closed after 11 p.m., but they'd persuaded the night clerk to sell them a bottle of Polish Merlot. They sat at a four-top in the middle of the room, surrounded by empty tables.

'It wouldn't be that unusual,' he went on. 'The number of people who are probably fucking Chiu Chiu in VR even as we speak . . . The reason I ask is, if I'm right about what you're leading up to – if you're about to tell me that the reason you're so fixated on the venomous lumpsucker is because you think it can fulfil this . . . fantasy or whatever it is? Maybe if you ask yourself what you *really* want, you'll realise there's some confusion about your goals. I mean, you might want to fuck the tiger, but you don't want to fuck the fish. Do you?'

'There are not many non-human animals that could be made to grasp the concept of extinction,' Resaint said. 'Among mammals, it would probably only be the higher primates: gorillas, chimpanzees, orangutans. You heard about that guy in Leipzig last year, with the orangutan and the bamaluzole?'

'He was trying to date-rape the orangutan. Which kind of proves my—'

'No. He wanted the orangutan to murder him.'

'What? How do you know that?'

'It's obvious. He planned to explain to the orangutan that nearly all the other orangutans were dead, and he'd helped kill them. Meaning not that he'd actually been there when it happened but that as a human being he was an accomplice. He was going to stir up the orangutan into such a rage that the orangutan would beat him to death. I assume he'd been laying the groundwork for months in advance.'

'So why did he try and slip the orangutan a roofie?'

'Higher primates are as capable of guilt as they are of anger. He didn't want the orangutan to remember what had happened, because he didn't want the orangutan to feel any guilt about it afterwards. Otherwise it would have been immoral to manipulate this animal into committing a murder.'

'OK, now I know you're taking the piss!' Halyard said. He topped up his wine glass, leaned back in his chair, remembered that it was a ruthlessly uncomfortable Japanese Minimalist knock-off, and leaned forward again. 'You're telling me this guy was trying to commit suicide by orangutan, and his main concern was that the orangutan shouldn't have any dark nights of the soul?'

'This guy was obviously close to the Black Hole. And, as I said, the Black Hole warps reality around it.'

'It makes you irrational.'

'No. It changes your sense of what is important and what isn't.'

'So in that case why don't you just try what he tried? If the whole thing makes complete sense to you.'

'I don't think it would have worked,' Resaint said. 'Balamuzole is a tranquilliser, like the ketamine in Stepanek's darts. Maybe there's some magic dose where the animal is still capable of violence but won't have any memory of the event, but it's incredibly improbable that you'd hit that on the first attempt. Anyway, where would I get access to a higher primate with well-developed language skills? That's not my field.'

'But so the venomous lumpsucker . . .'

'More than almost any other animal we know of, lumpsuckers are attentive to their own population size. They come together and make group decisions based on it. And they're the most intelligent fish on the planet. I believe they could be taught to grasp what was happening to them. They could become witnesses to their own extinction. Also, like we discussed, they're vindictive. They take revenge, not necessarily against the perpetrator, but against some passing member of the perpetrator's species. Even when they have nothing to gain from it, and even when their numbers are low. *Especially* when their numbers are low.'

'And they could kill you.'

'Yes, a sufficient number of venomous lumpsuckers could deliver a dose of venom big enough to kill me. And we have no reason to believe that they would feel any guilt afterwards.'

'They're cold-blooded.'

She gave him one of her Arctic looks (but the old Arctic, back when there was way more ice). 'The physiological meaning of that has nothing to do with the metaphorical meaning. But yes, fine.'

'And the venomous lumpsucker is the only species anybody's ever discovered that ticks all these boxes. So if it's extinct, that's the end of the line for your fantasy. Remember when you said that thing about how the extinction crisis fills you with puzzlement and incredulity?'

'Yes.'

'I think the extinction crisis is an absolute breeze to take on board compared to what you're laying on me now. I mean, this is deranged. You must be able to see that? And, you know what, it's OK to be deranged in your time off. We've all got our little things – mine is good food, yours is getting executed by a fish – whatever. What is not OK is when your thing starts to cause trouble for other people, as it did tonight, when we had a guy pointing a gun at us, and you basically invited him to shoot, because you're suicidal – and yes, that is the word, no matter how much philosophical icing you want to pipe on top of it.'

'That's not really what I want,' Resaint said. 'I don't want to just get shot by some guy in an orchard. It wouldn't mean anything.

I didn't want to watch him die, either. At the same time, when it was happening . . . Was part of me meant to be screaming out inside, saying, "This is wrong! He is wrong!"? Because there was nothing inside me saying that.'

When the instructor at the Hostile Environment Training had advised finding common ground with your captor, Halyard thought, he presumably hadn't meant you were supposed to take it quite as far as Resaint. As an exercise, Halyard pretended for a moment he was a boundlessly tolerant and empathetic person, and tried to imagine how such a person might regard the woman on the other side of the table. In Vienna the instructor had also explained that you could never predict how somebody would react to mortal peril, and there should be no recriminations afterwards if they behaved in what seemed to be very odd ways. But when he looked at Resaint, that was not what he saw. What he saw, more than anything, was his sister Frances.

'So what are you going to do now?' he said. 'Keep taking assignments until you find another species that's fit for purpose?'

'I don't think it's very likely that there's another species on earth that meets all the criteria. But yes, I'll keep looking all the same. When you told me you'd mined the reefs, I was on the point of giving up. But then I saw the news about the attacks on the bio-banks. And I thought, no, I have to hold on to this. I can't give up and go on with my life. Because we never stop destroying. We are irredeemable. The animals have to score a point, just once. What are *you* going to do?'

'I don't know,' Halyard said; and when a uniformed figure appeared in his peripheral vision, he jolted as if this, already, was his escort to a prison cell.

But it was only the night clerk, bringing them the two replacement phones that had just arrived from the fulfilment centre. They unpacked their new phones, logged in, and caught up on the last few hours.

Ever since the biobank attacks, Halyard had been getting a torrent of messages. He'd replied to a few on the train this afternoon, as vapidly as possible: 'I know. Crazy! Huge implications.

I'm in transit right now but let's talk later.' He was too nervous to go any further: he still had some faint hope of coming up with a cover story for what he'd done, but his fear was that if he discussed the extinction credits price spike in any detail with his colleagues at Brahmasamudram, there was no way of knowing what innocuous thing he might say today that would ruin his alibi later. Also, famously, liars always talked too much. However, the messages had continued to flood in since the last time he checked his phone, and at a certain point his near-silence through some of the most seismic events of his professional life was going to look odd in itself. He could announce to everybody that he'd been held at gunpoint by a terrorist in the middle of nowhere – how many people are ever blessed with the chance to deploy such a dazzling and conclusive excuse? – but that would also hasten the moment when he had to explain exactly what he was doing in Estonia, and he hadn't finalised a story for that yet, either.

Still deliberating, he let his scullion run through the rest of his notifications, and towards the end he came across a new result from an alert he'd set up earlier in the day. It was a video clip, and the first time he watched it, he gave a little gasp. After he'd looped it a few more times, he sent it to Resaint so that she could watch it too.

The footage had been shot inside the Tinkanen migrant labour camp on the south coast of Finland three days earlier, but it hadn't been uploaded until a couple of hours ago. The video it came from was several minutes long, but the relevant snippet was just a few seconds, and it showed two men cooking on a small charcoal grill. One of the men was picking fish out of a plastic bucket, and the fish on the grill looked like little herrings or sprats, but you could briefly see in his hand a more bulbous creature with bumpy skin. Halyard's alert, which was trawling every frame of the thousands of hours of video uploaded to the internet every second, had caught this fish in its extremely specific net.

They looked at each other. 'Do you think it could be?' Halyard said.

'It looks right. But, first of all, we don't even know if it's real.'

She meant that the footage was marked as having been shot on a phone with no verification chip. 'I'm looking at the channel it came from,' Halyard said. 'Seems like this person just films stuff around the camp – everyday life, fly-on-the-wall kind of thing. I don't see why she'd fake a venomous lumpsucker.'

As they were both aware, that hardly settled the question. The majority of fake videos on the internet were created for arcane motives that had little to do with their apparent content. Sometimes they might be a feint by one algorithm to manipulate some other algorithm, part of a struggle that was completely inscrutable to any human observer. Sometimes they might be a ploy to spoil somebody's forensic analysis, introducing a contradiction in what would otherwise have been a legally admissible timeline. For all Halyard knew, the entire channel was a fabrication, generated inside a server on the opposite side of the world from Tinkanen.

At the same time, Occam's Razor must apply here: most of the inhabitants of the camp probably had cheap phones with no verification technology. (After all these years, Halyard still didn't really understand how the verification chips in his own devices worked: something to do with cosmic rays and the blockchain?)

'Secondly,' Resaint said, 'just because one venomous lumpsucker found its way to the Gulf of Finland, that doesn't mean there's a second viable population.'

'If I go fishing and I catch ten herrings and one lumpsucker, and I already know there are ten thousand herrings in the bay, then it is reasonable for me to estimate there are one thousand lumpsuckers in the bay, give or take.'

'But if you go fishing and you catch ten herrings and one diamond necklace, that doesn't mean there are a thousand diamond necklaces in the bay, it just means somebody lost their diamond necklace once and now you have an amazing story from your fishing trip.'

'A venomous lumpsucker is not like a diamond necklace, it's a Baltic reef fish, it's exactly what you might expect to find somewhere like the Gulf of Finland—'

'It *is* like a diamond necklace, actually, because there are no reefs off the south coast of Finland that are suitable for venomous lumpsuckers to establish a breeding ground, and they're very particular about their breeding grounds, which means it has to have come from somewhere else. Anyway, in order to find out for sure, we'd have to survey the entire gulf with drones, every cubic metre of it, which is no more practical now than it was this morning.'

'We can go to this camp.'

'Go to Finland?'

'Yes. We can ask around. Someone will be able to tell us where they found this fish.'

'Even if they could tell us, that wouldn't necessarily get us anywhere.'

'It might.'

Resaint sighed. Perhaps she was wary of getting her hopes up again. 'I'm really tired,' she said.

But he already knew that they would go.

They went upstairs together, and this time, as they walked towards their rooms, he thought about asking her into his. No, they hadn't been doing anything resembling flirting, but it was 2 a.m. and they'd shared confidences and a bottle of wine and even a brush with death; he could have had barely half of that to work with and still felt compelled to take a flyer. But when he met her eye as the door of his room unlocked – perhaps he was imagining it, but all of a sudden he had the sense that she knew exactly what he was thinking and she was hoping he wouldn't sully them both with it by making her turn him down. So he just said goodnight.

*

After breakfast the next morning they sat in the slate-coloured lobby waiting for the police to arrive to take their statements. He'd noticed that Resaint's scullion, which she conversed with mostly in German, had a very distinctive singsong intonation. So he asked her about it.

'It's Marisa Tomei in *My Cousin Vinny*,' she told him.

'Is that a film?'

115

'Yes, from 1992.'

'Is she famous for her way with German?'

'No. I set it up as if for some reason the character from the film had learned fluent Basel German but still had a very strong New York accent.' Resaint shrugged. 'I just like the sound of it.'

Halyard went back to browsing the latest fallout from the bio-bank attacks. Global stock markets, rattled by the hacking of the unhackable, were down about a third of a percent, comparable to a rogue state testing a nuclear bomb or a major economy electing a mildly left-wing government. Several of the companies involved in scanning human brains after death had released statements insisting that their own data centres were still absolutely secure, but a meme of Saudi origin was now circulating in which the architects of the Egyptian pyramids used the exact same language with the pharaohs.

If the world was feeling any grief over the destruction of the Dead Bee Scrolls, then it was grief of a rather abstract, obligatory, great-uncle kind. Perhaps most people had the same attitude as Halyard and Resaint: that all those envaulted scans and samples didn't have any real significance if nobody would ever actually get round to looking at them. One exception was the vanishing Pacific kingdom of Tonga, which had used a WCSE grant for the multimodal preservation of several dozen species unique to its submergent islands, so that the 'Eua forest gecko and the spiny shore beetle could precede the nation itself into the realm of the immaterial: this morning a government spokesman had promised legal action against the biobanks, asserting that the Tongan people had been misled when they placed their entire ecological heritage into these fumbling hands. On the exact opposite side of the world, the extinction credit price spike accomplished what no amount of international outcry ever had: halting the construction of an Israeli settlement in the northern West Bank, because the settlers needed a moment to assess whether it was still feasible to flatten the last remaining habitat of the sooty orange-tip butterfly.

But these developments had only secondary claims on the world's attention, compared to the molten core of this story, the question of who was responsible. The internet was wild with conjecture and conspiracy theory. (Inevitably, Israel got brought up quite a bit in this context, too.) Assuming that the party or parties who hacked the biobanks were the same party or parties who had quietly cornered the market in extinction credits over the preceding weeks – and surely they had to be – they had pulled off an extraordinarily artful crime. There were estimates that they might profit by somewhere between fifty and four hundred million euros once they sold off all their hoarded credits. Which was a lot of money . . .

. . . and yet it wasn't *that* much money. Eight or nine figures. At that kind of net worth, there were dinner parties you could go to and still feel poor. So some people were asking: if you were wielding the most advanced cyberattack systems in the world, why on earth would you target the extinction credits market? Which was a niche as marginal as the habitats it purported to defend, such a small pond that for a while, according to Europol estimates, seventy per cent of the trading activity on the Paris marketplace was from criminals using credit sales to commit VAT fraud. Why wouldn't you just hack a few big banks or crypto exchanges? You could easily make ten billion. Halyard himself was enormously curious about this. The perpetrators had wrecked his life, but their scheme had in some ways been a mirror of his own. More than anger, he felt envy, and even admiration.

'You know who stands to lose their shirt if it happens?' Smawl had asked him re: the biobank reforms. That must have been an allusion to somebody with major extinction credit holdings. Halyard kept trying to remember what Smawl had said next, but that night he'd been as legless as . . . well, a legless skink. Could Smawl possibly have had advance knowledge of the market manipulators' identity? It was almost unthinkable that Barry Smawl, of all people, could have been carrying around this absolutely explosive intelligence like a pocket full of antimatter – but on the other hand he had brought it up in the context of somebody taking a big loss, when in fact they would have made a fortune after the hacks, so Halyard was reassured by the knowledge that Smawl's lifelong record of uselessness would remain untarnished. He'd sent Smawl a message but Smawl hadn't answered yet.

Two men in suits came into the lobby. One pointed out Halyard and Resaint to the other. These were the Estonian cops they'd been waiting for. 'Remember,' said Halyard, 'when they ask us about the guy last night, we don't mention that you were basically on his side.'

*

It took an hour to give their statements and then they were free to leave. They'd missed the day's only commercial flight from Tartu to Helsinki, and despite his promises to Resaint regarding his expense account, Halyard didn't dare book a VTOL two days in a row, otherwise the Brahmasamudram procurement scullion might start asking questions about just what he was up to that was so urgent. So instead they made another long journey by train: Tartu to Tallinn, Tallinn to Helsinki, and then Helsinki to a town called Kotka, about forty kilometres west of the Russian border.

'Did you know the Finnish national dance is the tango?' said Halyard to Resaint as they stepped off the last train.

'Really?' Resaint had exchanged the anorak of the day before for a parachute jacket in some kind of crumply sheer blue fabric, vintage-looking, drawstrings and zipper pulls flailing gently around her as she moved.

'Doesn't seem right, does it? Except then you find out that Finnish tangos are all in a minor key and they're about the longing for the old homestead and the sorrow of autumn rains, so actually it's exactly right.'

They walked from the train station to their only lodging option for the night, a run-down place that called itself a 'spa hotel' on the basis that it was across the road from the municipal swimming pool. They were both weary so they went straight upstairs. 'I wish there was an Inzidernil for hotel rooms,' said Halyard, stepping over a cleaning robot that was snuffling around with its vacuum nozzle beneath a water-damaged sofa.

'You take that stuff?'

'Almost every day.'

'Why not just eat what's in front of you and not worry about it so much?' Resaint said.

'The mere fact that you're asking that question tells me I would never be able to make you understand. Apicius, the most famous seafood connoisseur in Ancient Rome – when he couldn't afford good fish any more, he poisoned his own wine with hemlock.' Down to his last ten million sestertii and bereft of red mullet, very similar to Halyard's own situation.

'Last night you were calling *me* suicidal, but if suicide is just preferring not to experience your own life any longer – isn't this pill really a form of—'

'That's not what suicide is.'

She looked at him, surprised by the sharpness in his tone, as indeed he was surprised himself. 'Well, anyway,' she said, 'I suggest you don't complain too loudly about the quality of our hotel when we're at the migrant labour camp tomorrow.'

Before he went to bed, Halyard watched some more videos from the channel where his alert had caught the suspected lumpsucker. Its owner was an eighteen-year-old girl from the Hermit Kingdom who called herself ElsieVVVV. Like all her compatriots in the Tinkanen camp, she'd been sent over to Finland as part of the Hermit Kingdom's guest worker programme. 'I just wanted to do something good for my parents and my little brother and now I'm fucking stuck here,' she said in one video.

Over the past decade, milder winters in central and northern Finland had led to a vast expansion of the country's ranching industry, twenty million head of low-emission cattle crowding into the lakelands. Nobody had expected a concomitant expansion in job opportunities for ranch hands, because the industry was heavily automated. But lately Finland's cattle had been ravaged by an infection called kaptcha, which had originated in Russia and was now spreading all through Scandinavia. Like the diseases that killed the giant pandas and the Iberian oaks, it was part of the worldwide fungal insurrection that had arrived with the 2°C warming era. Kaptcha muddled the cattle's facial features, rendering them illegible to the biometric systems that tracked every cow on every ranch from birth to death. Because these ranches were so new, they'd staked everything on this technology: no barcodes, tags or microchips, just facial recognition cameras, which were supposed to be infallible. But now they were useless. It wasn't just that they could no longer tell one cow from another, it was that they no longer even recognised the cows as cows. So the infected cows didn't get flagged, quarantined or treated, they just spread the disease to their friends. Like antibiotic resistance, kaptcha was a remarkable example of evolution in action. Any strain that got caught by the cameras was wiped out; any strain that didn't would thrive and reproduce. And by now at least a couple of million Finnish cattle wore masks of fungus.

The livestock companies had rushed to find a fix, but although it was possible to teach a facial recognition system to identify any individual stricken cow, kaptcha's disfigurements were of an unpredictable and irregular nature which had so far defied any generalised solution. No matter how many examples you fed into the database, the next example always seemed to stump it. And in the meantime the Finns had no choice but to revert to antiquated technology – human beings – to wrangle their livestock.

By far the cheapest source of unskilled labour in northern Europe was the Hermit Kingdom's guest worker programme. Farmhands like ElsieVVVV, imported from the Hermit Kingdom, were paid about €600 a month for working long days on the ranches, and the majority of that went straight into the coffers of their government, leaving them with only about €200 a month to send home to their families. Nevertheless, because of the state of the Hermit Kingdom's economy, these jobs were so much in demand that you would often have to bribe an official to secure one.

Unfortunately for this spring's cohort of guest workers – thousands of them at dozens of ranches around the country – Finland was aflame. A freakishly hot April had brought early wildfires, the most demonic the country had ever seen. They galloped across the taiga until more than two hundred thousand hectares of boreal forest was on fire. 'We could smell the smoke,' said ElsieVVVV in one of her videos, 'but they were like, "No, we're fine, that's miles away. We've got these projections, everything's updated in real time, the fire's not coming here." And we were thinking, well, they're Finns, they know their shit. And then suddenly it was like, "We've got ten minutes, leave everything behind."' As the cattle ranches were engulfed by billows of glowing ash, there weren't enough buses and cars on hand, so some of the guest workers climbed inside windowless cargo containers to be borne away by heavy-lifter VTOLs, clinging to each other as the containers swayed in the fire's tornadic winds. Those who did have a view of their escape as they sped down the highway saw a landscape raging like the surface of the sun. The cattle, meanwhile, were roasted alive; the ranch managers couldn't risk opening the gates to let them escape, for fear of spreading kaptcha further south.

By agreement between Finland and the Hermit Kingdom, the guest workers weren't allowed to move freely around the country, so after they were evacuated they were brought to the south coast to await repatriation. The problem was that kaptcha, like ringworm, was zoonotic, meaning it could jump from animals to humans. After you spent a week working with infected cattle, you would look in the mirror and see swellings, rashes, sometimes even plaques of fungus as thick as the crust of phlebia on the bark of an oak tree. And even after the infection was chased away with anti-fungal medication, your appearance didn't quite go back to normal: it left behind not only scarring and mottling, but also small fatty deposits under the skin which could subtly alter and deform your features.

In most of ElsieVVVV's videos, she used a filter which reversed the effects of kaptcha, but in one of them – 'RAW AND HONEST comparison, old me & new me' – she contrasted a picture of herself from six months ago to her actual present appearance. Any misgivings Halyard might have felt about rigorously evaluating the physical appeal of a teenage refugee were alleviated when ElsieVVVV invited her viewers to do exactly that. In his judgement, she had been quite pretty before, and she wasn't any longer, not so much because of all her post-fungal blotches and pockmarks, which were no worse than freckles, but because of an ineffable change in the configuration of her features. She had become a knock-off or downgrade of herself. You couldn't quite put your finger on it, but those small fatty deposits must have ruined the symmetry that scientists said was the essence of good looks. (Halyard had a sense of his brain running its software exactly as evolution had intended, because part of the point of being attracted to symmetry was so that you wouldn't be tempted to fuck anyone who had anything living on their face.)

All of this would be correctible with a minor course of cosmetic surgery, but of course that was not readily available in a Finnish migrant labour camp. And kaptcha blanked out human faces in the eyes of the machines just like it did bovine faces. Nobody who knew the old ElsieVVVV would have a moment's difficulty recognising the new ElsieVVVV – nobody except for a facial recognition system, for whom the new ElsieVVVV might as well have been a dappling of sunlight or a graffiti scrawl.

Normally, this wouldn't have been an insurmountable issue, because there were so many other ways to ascertain a person's identity: voice, gait, fingerprints, retinas, the list was endless. The problem was that the Hermit Kingdom's databases were in such a shambles that the Home Office there refused to put their trust in any method except facial recognition – they were as reliant on it as the cattle ranches. So the repatriation of the farmhands fleeing the wildfires had almost entirely stalled, because kaptcha had left them unable to prove to their own government that they were who they said they were, and that government, like an empty restaurant who won't give you a table, was still very much wedded to the idea that their borders were under siege, even though it was probably a decade since anybody had felt any desire at all to sneak into the country. The Finnish Immigration Service had apparently proposed any number of common-sense solutions, but you couldn't reason with the Hermit Kingdom, so there were now three thousand guest workers whiling their time away in the Tinkanen camp, many of whom, like ElsieVVVV, had already been there for six weeks. Finnish government sources, speaking off the record to the media, said the guest workers were growing fractious and if they weren't repatriated soon it was possible that the camp would boil over into violence.

The video on ElsieVVVV's channel with the most views was called 'The worst thing about living here – RAIN OF GNATS!' The opening shot was of black specks drifting thickly down from a blue sky. It might have been ash from one of those wildfires to the north, until ElsieVVVV caught one of the specks in her palm and zoomed in on it. It was a tiny dead insect of the type you'd expect to find swarming around a pond.

'Most of the time we have these things falling on us,' ElsieV-VVV said. 'Not all the time. It's to do with which way the wind's blowing or where the sun is or something like that, I don't know. But most of the time. This is why we have to stay under cover even though the weather's nice. Because otherwise if you're outside you get loads of these in your hair. And everywhere else. Everywhere. Literally.' There were shots of a man sweeping the ground with a broom, gnats piling up in drifts against a water tank; and another man shaking a tarpaulin to empty out its folds; and a woman digging into a girl's hair with both hands to groom between the roots. Heaped up, the dead gnats looked like loose black soil. 'We don't even know where they come from,' ElsieVVVV said. 'I mean, obviously they come from that way, they come from the sea, but oh my god, how can there be this many? It's mad.' She told a story about a man who passed out drunk behind a cabin and his open mouth filled up like a grain hopper. The people who found him thought at first he might already be dead but when they turned him on his side he began a vomiting fit that continued on and off until morning.

And yet the following day, when a taxi brought Halyard and Resaint to Tinkanen, the air was unbugged.

Chapter Nine

The Tinkanen camp occupied fifteen hectares of shoreland, a neat grid of about a thousand white cabins with a little downtown of support buildings and storage sheds at the north end. Like Sanctuary North, it was bounded by both a physical fence of wire mesh and a virtual fence of cameras and sensors, but here the virtual fence shouldered a greater part of the burden, since on the south side the camp gave out on to the ocean, meaning that in theory you could simply paddle in or out. However, drones would dog anybody who crossed the perimeter, whether they were exiting with hopes of vanishing into the countryside or entering with hopes of preying upon the stranded.

It was possible, in fact, that the camp used the very same Antichain software to administer its humans that Delta Ecological Services used to administer their animals. Even after all the uproar about Kashmir, Antichain maintained a pretty dominant market share amongst the refugee camps of the developed world. Bad publicity never made much difference, not when they could do so much for a stressed-out government, transforming a 'jungle' or a 'tinderbox' into a perfectly transparent and predictable machine. (Just this week there had been a story about Ferenc Barka failing to turn up to a European Parliament hearing on civil liberties he'd promised to give evidence to. Nobody seemed to know where he was instead. And what was the European Parliament going to do about it? Send European Parliament gunships?)

So Halyard and Resaint presented themselves at the north entrance. There were no gnats falling from the sky at that moment, but everywhere you looked – every hollow in a tree, every cranny between two waste pipes, every last slot and furrow – was grouted by dried-up bodies. Resaint had seen videos of the locusts that now swarmed as far north as the Alps, billions and billions of them obliterating the wheat fields like some unthinkable weapon, but she'd never heard of anything resembling Tinkanen's chronic drizzle.

'You're here about a fish?' said the guard sceptically, examining their details on his screen.

'That's right,' said Resaint.

Yesterday, when Halyard had been wondering how they'd get into the camp, Resaint had suggested they simply tell the truth. This wild proposition didn't even seem to have crossed Halyard's mind, but it worked. On the journey from Tartu, they contacted a few people at the Immigration Service and its parent department the Ministry of the Interior, hoping that from Finland's relatively compact bureaucracy they might get a quick response. They explained that they worked on species conservation for the Brahmasamudram Mining Company and they had reason to believe that a critically endangered fish called the venomous lumpsucker might have a surviving population near the Tinkanen camp. Sure enough, that was all it took. This morning they had both downloaded waiver packages to their phones, which meant they wouldn't even need a minder when they were inside (although needless to say they would be watched just as closely as the inhabitants, just in case they tried to human-traffic any of these people even more than they'd already been human-trafficked).

'What happened to the . . .' Halyard made a fluttering motion with his hand to represent the fall of the insects.

The guard shrugged. 'It just stopped.'

ElsieVVVV's footage of the two men grilling the fish gave no indication of their location within the camp, but Halyard's scullion had found two other videos online which showed the same cabin with a bit more background detail, and by cross-referencing those with the plan of the camp supplied by the Finns it had pinpointed the barbecue at the south end, not far from the ocean. Once they were past the guardhouse, Halyard and Resaint set off down one of the camp's longitudinal avenues. Because the guest workers weren't supposed to be here for very long, the Finns hadn't bothered to pour concrete, so there were only wide dirt paths and the odd patch of dry grass subsisting where it hadn't already been trodden to dust. The basic layout of the camp had all the charm of a cargo terminal: just cabin after cabin after cabin, each of which was a steel box like a shipping container, and every four cabins a tall streetlamp, marking off distance all the way to the water. The regularity of it might have been oppressive to the eye if the residents hadn't jumbled the lines, with flags draped from the roofs, washing lines hung from the streetlamps, and tarpaulins strung up for shelter out of doors.

Although it was nowhere near as grim as some of the camps you saw in the news – there were no children here – Resaint nevertheless felt pretty self-conscious about strolling into this zone of misfortune as a tourist who could leave whenever she wanted. So it was a relief to her that people didn't pay them much attention, perhaps because their visit definitely wasn't the most exciting thing to have happened that day. In fact, the camp had an atmosphere of almost hysterical festivity. People had dragged plastic chairs out to the middle of the avenue, into positions that were very much in the way of everything, so that there was no reason why you would want to sit there except that it was emphatically, unsparingly *out in the open*. And even though it was not a particularly glorious day, with a blear of cloud so thick you could only guess at the position of the sun, people leaned back in the chairs, opening their bodies to the sky, gesturing upwards to each other as if there was nothing to talk about but the weather.

Some wore T-shirts and shorts, but others wore office shirts with shiny suit trousers or pencil skirts. Resaint had read that guest workers from the Hermit Kingdom continued to dress

126

according to their social position at home regardless of the work they had been sent to perform overseas, so if you thought of yourself as a white-collar professional you would wear a suit even to the cattle ranch. On almost every face she could see vestiges of kaptcha, but the Finns had assured them that there was no risk of infection in the camp, because everything and everyone that came from the ranches was purged before it got inside, and anyway human-to-human transmission was very rare compared to bovine-to-bovine transmission or bovine-to-human transmission.

'After the Holocaust,' Halyard said to her, pretty much out of nowhere, 'nobody was saying "We all have to kill ourselves out of guilt now, even if we had nothing to do with it." I mean, OK, wasn't there that one bloke who said basically "We aren't allowed to write poetry any more", and I suppose for poetry people that's a harsh sanction, but for the rest of us it's a relief if anything. Or take the Uighur thing. It was bad but nobody feels duty-bound to top themselves just for being alive when it happened. So why should anyone die over the extinction thing? Why should you?'

'The extinction crisis is not comparable to the Holocaust.'

'No, it isn't.' He glanced at her. 'Unless you're saying the extinction crisis is *worse*? Are you saying that? It's in really bad taste if you're saying that,' he added, in a tone which was almost but not quite enough to sell the idea that he was deeply invested in such niceties. 'What about all the suffering?'

'This isn't a question of suffering. The extinction of *Adelognathus marginatum* didn't involve any suffering. The injury is that it doesn't exist any more. That is irreparable. That's why it feels like a gash in the universe. Whereas the human race still existed after the Holocaust.'

'But millions of individual human beings didn't exist any more!'

'You mean that an individual human being has greater moral weight than an entire species?'

'I, an individual human being, wouldn't take a bullet for the last spiny shore beetle, nor would I expect anyone else to.'

'Four hundred thousand people are born every day,' Resaint said. 'If you or I died, someone else would soon be born who was very much like us.'

'No! Every human being is unique! Every death is the destruction of a whole world.'

'Do you actually believe that? You don't seem to me like someone who believes that. Isn't that just a platitude you've heard?'

'But all those people who died – what about the symphonies they would have written, and the novels, and the . . . well, again, not the poems, forget those, but you know what I mean. Isn't *that* irreparable? You can't get those things back.'

'I don't believe any individual human being has ever lived who was as remarkable as *Adelognathus marginatum* and the ninety-million-year evolutionary process it consummated, and I don't believe any work of art has ever been created which is as remarkable, either. Not even close. Not even within a couple of orders of magnitude.'

They passed four men who had climbed up on a roof for a boisterous picnic, old rock music playing from somebody's phone, one of them wearing a knotted cloth over his head to protect himself from the utterly negligible rays of the sun. 'OK, if you feel so strongly, why are you still living the same old life?' Halyard said. 'You still work in the extinction industry. You still took an assignment from Brahmasamudram.'

'I needed to hold on to my job so that people would keep sending me to evaluate the intelligence of endangered species. That's how I found the venomous lumpsucker.'

'But if it's so important to you, morally, shouldn't you just—'

'Kill myself right away?'

'No—'

'You know what they say – "the only way to be truly vegan is to die." That's more or less true.'

'No it isn't! You could go zero impact. Live off the land. Borrow a gnat broom from one of these poor fuckers and sweep the ground in front of you like a Buddhist monk so you don't squish anything.'

'That's Jainism, not Buddhism,' Resaint said.

'Or you could do some good. Take your considerable talents to some eco start-up that's trying to save us from all this shit. Or, to bring it back to the Holocaust, you could go Nazi hunter. Our friend from the orchard could probably put you in touch with the right people. There are still a lot of targets out there.'

She knew he was talking about the crusade, beginning in the late 2020s, to identify and punish those who had played the most inexcusable part in what was happening to the planet, before they all died of old age. This had quickly reached its zenith or its nadir, depending on your attitude, with the execution of Carl Megrimson. Newly surfaced documents from 1991 and '92 had identified Megrimson, a retired oil industry executive, as one of the chief architects of the industry's concerted sabotage of any political action on fossil fuels during that period. By 2028 he was seventy-seven years old, grandfather of eleven grandchildren, kindly-looking and wheelchair-bound and living in a Greek Revival mansion in north Dallas.

The footage of his death, anonymously released a few hours after the event, was shot from a drone that had been equipped not only with a camera but also with a one-gallon flamethrower of the kind used to clear debris from power lines. As Megrimson was being wheeled around the grounds by his nurse that morning, the drone hovered a few hundred metres overhead. But when the nurse left Megrimson alone for a moment, the drone swooped down upon the old man and squirted over him a fiery jet of what was later found to be diesel thickened with gelling agent – in other words, napalm. For the next forty-five seconds, the drone just hung there, filming, as Megrimson writhed and screamed in his wheelchair, and then went still. The very end of the footage, after the nurse had finally quenched him with a fire extinguisher, showed his blackened body caked in white foam, an object hardly recognisable as human. Nobody ever claimed responsibility for this tour de force, or was ever arrested for it. Afterwards, there were many copycats, but none ever made the same splash as the original; hence the turn, in recent years, towards the violent surrealism of the Chiu Chiu mega-tumours.

In the course of her job, Resaint had met people like Megrimson, executives who went into work and sat down at their desks and made decisions that ravaged the world. They didn't seem evil to her. They seemed more like fungal colonies or AI subroutines, mechanical components of a self-perpetuating super-organism, with no real subjectivity of their own. That said, she would have happily watched any of them die. And the reason she wasn't sure how to reply to Halyard was that, in truth, she had already contemplated all of the suggestions he was making: self-immolation, withdrawal, do-gooding, 'Nazi-hunting' (which in this context was something of a misnomer, because the Law for the Protection of Nature that Göring passed in 1935 was actually a model of its kind; the Forestry Department of the Third Reich even planned to rescue the auroch and the tarpan from extinction by artful breeding before setting them loose in a reforested Ukraine like the otters at Sanctuary North).

But these responses felt self-absorbed, internecine, meaningless, like the human race saying to the extinct species, 'You will be pleased to know that, following these unfortunate events, we have conducted a thorough internal review, which has yielded several important recommendations for the future.' They didn't exert the same pull on her as the dream of vengeance, because only the latter had the animals' participation. Without that, there could be no atonement. Certainly, in utilitarian terms, it was impossible to justify how she spent her time. It was impossible to justify her complicity with Brahmasamudram and Zhejiang-Lacebark and all the rest of them. It was impossible to justify her carbon footprint as a prosperous European who travelled all over the continent for work. It was impossible to justify breathing, really. This was at the back of her mind at all times, and if the guy in the orchard had shot her she would have accepted her end without protest. Yet, for as long as she was still alive, atonement was all she wanted. Sometimes she wondered if her work for all those harrowers and ruiners was really just a way of binging before she purged, fattening herself horribly on sin to make the final mortification an even greater thrill.

A smell on the air like rotting fish had been getting stronger and stronger as they walked south through the camp, and by now it was punchy enough that it fixed a sneer on your face if you didn't consciously relax your expression. 'What is that?' Halyard said. 'Is there a rubbish tip down here?'

'It's probably the gnats. The ones that come down on land will mostly dry up in the sun before they can rot, but a lot of them will fall into the water too. There must be mounds of them decomposing in the shallows.'

'But it smells like fish.'

'If you have enough insects decomposing in one place, that's what they smell like.' She knew that because of an incident during a previous assignment involving a housefly rearing module and a software crash.

'Jesus. I think this is worse than Pavel's toxic waste.'

When they reached the cabin that Halyard's scullion had located for them, Resaint recognised one of the two guys from ElsieVVVV's video, who was in the middle of shooing a pointy-eared black dog away from the door. 'Hello, excuse me,' Resaint said. 'Could we talk to you for a second?'

Wilson, as he turned out to be called, was a lollopy, balding guy in his forties. The more animated he became, the more his whole face spasmed in emphasis, eyes widening and eyebrows jumping as if he was being zapped with an electrode. Halyard took out his phone and showed him the video, with the venomous lumpsucker highlighted. When the screen creased it made that crinkly tinfoil sound that new phones always made for the first few days. 'We're looking for this fish,' he said.

Wilson's face fell. 'I'm awfully sorry, but we ate it.'

'Um, no—'

'That's the main reason we were cooking it, to be quite honest with you. I wish we'd known. Have you come a long way?'

Resaint explained that they weren't looking for that fillet in particular, but for the species in general.

'Oh! Well, I bought that fish from Gareth. He's a fisherman, so you'd have to ask him precisely where he scooped it up, but in terms of what I can tell you, I'd say a ninety-nine per cent chance it was the sea. The one per cent is in case he acquired it by some other means, which I can't altogether rule out, but his general modus operandi is that he catches fish in the sea.'

'Thanks, that's really helpful,' Halyard said. Wilson looked ecstatic. 'So where would we find—'

'About five hundred yards that way,' Wilson said, gesturing with his thumb.

'That's where Gareth is?'

'No, that's where the sea is.'

'And what about Gareth?'

'Ah – that's rather a fraught question, because nobody's seen him since the small hours of this morning. He went off in his boat with our other new visitor.'

'Who's that?'

'Well, I never set eyes on her myself,' Wilson said, 'but she dropped in like you two, except rather than coming to look for a fish, she was herself, as it were, fished! As far as I've been able to glean, Gareth was in his boat yesterday morning, around dawn, a long way out to sea, when he heard a woman calling out to him, just like a mermaid or a selkie in a folktale. Except she said to him, "Hark, I'm cast adrift upon the waves," or words to that effect, because she was.'

'How did she end up out there?'

'Evicted from her coralline abode, perhaps! No, the truth is I haven't the faintest – she was floating around miles from anything. By the way, can I offer you some tea? They don't give us the real stuff but we have a kind we make ourselves out of dried bilberry leaves, it's pretty dire but it's really not too bad . . . Absolutely sure? All right, well, as I was saying, Gareth helped this castaway into his boat, whereupon he was astonished to discover that she was from our little corner of the world, or at least she sounded like she was. He brought her home to the camp, hidden so the drones wouldn't spy her. And I do hesitate to gossip about a lady I haven't met, but I'm afraid it could be said that she rather trespassed upon Gareth's hospitality, and for that matter she trespassed quite literally, because that night – last night – Dr Shahad caught her robbing the medical centre.'

'What was she trying to steal?' Resaint said.

'I don't know for certain, but as I say, it was the medical centre' – Wilson hesitated, still visibly gripped by the desire to be of help – 'so perhaps it could have been some . . . ointment? Some bandages? Something of that nature? Anyway, our dear Dr Shahad is very merciful, very understanding, and I'm told that rather than summon a guard, she let her go. But of course the management were certain to get wind of the incident, meaning this lady could expect her welcome here to run out rather sharpish. I assume that was why she asked Gareth to take her back out to sea after her brief time in port.'

'Where was she going?'

'To rejoin her undinal sisters in the North Sea, I dare say!' Wilson laughed. 'No, that's just another little joke. The truth is, nobody seems to know their destination, including Gareth's wife, and Gareth apparently said he'd be back in three or four hours, but it's coming up on twelve hours and there's been neither hide nor hair of him yet. The Finns will have their unblinking eye on his boat, but they never pass us any intelligence even when it would be the most enormous help.' Wilson lowered his voice. 'There have been suggestions that Gareth and this lady – well, it's a hoary old tradition, isn't it, that mermaids turn the heads of fishermen? Again, not that I sincerely think . . .'

At that moment the dog trotted back out from behind the cabin and went straight up to Halyard. Beaming, Halyard bent to scratch its chin. 'Who's this cute little fella? Who's this? Who's this? '

This was the most cheerful Resaint had seen Halyard since they'd met. 'I hadn't realised you were such an animal lover,' Resaint said.

'If dogs ever went extinct – that's totally different.'

'Thank you again for your help,' Resaint said to Wilson. 'And I'm sorry about everything you've all been through.'

'Oh, don't be silly.' Wilson gave a half-smile, half-cringe, as if he was genuinely pained by this undeserved expression of sympathy. 'We've had a perfectly pleasant time.'

133

Halyard looked up from the dog. 'But you came here to work on the cattle ranches for eight euros a day, and then you all got a disfiguring fungus, and then you had to flee the wildfires, and now you're stuck in a camp because your own government won't take you back, and for the last six weeks you've had dead gnats raining on your head. It's fucking Biblical.'

'We certainly have had an eventful little holiday,' Wilson said. 'And when we get home it won't be a moment too soon. But I have no doubt we'll look back on it all with great fondness. Keep calm and carry on, that's what my mother always said! And when the weather is so splendid, you forget all your little troubles, don't you?'

'The weather today is mediocre at best,' Halyard said.

'Well,' said Wilson, as if that was very much a matter of opinion.

'Do you just mean that the gnats have stopped?'

'Certainly that has been a happy development, whether it's really Mrs Purleyswars' doing or not.'

'Who's Mrs Purleyswars?'

'She's the woman who's supposed to have talked to the gnats.'

'What?'

'Over the weekend Mrs Purleyswars told everyone that she was going to have a word with the gnats. See if they wouldn't give us a bit of a reprieve. I'm not sure I can swallow it myself, but the gnats stopped coming down precisely when she said they would, and people who know her say she *has* always had a way with animals, so in the absence of any better explanation . . .'

Halyard shot Resaint an expression meaning that this latest fairy tale was their cue to leave.

'Where is Mrs Purleyswars?' Resaint said. 'I want to meet her.'

'What?' said Halyard. 'Why?'

'I just want to meet her.'

'Our priority should be collaring this bloke Gareth so we can ask him where exactly he caught that fish. At this point he's the last lead we've got left. Which means we need to find out where he was headed with the "mermaid". I don't want to just sit around waiting for him to come back. We don't even know if he *is* coming back.'

'We can split up for a while. I'll catch up with you later.'

Halyard gave her a quizzical look. She knew he was asking for an explanation but she didn't feel like supplying one. Wilson begged for permission to lead the way to Mrs Purleyswars' cabin. And on the walk over there, while he burbled on, she thought about Kazu Horikawa.

Over the course of those three months on board the *Varuna*, Resaint had had frequent dreams in which she met her late predecessor. She knew so little about what sort of person Horikawa had been, nothing really to go on beyond the text of 'Social strategic behaviour of the venomous lumpsucker' and a few earlier papers. But one thing that had begun to fascinate Resaint about 'Social strategic behaviour', around her seventh or eighth reading, was Horikawa's arc of discovery. Just by watching and rewatching what little relevant footage she could capture each day on her underwater cameras, Horikawa had made such enormous leaps – leaps which she was then able to support with data (and which were reconfirmed years later by Resaint's own experiments), but leaps nevertheless. So little to build on, so little to work with, and yet she'd pulled these faint signals out of the noise. Clearly Horikawa had the intuitive powers of a great scientist. And Resaint wouldn't have felt any special longing for these powers, since ethology was just her day job, not her calling in life; except that she was now consumed by the problem of opening a line of communication between humans and animals, so that the animals could, in the words of the guy in the orchard, make their voices heard – so that an animal could look a human in the eye and understand 'You are my debtor', and the human could look the animal in the eye and understand 'You are my creditor', and the violence that followed would be an act of communication too, a payment sent over the wire. No real moral reckoning was possible between two beings unless those two beings apprehended each other, recognised each other, and that would be so much easier to arrange if you had Horikawa's empathy for the fish.

Of course she didn't believe that Mrs Purleyswars had really talked to the gnats. And yet as soon as Wilson had said that Mrs Purleyswars had 'always had a way with animals', Horikawa had come into Resaint's mind. If this woman from the Hermit Kingdom had known in advance that the gnats would stop falling, wasn't it possible she'd noticed something other people didn't see? Resaint would never have the chance to meet Horikawa, but mightn't there be other souls like her in the world? She told herself it was absurd, irrational, and yet as they came to the cabin – blinds closed, purple bellflowers potted in plastic buckets outside – she was tense with anticipation.

Wilson knocked on the door. 'Mrs Purleyswars?'

'Who is it?'

It's Wilson, Mrs Purleyswars. I'm here with a young lady who'd like to make your acquaintance.'

Chapter Ten

'You know, when I finally get home, I'll be rich,' said the man next to Halyard.

They were sitting in the waiting room of the camp's medical centre. This was another prefab building that had been trucked in at the same time as the farmhands, so the vinyl floors trembled slightly under the tread of your feet and everything in your field of vision was the exact same shade of off-white. It was a lot like the modular support structures he sometimes visited at Brahmasamudram's prospecting sites, except that this room had a huge decal of the Eiffel Tower up one wall which was presumably intended to have a jollifying effect on the interior but which looked absolutely nonsensical in context. The seating was that type of bench that's just a horizontal beam with three scoops fixed to it, and there was one empty scoop between Halyard and this man. The Finns handed out free plimsolls to anybody who needed them, so it must have been by choice that he still wore a pair of shiny brown fake-leather loafers with soles held on by duct tape.

Halyard barely looked up from his phone, because he wasn't particularly interested in engaging with some waiting room prattler. 'Really?' he said, out of politeness.

The man nodded. 'I've got a share in an extinction credit.' And Halyard realised that he might not be just a prattler after all.

One of the most baroque qualities of the extinction credits system was that it dealt so extensively in alternate histories and possible universes. Credits were not only allocated to companies like Brahmasamudram, they were also allocated to countries. And at the birth of the World Commission on Species Extinction, everybody had agreed that you couldn't determine how many extinction credits a country was entitled to simply on the basis of landmass. Imagine that every country of two million square kilometres got a certain number of credits a year. In that case, a country like Mexico – which was not only crawling with threatened endemics, but also had a strong economy and booming population that needed to be fed by constant new development – might have to more or less dismantle itself if it didn't want to exceed its allocation. Whereas a country like Greenland – which was the same size, but didn't have much wildlife, or really much of anything else going on, even in this age of thaw – could just lie back munching blubber. And it wasn't fair to penalise Mexico compared to Greenland just because Mexico started from a very different place.

So, instead, it was decided that credits would be doled out to countries on the basis of how many species *would have been* driven to extinction in the absence of any preventative measures. That way, if Mexico changed its ways, you could look at the gap between what had been averted (heaps of species lost) and what was happening instead (far fewer species lost) and reward Mexico appropriately, not for sinlessness but for temptation resisted.

The whole system was founded on this gap between the hypothetical worst and the actual not-so-bad. But of course this was a subject of Jesuitical perplexity, beetles scuttling underfoot in a garden of forking paths. Nobody could know for certain what the world would have looked like without the WCSE, because the WCSE had subtly reshaped the world. There were all kinds of sophisticated computer models to reckon with this, but different models advantaged different interests, so it was impossible to agree on one. Every country wanted to be classed as a Mexico, not a Greenland; every country insisted that, all other things being equal, they would have been absolutely scything through endangered species, dyeing their rivers red with the blood of unsuccessful tree frogs and esoteric deer mice, so if in reality they were only killing a handful, they should be garlanded for their restraint.

One proposal was that the baseline figures – the 'normal' rate of extinction in each country – should be taken from the day of Chiu Chiu's death, before the WCSE even existed, which would obviate a lot of the metaphysics. But many South American countries complained that when Chiu Chiu died they were still sunk deep in their post-pandemic recessions, and therefore that year wasn't a proper snapshot of their economic vigour. Why should a picture of you taken when you were sickly and greenish represent you for the rest of your life? So instead the WCSE decreed that the baseline figures should be taken from back in 2019, when many economies were still looking their most radiant.

Perhaps no nation benefited more from this compromise than the Hermit Kingdom. In 2019, the Hermit Kingdom was still the sixth biggest economy in the world. So that was its official baseline. But by the time of Chiu Chiu's death, well into the process of sealing itself off completely, it had fallen to around eightieth or ninetieth biggest (there was so little data leaking out that the analysts could only estimate from the industrial activity captured in satellite photos). In other words, the WCSE treated the Hermit Kingdom like a real bruiser – not quite a Mexico, because it didn't have the same tropical biodiversity, but certainly the sort of country you'd expect to be busy draining its marshes, spraying its fields, poisoning its rivers and tarring its air, eradicating plenty of species along the way. Whereas in fact none of that was happening any more: out of sheer poverty, it had become an environmental paragon. So a generous allocation of credits was grandfathered across to the Hermit Kingdom, almost none of which it had any use for, meaning it was free to sell them on the open market. For a while, in the early days of the WCSE, it looked as if extinction credits might be a nice boost to the Hermit Kingdom's shrivelled GDP; this was thought to be why the Hermit Kingdom happily signed up to the WCSE even as it was withdrawing from every other international treaty. Then extinction credits plummeted in price, partly because the Hermit Kingdom was just one of a number of countries flogging their surplus every year, and that hope died.

But now an extinction credit cost nearly four hundred grand. If you had even a share of one, in a country where people would fight over a job paying eight euros a day, you were really sitting pretty.

'What are you going to do with the money?' Halyard said.

The man smiled a bit awkwardly. He must have recovered from an especially bad case of kaptcha, because his features had the disordered quality of an old boxer's. 'Well, of course I can't just pick up the phone and say "I want to sell." There are controls on that sort of thing. But regardless of, you know . . . The fact is, I own a share of a very valuable asset. When I get home, no one can say I'm not rich.'

Not sure how to respond to this, Halyard searched for a pleasantry. 'Hope you're not here for anything too serious?'

'Sunstroke. Always been a bit susceptible but I still caught too much sun this morning. Silly of me.'

'What the fuck is wrong with you all?' Halyard exploded. 'There's no sun! It's not sunny! Just because it's not raining gnats any more, that doesn't mean it's sunny!'

'Well,' said the man.

'Mr Halyard? I have a few minutes.'

He looked up. Dr Shahad stood in the doorway. He got up and followed her down the corridor to her consultation room.

Why had he come to the medical centre to talk to Dr Shahad? His official pretext was that something must have transpired between Dr Shahad and the mermaid before the former let the latter go free, because no matter how understanding a person you are, the ransacking of supplies from a migrant camp clinic is not the kind of thing you just excuse without some sort of explanation. And so perhaps Dr Shahad might know something about where the mermaid had been planning to set sail with Gareth.

But that was mostly a post-hoc rationalisation. The real reason he'd come here was that it was the path of least resistance: wandering around the camp questioning people at random sounded exhausting, whereas Dr Shahad had the appealing qualities that 1. her name had already come up, 2. it was obvious where she might be found, 3. she would speak with at least a minimum of sense and authority because she was a doctor, and 4. she, too, was an outsider to this place, so he hoped she might be easy to talk to, the same way travellers can bond by complaining about the locals. Halyard would have been the first to concede that, in terms of initiative and tenacity, he was not a born detective.

However, his laziness paid off.

'I was in here working late when the alarm went off,' Dr Shahad told him, sitting with a cup of coffee beside her little built-in desk. He wouldn't have said she was dour, exactly – on the contrary, she seemed like someone who might be full of good cheer with her patients – it was just that the share of that good cheer she was willing to allocate to him, a healthy person taking up her time, was zero. 'I found her in the lab. She'd smashed a lock and come in through the back. At first I thought she must be stealing Inzidernil.'

'Oh, you take Inzidernil too?'

She looked at him as if she might want to add 'brain injury' to his medical chart. 'No, I don't take it. We give it to our patients here. Anybody the psychologist finds to be experiencing severe dislocation trauma, we give them two weeks of Inzidernil.'

'Why?'

'You understand these people are living mostly on nutrient bars? We distribute ten palettes a week, chocolate flavour and vanilla flavour. And they talk constantly about the food they miss – "shepherd's pie", "fish and chips". When you're a long way from home, the right food can feel very comforting, but the corollary of that is that the wrong food can feel very cruel. Demeaning. People resent the nutrient bars. But the Inzidernil really seems to make a difference. It takes away the sadness of a meal. Unfortunately the result is that people will do anything to get their hands on a dose. The pills have become a kind of currency inside the camp.'

Halyard wished Resaint were here to hear this. He felt vindicated. She had been wrong to mock his Inzidernil habit as a decadent indulgence. If these sooty waifs fought over the drug to make their lives bearable, didn't that prove it was actually a very meaningful and pragmatic invention? Forget that he took it primarily because he didn't like corporate catering. 'Are they using it in a lot of camps now?'

'I heard about a big trial in those privatised camps in Turkey. It's supposed to reduce the incidence of food riots.'

This wiped away Halyard's feeling of satisfaction. If the market for Inzidernil included all the hundreds of millions of climate refugees in the world, then the profits he could have made from an early investment in Henan Pharmaceutical Group were orders of magnitude larger than he'd ever imagined. By now he could have been blowing his nose on Bellotta ham. He tried to put that out of his mind. 'But she wasn't here for Inzidernil?' he said.

'I don't think so.'

'What was she here for?'

'I asked her but she wouldn't tell me.'

'And you still just let her go?'

'Yes. She told me there were people looking for her and her life was in danger if they caught up with her.'

'If I got caught stealing I might say something like that too.'

'I've worked in other camps,' Dr Shahad said. 'There's a look people get in their eyes after they've been running for their lives for a long time. That's what this woman had. It wasn't just a story. Anyway, I checked afterwards and there was nothing missing.'

'Did she say why these people were looking for her?'

She gave him a hard look. 'For all I know, you're one of them.'

'If I was, I would presumably already know what I wanted her for? So it wouldn't make any difference if you told me. But, to be clear, I'm not. I'd never heard of this woman until about half an hour ago when Wilson started talking about a mermaid.'

'She said they were looking for her because she knew some big secret about hacks that have been in the news.'

'You mean the attacks on the biobanks?'

Dr Shahad nodded.

'What did she know? Do you mean she knew who was behind them?'

'Yeah. Maybe. Something like that.'

'Fuck, really?' Halyard was thrown by this news, of course, thunderstruck, but he was also thrown by the casualness with which Dr Shahad had delivered it. She'd just met somebody who – if it wasn't all bullshit – had the answer to the question that half the planet was asking, and she didn't even seem curious. It was always a bit chastening when you met someone who was absorbed in a job that did some real good in the world and you saw how little they felt the need to keep up to date on everything. 'Did she say – I mean—'

'She didn't say anything else about that.'

'Fuck. Fucking hell.' Wilson had said that the mermaid sounded like maybe she hailed from the Hermit Kingdom too. Halyard thought about the guy in the waiting room. It struck him that even if that poor bastard would never be allowed to realise his gains, there were no doubt a few kleptocrats in the Hermit Kingdom's government who would do extremely well out of the price spike. Yesterday, he'd wondered why anyone would settle for making just a few hundred million euros after they'd designed a computer worm that could swallow the world like an Aztec god. But what if you were from a country where 1. that was an unimaginable fortune and 2. extinction credits were pretty much the only financial asset it was still possible to trade back and forth with the outside world? 'What about where she was going next?' he asked.

'She said she was going somewhere she could hide. She said Gareth had promised to take her there. And I said, "Are you sure Gareth's boat is going to get you where you're going?" He offered to take me out in it once and I said no. I don't know where he found it and I'd rather go to sea in an old tyre than that thing. And she said, "I'll swim if I have to."'

'Was she joking? You know, like, "I don't care if they cancel our flight, I'll swim if I have to!", or did she actually mean—'

143

'I don't know. After that I said, "Listen, next time you're on dry land for a while—" I was going to say she should rest, see a doctor, get her strength back. I was worried about her. She was worn down to the bone. But she said, "I really don't know when that will be."'

Halyard could not deny that these two remarks by the sea-borne woman lent strong support to Wilson's claim that she was a well-disguised mermaid. Through Brahmasamudram he had access to satellite tracking services that could retrace the recent movements of any of the larger vessels on the Baltic, but a fishing skiff would be beneath their notice. 'What about the surveillance grid for the camp? Wilson said it would have been tracking the boat. If we could get somebody to take a look at the data for us—'

'Where this woman was going is no business of mine. Why would I want to put Migri on her trail?'

Who the hell is Migri, Halyard thought? And then he remembered it was the abbreviation for the Finnish Immigration Service. He nodded. 'Right. No, I see.' He thanked her and left.

Outside, two men trudged towards the medical centre, supporting between them a third man who had his arms slung over their shoulders and was bleeding down his flabby shirtless chest and could be heard complaining that he was fine and just needed to sit down for a bit. Stepping out of their way, Halyard checked his phone, and saw that he had a message from Jan Busk, a colleague of his at Brahmasamudram. The two of them were not especially friendly. Busk was a member of a Polish neo-traditionalist Catholic movement, and he was rumoured to have an app installed on his smart glasses that blanked out any cleavage in his field of view that didn't belong to his wife.

'Hi Mark, I know you'll be joining us for the call this afternoon, but I was just wondering if you could help me pin something down in advance of that.

'As you know, Pia has been keen to reassure Mumbai that we don't have too much exposure to the volatility in the EC market, and she wanted to double-check all the numbers before she talked to them.

'Sorry if I've stepped on your toes a bit here, but since you're still travelling [Halyard recognised this as a euphemism for his having been virtually incommunicado for the past three days] Pia thought it would be quicker if I just got in there myself.

'Everything looks fine except for one thing, which is the thirteen credits we bought in advance of the Bothnia op. Right now those aren't showing up in the database for me. Do you know why that would be? I'm probably missing something obvious! But it would be great if you could fill me in before the call.'

There was a mindfulness technique Halyard sometimes used where if you felt gripped by stress you simply made the choice to reframe it as a stomach ache, a bodily signal with no emotional valence, and after that it was much easier to push into the background. But what he felt after he read this message was not an intensity of stress you could just pretend was a stomach ache, unless it was the kind of stomach ache you got from drinking a tall glass of weedkiller while somebody hollowed you out with a garden fork.

He had never even considered the scenario that the absence of the credits would be noticed this fast. Yes, once the extinction of the venomous lumpsucker was confirmed, and Brahmasamudram had to settle accounts with the WCSE, the hole would be impossible to conceal. But that should have been weeks or months away. There was no reason for anybody to poke around like this. It was as if your office had a supply cupboard stocked with paperclips, and then you found out there was a worldwide paperclip shortage, so you audited the shelves to make sure you had enough paperclips, even though nobody had used any paperclips since the last time you ordered a box. You would have to be a neurotic. Jan Busk should have had better things to do with his time.

His tactic so far, staying as quiet as possible so that he wouldn't make any mistakes, wouldn't say anything which might hem him in later, was now revealed as idiotic — so idiotic, in fact, that he found it impossible to reconstruct what had made him think it was a good idea as recently as a few minutes ago. What he should have done was stride cheerfully into the middle of everything, take charge, volunteer the answer to every question before it was asked, so that the whole matter would be dropped from the agenda because he so conspicuously had it in hand.

Now it didn't matter any more whether the venomous lump-sucker was dead or alive. Brahmasamudram knew the credits were gone, and there was no explanation he could come up with on the fly that would withstand even a day's scrutiny. They were going to throw him in jail like Pratury. Really, all his efforts to save himself had been futile. His fate had been sealed the night all those animals in the biobanks were cooked down like roadkill in a drum of lye.

And that made him think again about what Dr Shahad had told him. 'She said they were looking for her because she knew some big secret about the hacks.'

The idea that she knew not just a big secret but the biggest secret in the world – this nameless woman passing through a migrant labour camp, this flotsam from the sea, this cornered thief – was about as plausible as the idea that Barry Smawl knew it.

And yet if somehow she did . . . That made everything else unimportant. Dr Shahad had demonstrated by her forbearance how people would make allowances for someone who was pregnant, Madonna-like, with some world-historical revelation. Halyard, too, wanted to be let off for stealing. If he could talk to this woman, and become one of the very first conduits for whatever she knew, how could anyone care any more that he'd dipped into the till at work? He would be operating at a new, grander scale where such trivialities receded to imperceptible size. That guy who solved Jeffrey Epstein's murder had turned out to be a vindictive weirdo who kept trying to drive his neighbours out of their homes with campaigns of psychological attrition, but everyone just ignored that most of the time, and it didn't come up at all in the film version that portrayed him as a hero.

This could be his rescue. And he had nothing to lose and nowhere else to turn.

He told his scullion to look through ElsieVVVV's videos until it found a boat that might be Gareth's. Sure enough, in one of the

146

videos there was a shot of a cricket match on the beach, and in the background you could see a fishing boat, about ten feet long, pretty clapped out, the gunwale cracked and the hull painted with black mildew, presumably salvaged from abandonment somewhere along the shore. Halyard's scullion, identifying the boat's outboard motor as an 8-horsepower Yanmar electric, informed him that in three hours, at top speed and in calm waters, such a vessel could manage a round trip of about fifty kilometres total. Meaning that if Gareth had genuinely been expecting to get back to camp within 'three or four hours', twenty-five kilometres was about the furthest away he could have been planning to ferry the mermaid. Or call it thirty-five kilometres, even forty, in case Gareth was one of those people you sometimes find yourself dealing with who are always late because they have some sort of brain defect that makes them undercalculate how long everything will take. The mermaid's destination ought to be somewhere within a forty-kilometre radius of Tinkanen. 'Somewhere she could hide.' But not 'dry land'. Therefore not, if she was to be taken literally, any of the dozens of rugged islands that speckled the Gulf of Finland, nor the shores of Vyborg Bay across the Russian border.

There was only one place on the map that made sense. Surface Wave. The city floating in the gulf.

He called Resaint. 'We need to go to Surface Wave,' he told her. 'I'm pretty sure that's where our fisherman was going.'

'That's funny, I was just talking about Surface Wave.'

'With who? With this gnat woman? Dr Dolittle?'

'No.'

'How did it go with her?'

But from the barely audible sigh that followed, it was clear that Resaint preferred not to talk about it.

147

Chapter Eleven

Like a small child defending an obvious lie, Mrs Purleyswars had managed to answer only two or three questions before her story ran out. She was a stout hippyish woman in her fifties who, until she became evasive, spoke in the unctuous tone of somebody forever celebrating life's lovely little surprises, a voice like a hug that goes on for too long. As the two of them sat there in the dim, airless cabin – Mrs Purleyswars perched on the bottom bunk of the bunk bed, Resaint on a stool sipping from a plastic tumbler of bilberry tea she had felt no choice but to accept – Mrs Purleyswars chuckled, hummed and sighed through her explanation of exactly what she meant by 'having a natter with the gnats', and Resaint was certain that this was the first time she'd been pressed on the subject by an outsider. Once Mrs Purleyswars could see that Resaint could see that she was talking nonsense, she did seem sheepish. But only mildly. Whereas Resaint was scolding herself for being such an idiot.

After all, Resaint thought, what was more demeaning: for an adult woman to pretend she could talk to insects, or for an adult woman to nearly believe her? Part of her had known in advance it was silly but part of her, enough to matter, had longed for it to be true. She asked herself again how she could have got her hopes up like that – it was extremely out of character – and she knew it had to do with the sadness she felt about Kazu Horikawa:

about the dismissal of her ideas, about the curtailment of her career. If Horikawa had died as a sort of exile, wasn't it possible that amongst the exiles on this putrid Baltic shore one might find languishing another like her, a savant of little nibblers, somebody who understood these gnats like a Siberian hunter understood tigers, and that when Resaint met her it would be like the many meetings she'd had with Horikawa in her dreams?

The cabin door opened and a girl came in. She was about eighteen or nineteen, and she had that low-contrast colouring that was in fashion for white women at the moment, tawny eyebrows hardly standing out against the skin, although it was now a bit measled by kaptcha marks. Resaint recognised this girl but couldn't place her right away. 'Nathan said he left his charger here,' the girl said. 'Do you know where it is?' She looked at Resaint. 'Oh, hi?'

'Elsie, this is Karin,' Mrs Purleyswars said. And so Resaint realised where she'd seen the girl before: this was ElsieVVVV, who posted all those videos about life in the camp. She had burst into the cabin with such familiarity that Resaint wondered if she might be Mrs Purleyswars' daughter, although there wasn't much of a resemblance.

'Are you from Migri?' Elsie said.

'No, pet, she's from Switzerland. She came to talk about . . .' Mrs Purleyswars tailed off. The conversation they'd just had was like a pool of vomit in the corner of the room that neither of them wanted to acknowledge.

But Elsie frowned and said, 'This isn't to do with the gnats, is it?' She was watching Mrs Purleyswars' face, and from it she must have got her answer. 'Oh my god, oh my god.' She turned to Resaint. 'I can't believe you're from *outside* and she got you to listen to her. She only came up with the whole thing because she wants attention. Linda, you have to stop doing this. It's really pathetic at this point. Nathan hates it too.'

Mrs Purleyswars smiled as if she hadn't heard any of that. 'Do you want a cup of tea, pet?'

'No! Where's Nathan's charger?' Elsie spotted it lying on the duvet behind Mrs Purleyswars. She snatched it up and went to the door. 'If you're from outside, I seriously do not understand why you're in here listening to her drivelling on. But, fine, whatever,' she added, shrugging as if she could not be held responsible for Resaint's terrible choices.

After Elsie closed the door behind her, Mrs Purleyswars gave a knowing sigh as if to invite Resaint's participation in a little chuckle about the young, perhaps seeing an opportunity to reset the atmosphere between them. Resaint, rejecting this invitation in the strongest possible terms, put down her tea and went outside to catch up with Elsie on the avenue. She was grateful to the girl for her contempt, for lancing the shameful encounter like a pustule. She remembered the contempt she had felt herself at that age for adults who chose to accept each other's lies: nothing else like it, nothing so intense in the whole solar system, a jet of plasma that could take out satellites and power grids. Her father had told her she would become more forgiving of adults once she knew what it was like to be one. But for the most part that had not turned out to be true. The opposite, actually. All those mitigating facts that her father implied would explain everything, the sealed evidence for the defence: now she'd seen the file for herself, she knew there was fuck all to it. The teenagers had it right.

She was still reminiscing about the unshakeable granite fixity of youthful indignation when she said 'I watched your videos' and instantly saw any trace of it vanish from Elsie's face.

'Really?' Elsie said. 'You've really seen them? I know they're not very good. I've only been posting stuff for a few weeks. I've always wanted to but at home I wouldn't have been allowed to, so . . .' Up at the ranches the guest workers' internet access had been routed through servers in the Hermit Kingdom so that it could be restricted as normal, but whether by neglect or by design the Finnish government had put no such measures in place at the camp.

Resaint gestured back at the cabin. 'Is she your mother, or—'

'Oh my god! No. She's Nathan's mum. My boyfriend. She's so full of shit.'

'What I still don't understand is that right before the gnats stopped, she was telling people they were going to stop. So she must have known somehow.'

'Yeah, because—' Elsie looked around and lowered her voice. 'The gnats stopped because of what Nathan did. And he told her he was going to do it before he did it. So she was like, "If I make up some shit about this, about how I did it, everyone's going to think I'm really special, and want to talk to me, and be really interested in me." Because that's what she's like. So she started telling people this thing about talking to the gnats, which is so fucking stupid, oh my god. But some people believed it.' Elsie rolled her eyes.

'What did Nathan do?'

'I'm not supposed to talk about it. But if you come and talk to Nathan he'll probably tell you.'

Resaint hesitated. *Another* gnat whisperer? She didn't want to glide without resistance from one let-down to the next like one of those grandmothers who give half their savings to a con man and then the other half to a second con man promising to get the first half back. But whatever this new story was, she believed, at least, that Elsie believed it.

So she went with Elsie to meet Nathan. On the way there, Elsie asked Resaint a lot of questions about herself, and Resaint realised that she might be the first human being Elsie had met since she was a little girl who was not a citizen of either the Hermit Kingdom or the Republic of Finland. This seemed to Resaint a greater responsibility than she was qualified to bear and she felt guilty that she wasn't more exotic. Amidst the questions, Elsie mentioned that Nathan's father had come out to Finland as well, but he had been sent home in disgrace after the managers of his ranch accused him of deliberately spreading kaptcha to healthy cattle. Nathan's father had denied it, but everybody knew that before the fires this sort of thing had been going on: after all, if a ranch had ever succeeded in eradicating kaptcha, there would have been no more paid work.

They found Nathan lying in a hammock fixed between two vacant cabins at the western edge of the grid. The hammock was

151

made from a sheet of white logo-printed material that looked like that stuff they wrapped buildings in during construction to stop moisture getting into the walls. Compared to the freight-yard corridors of the rest of the camp, this spot had almost the feeling of a verandah, because beyond the wire fence you could see out to the pines – smart dignified ranks of them apart from one dead one at the treeline whose leaflessness exposed the wormy and demented pattern of its upper branches, raising serious questions about what the others were really like underneath. Nathan looked up from his phone, took the charger from Elsie and kissed her.

'This is Karin,' Elsie said. 'She's from Switzerland. I told her you'd tell her about the gnats.'

Nathan looked at Resaint and then looked at Elsie with an expression as if she'd summoned a police tactical unit here to arrest him.

'It's fine,' Elsie said. 'You can tell her.'

'Els.'

'I promise it's fine.' But Nathan still refused, and Elsie ran out of patience. 'Nathan found out that the gnats were coming from Surface Wave—'

'Els!'

'That's not a secret!'

'How could they have been coming from Surface Wave?' Resaint said.

'We still don't really know,' Elsie said. 'But so after he found out . . . just tell her what you did! She's not from Migri. Everyone's celebrating because the gnats stopped and you won't even take credit.'

'She could be recording or something,' Nathan said. He was mirthless and pale and hollow-eyed, but handsome too, exactly the sort of boy Resaint was interested in at Elsie's age – *zerbrechlich* her mother used to call those boys, meaning frail.

'He's worried that if Migri find out he's been hacking over the camp network they'll take away his internet.'

'*Els!*'

'If you don't want to tell me, you don't have to,' Resaint said.

'Oh my god,' Elsie said to Nathan. 'Why are you being like this? I told her you'd tell her!'

'You said he might. It's OK. Really.' Resaint felt her phone tingle. It was Halyard.

'We need to go to Surface Wave,' he said. 'I'm pretty sure that's where our fisherman was going.'

'That's funny, I was just talking about Surface Wave.'

After Resaint hung up, Elsie said with unabashed nosiness, 'Was that the guy you came here with?'

Resaint nodded.

'Can we meet him?'

'Why would you want to meet him?' Resaint said. But then she reminded herself that they knew of Halyard only as another fascinating stranger, not as a slippery, self-interested mining exec who was, at best, intermittently good company. So she told them they were welcome to come with her to rendezvous with Halyard at the north entrance. Nathan stared at the ground as he followed a few steps behind, close enough to listen to Elsie resume her interview with Resaint. Resaint had the sense that he was just as keen as Elsie to mingle with the foreigners but a few minutes ago he had ostracised one of them as a potential pawn of the Finnish surveillance apparatus so now he was feeling a bit awkward about the inconsistency.

For some reason Halyard arrived twenty minutes after they did, even though Resaint thought he would be coming straight from the medical centre. Unlike her, he recognised Elsie from her videos without any help. Based on this statistical sample of two, 100% of people in the outside world were fans of Elsie's channel, and Resaint observed Elsie's excitement as she began tentatively to reconceive of herself as an international celebrity. In her high spirits, she described Nathan to Halyard as 'a hacker, he's amazing, he can do anything, literally anything,' and once again Nathan glared at her.

'In that case—' Halyard began, but then all four of them had to shuffle along to make way for the van that collected waste from the composting toilets. 'In that case, I have a question for you.

The attacks on the biobanks. Could it have been your country? Your government?'

Nathan shook his head. 'They couldn't hack a vending machine.'

'Are you sure?'

'Last year there was this big leak of GCHQ's "hacking tools". I had a look at them. They were like if someone gave you a car and it wouldn't start, so you opened up where the motor was supposed to be, and it was just full of, like, old socks and twigs and stuff. Whereas the biobanks thing – there are people online who are saying it must have been time travellers or aliens or something. I mean it's that good. It's unreal. The morons at home had nothing to do with that.'

'But some of them must be doing really well out of the price spike.'

'Yeah, well, that's why they're never going to let us go back.'

'What do you mean?' Resaint said.

'He's just being paranoid!' Elsie said.

The Hermit Kingdom had citizenship laws, Nathan explained, stipulating if you were out of the country for long enough you forfeited certain rights, including the right to own a share of an extinction credit. If the guest workers had to stew in this camp all year instead of going home, it wouldn't be their fault, so would the citizenship laws be waived in their case? No, they certainly would not; at the Home Office, rules were rules. Meaning anybody here who owned such a share would find that it had reverted back to the state. And the bureaucratic riffle shuffle of this reversion would present an excellent opportunity for officials in the government to quietly pocket most of the shares. 'So all those cunts are thinking, "Credits are worth a packet now because of the hacks. We fancy a bit of that. So let's wait it out." They can't *only* keep out the people who have shares, because that would make it too obvious, so they're going to keep us all out. And they'll carry on saying it's because of kaptcha.'

'I hope you're mistaken,' Resaint said. 'I hope they sort it out and you can go home.'

Nathan shrugged. 'The ranch was shit, but it's not that bad here – I mean now the gnats have stopped. We can get on the real internet, and it's way faster.'

'Also you met me here,' Elsie said, touching his arm fondly.

'And Finland's a proper country – as soon as we got to the ranch they gave us all vaccinations because they know the ones we get at home don't work. Els misses her brother, and I hate sharing a cabin with my mum, but apart from that . . .'

Resaint could not have anticipated that, for all their generational differences, Wilson and Nathan would be united in their position that life here wasn't really anything to complain about. She wondered what on earth those Finnish government sources had been talking about when they said the camp was on the brink of combustion, and then it occurred to her that they probably just came up with that because they wanted the guest workers off their hands as soon as possible. 'You don't miss the food back home?' Halyard asked.

'Have you seen the food back home?'

His curiosity satisfied, Halyard suddenly seemed very impatient to leave. 'Is there anything either of you need?' Resaint said. 'We can have it delivered to you.'

'Concealer,' Elsie said.

'Sorry?'

'Kaptcha is going to spread, right? No chance they're going to contain it up here. Loads more people are going to get it. And those people will be looking for tutorials on how to do your make-up, like if you've already had kaptcha but you haven't been able to get laser treatment and you have to go on a date or something. Nobody's doing them yet, so if I'm the first one, that will be massive for my channel. But I can't do make-up tutorials because I don't actually have any make-up.'

Resaint took out her phone so Elsie could dictate to it.

'Ricercar No-Sebum Blur Primer Jeju Cushion Primer 3SL Silky Smooth Balm Ricercar Double Lasting Serum Foundation Ego Dominus All Stay Foundation 3SL Bright Up Foundation Ricercar Big Cover Cushion Jeju Gel Cushion Ricercar Advanced

Smoothing Concealer Jeju Cover Perfection Tip Concealer Ioppa Mineralising Creamy Concealer Nu Veronica Pure Weightless Concealer 3SL Big Cover Skin Fit Concealer Pro 3SL Nano Emulsion Ioppa Advanced Renewing Cream,' Elsie said.

Resaint looked at her phone. It came to €590.

'Can you expense this to Brahmasamudram?' she said to Halyard.

He looked at the total. 'You know this represents about 120 tons of manganese ore that somebody is going to have to mine?'

Resaint felt something on her wrist. A single dead gnat lay there. She brushed it off, and then looked up, but there were no more.

As they were saying goodbye, Elsie said, 'I'm glad you're going to Surface Wave.'

'Why?'

'Because you'll see what Nathan did.'

Chapter Twelve

When Halyard went to meet Resaint, there was something he didn't tell her.

Well, in fact, there were a number of things he didn't tell her. He didn't tell her that he was now a condemned man at Brahmasamudram. And he didn't tell her that he was no longer interested in saving the venomous lumpsucker, only in finding the mermaid so he could learn the truth about the biobank attacks. But there was one thing in particular he didn't tell her, about what had happened since they spoke on the phone.

Just as Halyard was ending the call, Wilson had come riding up to him on a bicycle, ringing his bell like a fire alarm. 'Rather electric news!' Wilson had called out. 'Glad I could find you. Gareth's just got back. He still won't tell anyone where he was going, but he says his engine conked out on the return leg so he had to paddle part of the way, that's why he was so long. Hop on and we'll whizz down there and you can ask him about the fish.'

Halyard couldn't help feeling some irritation that his feat of deductive brilliance in tracing the mermaid to Surface Wave had almost immediately been rendered redundant. Nevertheless, he accepted a ride, straddling the seat while Wilson stood on the pedals so they could rattle top-heavy down the avenue, cabins zipping past on either side like the carriages of a train. 'What a day!' Wilson exclaimed. 'What an eventful day!' You had to be wary about getting into Hermit Kingdom politics with a guy like this, Halyard thought, in case his wonderful talent for finding the bright side of everything also extended to famines and purges. Safer not to find out. As they neared the water's edge the smell once again rose sickeningly in his nostrils, and along the shingle beach there were snaky black rinds where the tide had deposited its scum of gnat jelly. Wilson parked the bike against a tree and they made for a crowd of about twenty people who were congregating around the boat Halyard recognised from the video. Their attention was on a man who sat on the prow of the boat with a can of Nobelaner in his hand.

'And then,' he was saying, 'like I say, I spent a long time trying to get it going again – hours, probably – but . . . well, like I say . . .' He hesitated as if casting around for something further to add. Halyard got the sense that Gareth was already on perhaps his third or fourth telling of a story that simply did not have enough content to sate the appetites of his excited welcoming party.

'Gareth, this is the chap I was telling you about,' Wilson interjected. 'He's here on very important fish business and he has some questions to ask you.'

Although it no longer mattered in the least to Halyard whether the venomous lumpsucker was still down there solving differential equations, it seemed easier to carry on with what was expected of him. He took out his phone and showed Gareth the same clip from ElsieVVVV's video that he'd shown Wilson, a few of the onlookers craning over the fisherman's shoulder to see for themselves.

'I remember it,' Gareth said. 'Yes, I do. The funny-looking little fish. I never saw one before. I wasn't sure if anyone would want to eat it. Oh, yes, I remember that fish very well. Ask me anything you like about that fish.'

'Where were you when you caught it?'

'Haven't the foggiest.'

Privately Halyard gave thanks that this fisherman's testimony was no longer the sole focus of his existence. He asked Gareth if they could speak in private for a moment. Gareth looked relieved to be rescued from the hungry crowd, and they walked a few metres up the beach. A few swans circulated amidst the boulders that poked reddish-grey from the shallows here, glacier dandruff from the last ice age. These were the same sort of boulders that the lumpsuckers could breed around if they were a bit further out to sea, but the lumpsuckers could never use *these*, no, of course not, that would be too much to ask, because god forbid the lumpsuckers should meet us halfway for once in their lives, god forbid they should make some kind of reasonable compromise, like for instance becoming slightly amphibian.

'Wilson says you won't say where you were going with this woman,' Halyard said quietly, 'but you can tell me. I'm from outside. I'm not part of the rumour mill here. Nobody else in the camp will hear about it.'

'No. I promised her. I'm not telling anyone.'

'I can get you anything you want. New fishing tackle. Shepherd's pie. Inzidernil. I have Inzidernil on me.' Halyard reached into his jacket. 'I can pay you right now.'

'Sorry, mate.'

Halyard looked Gareth in the eye. 'It was Surface Wave, right? She was going to hide on Surface Wave?'

'No, it wasn't,' Gareth said. But he was not a good liar. 'And you can piss off and all.' He turned to go.

'Did she say anything about the hacks?' Halyard called after him, but Gareth just carried on back towards the crowd.

Halyard didn't follow, and after a moment Wilson came over to join him. 'I trust Gareth was helpful to you even if he wasn't sure about your endangered species.'

'I confirmed something important, yeah.'

'That is to say, I trust he brought back more in his fishing boat than just—' and at this moment Wilson fixed Halyard with a truly manic look '—*red herrings*!'

Halyard gave him a polite smile in return.

'As I'm sure you know,' Wilson added, 'the Baltic is replete with delicious herrings, or *silakka* in Finnish – we cook them quite often – so the pun could hardly be more apposite.'

'Right, yeah.'

'Now, I must ask: in your tête-à-tête just now, did he let slip anything about . . .'

'What?'

With a meaningful wink, Wilson made a motion with his hand like he was wafting gas away from his arse. It took a long moment for Halyard to realise it was supposed to represent the graceful undulations of a scaly tail. 'I'd better go and find Karin,' Halyard said.

'I hope she won't be too disheartened by this little setback.'

'Yeah, I hope so too.'

What Halyard was actually thinking was that once Resaint found out, she wouldn't have any reason to travel with him to Surface Wave. As far as she was concerned, they were only headed there to track down Gareth and ask him where he'd caught the fish from the video. And he was the last lead they had. So when Resaint learned that Gareth had just revealed himself as a busted flush, that would be it. The end of the story. They would go their separate ways.

But no matter that there wasn't much warmth between them – no matter that he still resented her for almost getting them killed in the orchard – no matter that she still looked at him like he was a fucking tapeworm (except that wasn't quite right because knowing her she probably looked at tapeworms with tremendous affection and respect) – he didn't want it to be over yet. He would much rather go to Surface Wave with her than go alone. At this moment there were only two people in the northern hemisphere he felt could be entirely honest with, and one of them was the scullion on his phone. He still hadn't told Resaint all the gory details of how he'd got into trouble with the extinction credits, but ever since Sanctuary North he'd dropped any pretence that there was some sort of innocent explanation. He didn't have to worry about her opinion of him because it had already sunk as far as it could go, which made her very relaxing to be around. And that – the rare freedom of having no facade or persona to maintain, because she already knew the worst of him – only deepened how much she

160

reminded him of his sister. In Tartu, the morning after their long talk in the hotel restaurant, he'd woken up with this impression still clear and plangent in his mind, eclipsing any residual sense of Resaint as a sexual prospect. (Which, to be clinical about it, was not an absolute guarantee that these two incompatibles wouldn't coexist again the next time he had a few glasses of wine; after all, she didn't *look* anything like Frances.)

Of course, if his reason for withholding from Resaint the news about the venomous lumpsucker was that he so loved being honest with her, there would be a pretty uncomfortable irony to that. So he really ought to tell her about Gareth and 'the foggiest' and the former's critical shortages of the latter. He knew that.

But when he found her at the north entrance, it was one of those situations where if you don't do something at the first possible moment, the ship pretty much sails on any prospect that you ever will. By the time he worked out for sure that she hadn't already heard about Gareth's return, that ship was somewhere in the Danish Straits. And then, after he was distracted for a moment by consulting with Nathan about the biobank attacks, he remembered that the teenagers might at any moment see a message in a group chat announcing the sensational news. So he tried to hurry Resaint away from them as fast as he could.

He knew that, from that point on, he was wasting her time. And she would hardly be the first woman whose time he'd wasted – like ZymoD he was a liability to his investors – but this was a starker example than usual. He tried to ruffle his misgivings with the thought that if they found the mermaid on Surface Wave, and she really *was* a mermaid, maybe she could tell them where the venomous lumpsucker lived. Unless that was racist, to just assume that a mermaid was friends with all the other sea-life . . . Also, the conversation might get a bit frosty once she found out who he worked for. Mermaids were probably not a constituency very well disposed to ocean-floor mining operations. You couldn't use the old 'Tut all you like, but next time you get in a taxi where do you think the manganese in the battery is going to have come from?' argument on a mermaid.

*

Surface Wave floated ten kilometres off the coast, where Vyborg Bay opened out into the gulf, in waters that would once have belonged to Finland but had changed hands during the grinding Russo-Finnish Wars of the 1940s. The barrier spits to the east were featureless but for Red Army gravesites, which made you wonder if they'd fought that war just so they'd have somewhere to put their dead from fighting it.

Architecturally, Surface Wave had a kind of gaseous, ungraspable quality, so that no matter how long you looked at it you could never quite visualise it afterwards. One might have compared it to an ugly Modernist chandelier, but it also vaguely evoked an old-fashioned cartoon Martian, a little green man or Great Gazoo, with his overabundance of arms, legs, ears and antennae sprouting from a rounded body.

The core of it was a circular structure like an amphitheatre, about two hundred metres across, which held most of Surface Wave's laboratories, workshops and residences. The undular roofs were gardens planted with evergreen trees, and at treetop height there were walkways, terraces and VTOL landing pads. From underneath the amphitheatre, three columns splayed out in a tripod, disappearing below the surface of the water. These columns looked like solid concrete, but were in fact packed with styrofoam beads inside a concrete shell, so that instead of dragging the city to the bottom of the ocean they enabled it to float. Braceleting one of these pillars at sea level was a disc-shaped dock spoked with moorings, and from that dock a freight elevator ran up the full height of Surface Wave to a terminal hooked over the rim of the amphitheatre. Lastly, radiating from the main body of Surface Wave were six stubby arms, and at the end of each arm was a cylindrical outbuilding part-submerged in the water. Each of these – the lightbulbs of the chandelier, so to speak – was a cavernous workspace for larger operations.

To visit Surface Wave you needed an invitation. After a little bit of research, Halyard learned that the quickest way to get one was to make an appointment with one of the tenants there on the pretext of doing some in-person business. So Halyard chose one at random and got in touch with its secretarial scullion. His answers to the scullion's questions were pretty vague, and any human interlocutor would have sensed he was bullshitting, but evidently the scullion judged him to be a respectable individual because it issued him an invitation right away.

When he tried to book a VTOL, however, he was told that because of weather conditions it wasn't possible at the moment to fly there. This was a surprise, since the weather on the coast this morning was as fine as everyone at the camp had been pretending it was the day before, but Halyard guessed there might still be high winds further out to sea, the price of living on the Baltic. Early on, the consensus had been that seasteads would be anchored at tropical latitudes, where you would have beautiful blue skies nearly all year round. But then AEolia – the first major seasteading community, established in the Atimaono Lagoon in Tahiti by agreement with the French Polynesian government – was broken in half by Cyclone Josese. And the following year Mainspring 1 – the second major seasteading community, established in the Gulf of Mexico with backers including Antichain's Ferenc Barka – was captured by the gunboats of the Los Zetas cartel.

After that, the seasteading movement started to refine its criteria beyond 'hours of sunshine per year'. It was noticed that the inland seas of the Baltic had some of the lowest waves in the world, which would really help to calm people's nerves vis-a-vis the AEolia disaster. Also, with the notorious Lyudinovo Special Economic Zone, the Russian government had already shown their broad-mindedness about slashing red tape in the name of progress. And that was the whole premise of Surface Wave, which shared with its predecessors a philosophy of entrepreneurial statehood, of disrupting the incumbents (i.e. existing sovereign nations) with innovative thinking. Here, there would be none of the restrictions on cutting-edge biotech that were set out in the laws of nearly every developed country as well as a number of international treaties. Nobody could tell you what you were allowed to do in your own laboratory. Which was apt, because seasteads themselves were supposed to be like laboratories, experimenting across the

163

whole spectrum of political possibilities to find out which worked best for modern human beings (although so far the whole spectrum of political possibilities apparently ran from 'no personal income taxes' to 'no taxes of any kind whatsoever'.)

A deal was struck, like a more extreme version of the one between Sanctuary North and the Estonian government, whereby Surface Wave would float in Russian waters and pay royalties to the Russian treasury but it would not be subject to any Russian laws that didn't involve warfare or terrorism. And, sure, when winter drew in at 60° north the nights were long and the days did not exactly bring daiquiri weather: even in this era of warmer seas, it was sometimes possible to climb down from Surface Wave's dock on to solid ice. But Surface Wave had lasted six years so far, which was a lot longer than either AEolia or Mainspring 1.

Because there were no VTOLs landing on Surface Wave, the city's management had organised a water taxi service from Kotka. The morning after their visit to the Tinkanen camp, Halyard and Resaint checked out of their hotel and walked down to the marina. There were eight seats on the boat but when they boarded there was only one other passenger on the ramp with them, a bearded guy in a suit and tie carrying a duffel bag. The interior was narrow, which led to an incident where the guy bent over to get something out of his bag and got whacked in the side of the head by Resaint's backpack. Resaint apologised to him, although not as effusively as a lot of people would have; Halyard had noticed she wasn't much affected by small embarrassments.

The guy waved it off. 'Do you live out there, or are you just visiting?' he said – or, to be precise, his earpiece said it, after he muttered something in another language.

'We're just visiting. You?'

The tiny latency you could perceive in a person's expression as the translation in their ear tarried just a moment after the source. 'Yes, just here on business.' He was from Turkey, he told them.

Everyone took their seat. The water taxi set off, out past the cranes and the warehouses and the town's maritime museum, which was not, as you might expect, a nice little converted customs house, but rather a gleaming blue pyramid on an absolutely megalomaniac scale. This boat was a hydrofoil, so as it gained speed it rose so high on its skids that the hull wasn't even grazing the water; from a distance it would look as if it was levitating. 'Would you take a bullet for dogs?' Resaint said to Halyard.

'Whose dogs?'

'You said you wouldn't take a bullet for the last spiny shore beetle. But then you said that if dogs ever went extinct, that would be totally different. So would you take a bullet for dogs?'

'If we ever get to the point where there's only one surviving dog, I hope I'm already dead.'

'OK, but—'

'Someone's made a bioweapon that will kill all dogs and it's in a canister beside me and if the canister is shattered then it will diffuse into the troposphere,' Halyard said. 'Would I catch a bullet with my face to stop it hitting the canister?'

'Yes.'

'Obviously I would. I would be the greatest hero in human history.'

Resaint gave him one of her unindulgent looks.

'You think I'm a species philistine,' Halyard said. 'I'm a fan of dogs merely because they offer joy and companionship to millions of people. How bloody childish of me.'

'I agree it would be sad to lose dogs. Just as it will be sad to lose the spiny shore beetle. But we're not losing only the spiny shore beetle. We're losing the spiny shore beetle and at least another ten thousand like it every year. You say you'd rather die than lose dogs, but to lose those ten thousand a year doesn't trouble you at all.'

'Christ, you people never stop talking about your ten thousand a year, it's like being in fucking Jane Austen. The difference is, dogs actually do something for us. Most of the others are no good to anyone. I mean, look, if it's not about nice or not nice or useful or not useful, if it's just about *interesting*, then why don't you care about kaptcha? Why aren't you talking about what a tragedy it would be if we eradicated a fungal infection? If you're going to be consistent about this you ought to care about kaptcha too.'

He thought for a moment he'd scored a point, but Resaint replied, 'I do care about kaptcha. I do think if we eradicated it that would be a tragedy. Kaptcha is as remarkable as honey badgers or birds of paradise.'

'Oh, come on!'

By now they were threading between the islets that Halyard had seen from the beach at the camp, platforms of rock as smooth and flat as poured concrete. People complained about Brahmasamudram's surface mines just because they notched a few hilltops, but the Pleistocene ice age had so thoroughly fucked with the landscape up here that if it were happening now the EU would definitely try to legislate against it.

'You really don't believe that anything can have a value of its own beyond what function it serves for human beings?' Resaint said.

'Value to who?'

Resaint asked Halyard to imagine a planet in some remote galaxy – a lush, seething, glittering planet covered with stratospheric waterfalls, great land-sponges bouncing through the valleys, corals budding in perfect niveous hexagons, humming lichens glued to pink crystals, prismatic jellyfish breaching from the rivers, titanic lilies relying on tornadoes to spread their pollen – a planet full of complex, interconnected life but devoid of consciousness. 'Are you telling me that, if an asteroid smashed into this planet and reduced every inch of its surface to dust, *nothing* would be lost? Because nobody in particular would miss it?'

'But the universe is bloody huge – stuff like that must happen every minute. You can't go on strike over it. Honestly it sounds to me to like your real enemy isn't climate change or habitat loss, it's *entropy*. You don't like the idea that everything eventually crumbles. Well, it does. If you're this worried about species extinction, wait until you hear about the heat death of the universe.'

'I would be upset about the heat death of the universe too if human beings were accelerating the rate of it by a hundred times or more.'

'And if a species' position with respect to *us* doesn't matter – you know, those amoebae they found that live at the bottom of the Mariana Trench, if they're just as important as Chiu Chiu or my parents' dog, even though nobody ever gets anywhere near them – if distance in space doesn't matter, why should distance in time? If we don't care about whether their lives overlap with our lives, why even worry about whether they exist simultaneously with us? Your favourite wasp – Adelomidgy-midgy—'

'*Adelognathus marginatum*—'

'It *did* exist. It *always will have* existed. Extinction can't take that away. It went through its nasty little routine over and over again for millions and millions of years. The show was a big success. So why is it important that it's still running at the same time you are? Isn't that centring the whole thing on human beings, which is exactly what we're not supposed to be doing? I mean, for that matter – reality is all just numbers anyway, right? I mean underneath? That's what people say now. So why are you so down on the scans? Hacks aside. Why is it so crucial that these animals exist right now in an ostensibly meat-based format, just because *we do*? My point is you talk about extinction as if you're taking this enlightened post-human View from Nowhere but if we really get down to it you're definitely taking a View from Karin Resaint two arms two legs one head born Basel Switzerland year of our lord two-thousand-and-whenever.'

But Resaint wasn't listening any more. 'Look,' she said, pointing out of the front window of the boat.

Surface Wave was on the horizon. But it didn't look right. Of course, you could never quite retain in your mind what it looked like, but he was sure it wasn't supposed to look like *this* – like a black cloud caged in vertical white bars. He got up from his seat and walked down to the front of the boat for a better look, Resaint following behind. And that was when he recognised the triple rotors spiring over the sea.

Spindrifters.

Two days ago, from the VTOL over the Gulf of Bothnia, they'd seen five of them on their way south. And now here they were, those five and more besides, a circle of maybe ten or twelve, wheeling counter-clockwise around the city like dancers around a bonfire.

Resaint was laughing now, the hardest he'd seen her laugh in the three days they'd known each other. 'What is it?' he said. 'What are you laughing at?'

'Now I know why they were migrating,' she said.

Chapter Thirteen

The boat seemed to hesitate as it approached the ring of spindrifters, like a pedestrian timing a dash across a roundabout. The spindrifters had spaced themselves about a hundred metres apart, so after one went by you had a good fifteen seconds' grace before the next came along, but nevertheless Resaint respected the water taxi's caution; back in the Gulf of Bothnia, that lone spindrifter had turned aside from the *Varuna*, but how could you be sure the same would happen here? Especially considering at least one of them was already trailing debris: Surface Wave was surrounded by aquaculture installations, and snarled around the twin hulls of the spindrifter up ahead you could see netting that had probably been a crayfish pen before the spray vessel smashed through it, like when you get a cobweb in your face while you're jogging in the woods. It was easy to imagine getting ploughed under the water by those same unflinching hulls.

But instead their boat darted through a gap in the procession. And then the daylight dimmed in the cabin as the windows filled up with a boiling darkness, a photonegative snowstorm, a black migraine swirl as thick as tossed gravel. They'd been ferried into hell.

Strange that there was no better word for it in either English or German than swarm or *schwarm*: that had to cover, say, twenty insects in one place, and it also had to cover whatever the fuck this was. The boat was only just across the threshold, but already you would think the maelstrom went on for an infinite distance in every direction. A gnat was too tiny to thwack like a bumblebee against a window, so if there was any sound at all from their impacts against the hull, it was lost beneath their enveloping wingbeat hum. Just like when that spindrifter had dragged its storm across the *Varuna*, Resaint was frightened at first by the force of it. And she could see Halyard was freaked out too, as he stood there swearing under his breath, while the Turkish guy was just staring open-mouthed. Although your eyes were desperate for purchase as you looked out of the windows, it was impossible to fix on any individual gnat and follow its path; the roil seemed discontinuous from instant to instant, like the flicker of dirt on an old film reel.

'This is crazy,' Halyard said. 'In the videos from the camp it was just drizzle. It wasn't like this.'

So Resaint explained what had happened here, as best as she had been able to reconstruct it in her mind.

For reasons still obscure, this plague of gnats had originated at Surface Wave. For weeks they had blown west along the Finnish coastline, blighting the Tinkanen camp. So when Nathan found out where they were coming from, he searched for a way to stop them. And he fixed upon the spindrifters, which were still out there, tramping the Baltic, vaping seawater to repel the sun, but now disowned, forgotten, their security software years out of date, easy pickings for anyone with a modicum of skill. He took control of the spindrifters and sent them to converge on Surface Wave, one of them incidentally goosing the *Varuna* on its way south. Once they arrived, they made this carousel, braiding their strange airflows together into a wreath around the city. Whereas at Tinkanen the gnats simply drifted to the ground, here the wash from the spindrifters' rotors kept the gnats aloft in this teeming, choking dance. That was why it was so much worse than in the videos from the camp. The spindrifters were throwing the gnats right back in Surface Wave's face. Or better to say Nathan was. She knew now why Elsie was so proud of him.

'If the gnats are coming from here, why don't they do something about it?' said Halyard.

'I have no idea.'

Now the intensity seemed to wane, though the light in the cabin didn't get any brighter, and she realised they were passing underneath the main body of Surface Wave, so they were sheltered somewhat in its shadow. Here were the three flotation columns rising to the base of the seastead, forming a cavern of raw concrete like one of those dead zones under an elevated highway. As the water taxi nosed towards the dock that ringed one of the columns, Resaint made out a golf-cart-type vehicle driving in their direction. The golf cart stopped at the edge of the dock and out of it slid a figure in a yellow coverall. Once the boat had found its mooring, the mission of this figure turned out to be the delivery of three mosquito nets through the hatch.

The sprint from the mooring to the golf cart was pretty brief, but Resaint was still grateful for the mosquito net draped over her like a burqa, because even here the hail of gnats was heavy enough that it gave you a fairly powerful urge to curl up on the ground with your arms flung over your face. Unlike a real golf cart, this one was sealed on all sides, but there was no way to stop gnats surging inside during the few moments the doors were open to let everybody on board, so Resaint had to brush them off the seat before she sat down with her backpack on her lap, and every time her feet shifted in the footwell she could feel the grit of their bodies under her trainers. The man in the yellow coverall, introducing himself as Daniel, welcomed them to Surface Wave and apologised for 'the situation'.

'What's that thing where the three ghosts are chasing the yellow guy?' Halyard said.

'Is that a folk tale?' Resaint said.

'No, it's a video game.' Nobody knew, so he asked his scullion. Apparently it was called Pac-Man, although in fact there were four ghosts. 'We must have looked like Pac-Man just now,' Halyard said.

*

171

Being on Surface Wave wasn't anything like being on the *Varuna*. Here you could smell the ocean but you couldn't feel it, and the public areas were bone white polished to a high shine, lots of curves and ribs and lattices, the kind of architecture Resaint associated with crown-jewel R&D facilities built by prosperous industrial firms, functionalist and show-offy at the same time. Except that every window to the outside had become a TV tuned to black gnat static, the picture blurred by the mucoid residue of a million glancing contacts. It swelled in fury as each spindrifter approached and then ebbed as the spindrifter receded. Like snow you could just stand there and watch it, but unlike snow it didn't fade from consciousness when you tried to pay attention to something else. In your peripheral vision the effect was particularly unsettling, like catching a glimpse of something trying to get into your house.

The closest thing Surface Wave had to a mayor was Ovet Ganf, co-founder and head of the executive committee. They asked Daniel about the easiest way to get a meeting with Ganf, and Daniel said he was pretty sure Ganf was at the health club. So they dumped their bags on a service robot and went straight there, one long elevator ride and then one short one. Resaint was excited to see that the health club had squash courts, because she hadn't played squash in four months. However, there was no sign of Ganf in the squash courts, nor in the Pilates studio, nor in the cryotherapy facility. Then they looked in another room and found a small woman shouting at a spinning orb.

'I have buyers visiting next week!' she was saying. 'When my buyers visit I always like to start with a walk in the gardens! Have you tried to take a walk in the gardens recently?'

Resaint recognised the orb because she'd once almost got inside one herself, in Berlin a few years ago, during her fling with the venture capitalist with the ludicrous penthouse on Rosenthaler Platz. It was an immersive neurofeedback rig. The orb was made of transparent plastic, like a human-sized hamster ball, braced on the inside by a steel frame of tessellar pentagons. You put on a VR headset, then you climbed inside, strapped yourself into the foam seat, and let the hatch close behind you. Wheels in the base could spin the orb 360 degrees on every axis so it gave you a pretty good sensation of floating untethered, and sensors inside picked up the smallest movements of your body so you could glide at will through the psychedelic starfield shown to you by the headset. However, this wasn't just any psychedelic starfield: it was generated moment to moment by the brain waves the headset was reading off your scalp. The idea was that you swooped and dived through this galaxy of your own emotions (which sometimes became a mountain range or a cell nucleus or a Twombly painting) and as your emotions fluctuated you saw them reflected around you, and gradually this shimmering feedback loop taught you to take conscious control of them, until there was no difference between inner world and outer world, between pulling out of a barrel roll and calming an intrusive thought. To Resaint it was basically as if the words 'Take a deep breath and count to ten' weighed half a ton and cost a quarter of a million euros.

The guy inside the rig said something, but it was too muffled to hear over the whirring of the machinery.

The woman knocked on the plastic as if she was trying to irritate a zoo animal. 'I can't fucking hear you, Ovet!'

This time, when the guy spoke, his voice was piped out of a speaker in the base. 'I'm very happy to talk about this later, but right now I'm in the middle of a session.'

'Why don't you get out of that thing and do your fucking job?'

'I cannot carry out my duties at peak effectiveness unless I have complete mental clarity, so sustaining that mental clarity *is* part of my job. It would be irresponsible if I *didn't* do this.'

'Ovet—'

'You're breaking the immersion,' Ganf said. 'This is totally pointless if you break the immersion. I'm probably going to have to start again from the beginning.'

'Ovet, there are insects raining on us! It's a fucking living nightmare! This is not what I pay rent for! Just turn off the power to Module 3. That's all you need to do.'

Resaint knew that Module 1, Module 2, Module 3 and so on were the names of those big beer-can-shaped workspaces at the ends of Surface Wave's radial arms. 'Is that where they're coming from?' she said.

'Who's that?' said Ganf. 'Who else is here?'

For the first time the woman turned to look at Resaint. Most of the Surface Wave townsfolk Resaint had seen so far sported some configuration of business-bland or STEM-bland, but this woman wore cosmetic implants under the skin of her face, a sharp ridge flaring out from each nostril and pyramidal studs at her temples and cheekbones like the spikes on a thorny lizard. 'Yes, that's where they're coming from,' she said. 'You can see them streaming out of the flue. They're breeding in there.' She turned back to the orb. 'Ovet, you have to cut off Module 3. Whatever's running in there, we need to starve it.'

'I can't.'

'Yes, you can.'

'No, I can't,' said Ganf. 'I literally can't. It's a smart contract.'

She thumped the side of the orb. 'Nobody cares about your fucking smart contracts!'

'That couldn't be further from the truth. People flock here because of our smart contracts. They flock here because they want to escape their arbitrary and capricious governments. If I could just cancel a smart contract, the whole thing would be a joke.'

'Ovet, you *are* a joke! Cancel the contract!'

'It can only be cancelled by mutual consent. You know that perfectly well. This is out of my hands.'

The category of smart contracts included the non-disclosure packages and waiver packages that were a routine part of Resaint's working life, but at Surface Wave they were used far more extensively. Like making a bargain with a witch or a goblin, signing a smart contract was not just agreeing to be bound by it, it was *becoming* bound by it, instantly and inescapably. The reality in which you lived changed from the moment you signed it, because in essence a smart contract added a few lines to the code of every computer system around you, constraining those systems to operate within its terms. Ganf was saying that if he'd signed a smart contract with one of the tenants of Surface Wave to provide power to Module 3, there was no way for him to cut off that power, since that would breach the contract, which was a technological impossibility.

'Then we have to go in there—'

'The contract doesn't allow that either. Anybody who tries to get through that door – even me – they'll be repelled by the security system. And I can't unilaterally disable the security system any more than I can unilaterally disable the electricity supply.'

'What does the contract say we're supposed to do if little bugs are gushing out of that pipe like sewage with wings, and they're getting blown all over the place, and we can't go outside, and we can't eat in the restaurants because the patio doors make you want to scream, and I keep finding them in my clothes, and there's nobody inside the module who can turn it off?'

'The contract anticipates a vast range of eventualities,' Ganf said, 'but unfortunately not this one. Nothing like this has ever happened here before.'

'I certainly don't remember any mention in the fucking promotional materials!'

Rather listlessly the orb continued to nod and tilt, meaning Ganf still refused to abandon his neurofeedback session, or at least he refused to be seen to abandon it. If he could have looked at himself from the outside, perhaps he would have reconsidered whether conducting parts of this discussion at a forty-five-degree angle was a net positive for his dignity. Resaint had never actually got as far as encapsulating herself in the rig at the venture capitalist's apartment, because the feeling of his fingertips on the back of her head as he helped her on with the headset had made her realise what even sexual intercourse had not, which was that she found him risible and disgusting. 'I strongly believe that we're better off focusing on the spindrifters,' Ganf said. 'Until the spindrifters arrived, the insects just flew away and disappeared.'

'That's not exactly true,' said Resaint.

'The spindrifters are not parties to any contracts here, so we have a free hand. We're going to have them towed away.'

'And why is that taking so long?' the woman said.

'Nearly all of the contractors I've approached have told me they won't attempt a towing operation on a large moving vessel. However, we are now in negotiations with a company in St Petersburg and I'm optimistic that by early next week—'

'Fine. If all you want to do is hide in your fucking snow globe, then the rest of us will do your job for you.' She turned to leave, giving such an extravagant roll of the eyes on her way out that you would have thought they, too, were capable of 360-degree motion.

There issued from the speaker in the base of the orb a little sigh of relief.

'Mr Ganf—' Halyard said.

'Who is that?' Ganf yelped. 'Why are you still here? I thought everyone had gone!'

Resaint knew that their pretext for visiting Surface Wave was a meeting with a biotech firm, and Halyard, presumably feeling it was more tactful not to contradict this outright, related their search for the fisherman and the 'mermaid' in a manner implying this was just one of a number of items on their agenda. 'They would have arrived some time last night,' he explained. 'Both of them or maybe just one of them.'

'Privacy is one of the values at the very centre of our value mandala,' Ganf said. 'We don't just gossip about our visitors to anyone who asks.'

'No, of course not, but these people, or this person, are not, you know, legitimate visitors like us. I mean, they came here in a fishing boat from the migrant labour camp near Tinkanen.'

'As I said, we don't gossip about our visitors.' Ganf paused. 'However, I can absolutely guarantee you that nobody is rowing to Surface Wave from a refugee camp. We have very good perimeter security to prevent exactly that kind of scenario.'

'OK, but if they do turn up, maybe you could let us know?'

'I'm sorry, that's just not how we operate. Now, I would appreciate no further interruptions.'

As they were leaving the health club, Resaint looked longingly at the squash courts. It might have been OK if she hadn't known they were here, but nothing renders a pressure more unbearable than the foretaste of release – the accumulated pressure, in this case, of those three months of cramped quarters and these three days of incessant travel, making her vibrate like a steam boiler. She asked Halyard if he played. He did not. But then, when the lift arrived, the first person to come out of it was the Turkish guy from the water taxi, still carrying his duffel.

They said hello, and maybe it was just because he had an athletic build that Resaint found herself asking him the same question: 'Do you play squash?'

There might have been a bit of woolliness in the translation of the present tense, because he answered, 'No, I'm just going to use the stationary bike.'

'I mean, are you capable of playing squash? Would you play a game of squash with me?'

He smiled. 'I can play, but it's been years. I'd be terrible.'

Without mercy she dismissed this objection, very much as she dismissed Halyard to go and snoop around Surface Wave on his own for an hour. The T-shirt and trainers she already had on were just about viable, but not her wool-rayon crops, so she bought workout leggings from the same vending machine where they rented a couple of Yonex rackets. The Turkish guy turned out to be called Selim. He was in his forties, handsome, with a beard as dense as doormat coir, touched with silver at the sideburns. Sure enough, he was a wretched player. It was not in her nature to demean them both by going easy on him, but his tottery serves in particular she found she had no choice but to pass back like warm-ups; that way they might at least get a rally going and she wouldn't feel too much like a hydraulic device repeating a single mechanical action as she punched each hopeless ball beyond his reach. They barely spoke until their second game ended, when he said, 'Let me give you my mother's address in Gaziantep.'

'Why?'

'So you can arrange for my remains to be returned to my family.'

She laughed, pleased that he seemed neither resentful nor embarrassed. 'I play a lot.'

'There was a time when my squash and my English were both pretty good, if you can believe it. Actually, I can still understand fine, but ever since I started using this' – he gestured at the earpiece that was translating for him – 'I've forgotten how to say anything. Are you in biotech?'

'No, I'm a species intelligence evaluator.'

'Oh, on the boat I overheard you talking about extinctions. That explains it. You're not the first one I've met. I work for the Ministry of Forest and Water Affairs.'

'So what are you doing on Surface Wave?'

He gave an apologetic smile as if he was about to make a confession. 'Well, you know we have a lot of endangered species in Anatolia?'

'Yes.'

'I'm here to make some more.'

Selim explained that he was the deputy director of the ministry's Regional Directorate for Southeastern Anatolia. By the end of the year, the Turkish government was finally due to break ground on a high-speed rail line connecting the cities of Adana, Gaziantep and Diyarbakir, right through his turf. Because this was a region of high biodiversity, the WCSE mandated a thorough survey of the route to find out whether the construction of the line was likely to finish off any endemic species that had already been backed into a corner by some combination of climate change, hydroelectric dams and overgrazing by insatiable herds of goats. Such surveys used hummingbird-sized drones to comb through every inch of the terrain, and they frequently made new discoveries that centuries of galumphing human naturalists had overlooked, analysing the DNA in a lizard dropping or an insect carcass to prove that this was not a member of any known species.

178

Under WCSE rules, this rail line was not regarded as an out-rageous debauch on Turkey's part. Rather, it fell within the country's baseline level of economic development. Turkey was perfectly entitled to build itself a 600-kilometre rail line every so often. Which meant that Turkey would not be penalised for the species it wiped out by building the line. Dues could only flow in the other direction: Turkey would be *compensated* if it *did not* build the line. Supposing it managed to restrain itself, then for every critter saved, Turkey would be allocated one extra extinction credit, which it could either spend elsewhere or sell on the open market.

But the truth was, Selim told her, the Turkish government didn't actually want to build the railway, and it hadn't for a while. For fiscal reasons totally unconnected to the imperilled fauna of the Anatolian plateau, it was planning to nix the whole project. It couldn't announce its decision quite yet, otherwise it would open itself up to various legal liabilities, but at this point it was just going through the motions, crossing its fingers behind its back every time the subject came up.

So it would definitely be getting those extra extinction credits from the WCSE as a reward for its forbearance. And back when a credit sold for less than €40,000, that wouldn't have meant much. But now that the price had spiked to ten times that, there was real money at stake. When those drones inspected the route, if they found, say, fifty endangered species instead of just forty, that was an extra four million euros in the bank. Which made it worthwhile for Selim to travel to Surface Wave, commission ten new endangered species, and set them loose upon those orchid-purpled steppes. A friend of his in the Ministry of Environment and Urbanisation had promised that half of that four million euros would be quietly funnelled back to Selim's directorate, where-upon Selim could use it to supplement his meagre budget for conservation work.

'What do you mean, "commission" new species?' Resaint said. Just occasionally, she could sense that the translation had miscon-strued a word or two, but the real meaning was generally clear from the context. What was more noticeable was the way the translation sometimes paused for a while and then gabbled like an auctioneer in its hurry to catch up; she remembered hearing once that Turkish could be a real bastard for interpreters because it so often left the pertinent verb until the very end of a long sentence.

'There's a company here,' Selim said, 'you give them the DNA from some little snake or butterfly, and they tweak a few base pairs on COX1. You know, change the barcode. They make a hundred of the new snake for you, and then you put it where the drones will find it. The drone thinks it's genetically distinct enough that it's a newly discovered species, so you get your extra credit. And if you commission ten at once, you get a nice discount. So when everything shakes out we should make enough of a profit that we can hire some researchers for our watershed rehabilitation project in Urfa.'

Resaint was disheartened to learn that Selim was, to borrow Halyard's expression, 'just another extinction industry cunt'. Leftists sometimes asserted that within a capitalist framework there could never be a solution to the extinction crisis that was untainted by profiteering and abuse, because the free market was like some malevolent AI, infinitely more devious than the humans who thought they could constrain it; but Resaint's own proposal was simply that each of the hundred thousand wealthiest individuals on earth should be randomly assigned a vulnerable species and then informed that if their assigned species were ever to go extinct they would be executed by hanging.

'Is cloning really that cheap here?' she said. On the *Varuna* she'd wondered about cloning the venomous lumpsucker to rebuild their population, but she'd never been sure where the funding would come from. Anyway, a cloned lumpsucker wouldn't satisfy her private agenda. It would be nonsensical for a fish to take revenge on you for pushing its species into the abyss if in fact the only reason that particular fish existed was because you had gone to enormous lengths to pull it back out.

'Well, the new snakes don't have to be reproductively viable or anything like that – they barely have to function at all, really – so they can take a few shortcuts and it keeps the cost down.'

'And you think you'll get away with it?'

'Before the biobank hacks, I probably wouldn't have taken the risk. But now that everything's in such a mess . . . Who's going to notice?'

'So just at the moment we have to begin rebuilding everything we lost, you're inserting spurious data. Fake species.'

'There was a time when that would have kept me up at night,' he conceded. 'You probably won't believe this but I used to be an idealist.' As he spoke, he was reading a message on his phone.

'What happened?'

He looked up. 'Do you feel like a coffee? I mean after I take a shower?'

'Shouldn't you be going to find your bioengineers? I assume you didn't come all the way from Urfa just to play squash and drink coffee.'

'You're right, I was supposed to be meeting with them right now. They just told me they're stuck in a lift.'

*

She was about to sit down when Selim darted past her and claimed the bench seat for himself. It took her a moment to realise he was making sure she wouldn't have to sit facing the gnats; a chivalrous gesture, newly coined. Like nearly all the public spaces on Surface Wave, this café was walled in glass, and although somebody had switched on the electrochromic tinting that would normally be used to dim the glare of a low sun, it didn't help that much. She sat down opposite him and took a sip of her Americano. As in the health club, the architects had permitted here a minor relaxation of the white fibreglass aesthetic, and the tabletops were made of that GM teak that grew with a grid pattern in its wood like slightly wobbly graph paper.

For a long time, Selim told her, he had been married to the pallid nuthatch. He had first encountered the bird as an undergraduate, on a trip to Nemrut Dagi National Park with the Dicle University Birdwatching Club (at that time convulsed by the acrimonious break-up of two of its four members). There, the last surviving colony of *Sitta petronia* nested in the cliffs. Selim learned that the pallid nuthatch had been identified as the species that the great Anatolian folk poet Yunus Emre was referring to in one of his most beautiful verses – in other words, it was part of the country's cultural heritage as well as its ecological one – yet without anyone really paying attention its numbers had dwindled to less than a hundred. All the pallid nuthatches in the universe weighed not much more than his liver.

The moment he found this out, the bird seemed to transform before his eyes. Beforehand, it had been just another short-tailed passerine, unexceptional, colourless, with grubby-looking breast feathers and a high-pitched call that cracked in the middle like a ragged human scream played back at triple speed. But afterwards, every hop and twitch seemed precious, historic, full of grace and defiance, as the nuthatch solemnly persisted with its work, ignoring the approach of extinction. Right away Selim felt as if he had a personal responsibility to this dying immortal. Elsewhere in Turkey the northern bald ibis and the white-headed duck had their guardians, but nobody was looking out for the pallid nuthatch. He returned again and again to the cliffs, and when he went on to his MSc he made the nuthatch the focus of his fieldwork, and after that he won funding from a conservation foundation in Switzerland to continue his research into how it might be saved. He still remembered the day he got that email as the happiest day of his life.

And sure enough, for several years he lived blissfully with the nuthatch. The females would lay a second time if the first egg disappeared from the nest, so Selim would climb the cliffs with a ladder to swipe the eggs, then hatch them in an incubator, hoping to multiply the nuthatches' output. He fitted the entrances of their nest cavities with wooden baffles so that invasive myna birds couldn't muscle their way in, and he even bought a BB gun to roust the mynas, although he was never fast enough to use it. He loved the sense of mission, his alone, and his alone, too, the study of the nuthatches' lives; like a fissure in the cliffs, from the outside it looked narrow but once you got inside it widened out forever. Willingly he would have mantled himself in their feathers, anointed himself in their guano. If you set aside all the grant applications and the networking at conferences and the fiddling with the tracking software, it felt honest, natural, a job that, like an animal, did not need to be justified. Once, he fell off the ladder and broke his ankle. More than once, he got stung by scorpions and it hurt so much he vomited. He hardly minded.

But then, about a decade into his time with the nuthatches, there was the incident with his friend Necla's husband. The war photographer.

Whenever Selim had to explain his work to a relative back in Gaziantep, he was as straightforward as possible, knowing that none of them could really understand what he'd made of his life. But whenever he had to explain it to some accomplished, worldly person from Istanbul or beyond, he had a routine. 'I just look at birds all day,' he would say, affably, self-mockingly, as if ruing his own craziness. 'That's all I do. It's a very boring life. Very nerdy.' And the other person would contradict him, saying, 'Wow, no, that sounds fascinating, much more worthwhile than what I do, conservation is wonderful, birds are precious, I wish I could spend more time in nature, isn't climate change awful?' or some permutation of the above. And in response Selim would humbly concede that yes, maybe his job did have some value, after all. This was how it almost always played out. People understood their roles.

But not this time. Necla was his only truly glamorous friend: she had been the most beautiful girl in their high school, and around the time of their university entrance exams she'd been scouted on Instagram by a modelling agency in Paris, and after working all over Europe she'd married this war photographer. He was Turkish too, but they'd met on a glacier in Iceland after Lanvin hired him for ten thousand euros a day to shoot an ad campaign, presumably hoping he'd imbue it with a haunted, prestigious quality. Selim had been forced to miss their wedding after a freak summer storm blasted the nuthatch cliffs like a water cannon, but some years later, finding himself in Istanbul for a few nights, he went to Necla's apartment for dinner and met her husband for the first time.

From him, there was no generous riposte when Selim explained what he did. Just a puzzled, contemptuous look, as if he could hardly make sense of what Selim was saying because it so defied belief that an adult man would spend his time in such a way. So Selim kept chattering on about the birds, and Necla's husband still said nothing, until Selim mentioned the time he spent up ladders screwing wooden baffles into the cliff face.

'You make little gates? For the little nests?'

Selim nodded.

'Sounds like performance art.'

One week later Selim was up a ladder with a nuthatch egg in his latex-gloved hand and he felt an almost uncontrollable urge to hurl the egg down and see it smash on the ground.

Brief as it was, that conversation in the apartment in Beyoğlu, Necla's husband's refusal to play along politely, had punctured something inside him. In later years he sometimes wondered whether the exchange would have had quite such brutal revelatory force if it had been with anyone other than the alpha male, the hero of battlefields, the wooer of fashion models. But what was running through his head up the ladder couldn't have come out of nowhere. There was too much of it, too profuse an explosion of magma and pus. It was like when you're having what promises at first to be a minor quarrel with somebody and then you realise that in fact they are only just transitioning from their opening statement into the first of many subsectioned arguments and you think, 'Wow, I had no idea they'd been brooding on this for so long,' except that in this case the other person in the quarrel was himself, Selim.

What was the point of all this? Wasn't it, indeed, an empty ritual, a performance for nobody? Wasn't it just solipsistic fidgeting, circular busywork of the kind you'd devise to occupy a surplus person? Wasn't it difficult even to imagine a vocation that could have less of a purpose? What pathology or delusion had enabled his younger self to find this work inherently profound? Hadn't he thrown his away his prime? Wasn't he an embarrassment to his parents? Hadn't he had real potential once? Maybe he wouldn't have been a war photographer, maybe he wouldn't have travelled the world and documented atrocities and had babies with Necla, but couldn't he have had at least *some* fun, made *some* contribution? Why should he have to spend so many days in the rain and snow? Hadn't he been numbingly lonely for ten years? Weren't the pallid nuthatches just an evolutionary dead end, and out of misplaced reverence for them hadn't he made himself into one as well? Hadn't his very first impression of them been correct, that they were basically a banal, shoddy creature, no more than filler in the Book of Nature? Weren't they just witless, ungrateful, screeching little vermin?

And wasn't this all their fucking fault?

He raised the egg in his hand.

*

'Did you break it?' Resaint said.

'No. I couldn't.'

'But after that you left?'

'No. Not for two more years.'

She raised her eyebrows in surprise. 'Did you have second thoughts?'

'No. I loathed the birds more every day. But it took a while to really extricate myself. Psychologically, but also – you know, the funding, the partnerships. There was no one to replace me. But finally I moved over to the Ministry.'

'And now all you do is game the system?'

'No, we do good work there,' Selim said. 'We're trying to stop Anatolia turning to desert. We'll probably fail, but we won't regret trying, and any goatherd would understand why we did try. You can put all your hopes and dreams into something like that and it will fit them easily. But if you try to put all your hopes and dreams into this little . . .' A gesture with his fingers like a fluttering bird. 'Animals aren't really built for that. They don't have the capacity. It should be obvious when you look in their eyes, but

185

people forget.' He paused. 'You only spend two or three months on each species, right? That's good. You don't have time to get too attached.'

'You'd be surprised,' Resaint said.

Selim gave her a quizzical look.

'There's a fish—' she began.

'Selim? We're so sorry.'

Resaint looked up. A man and a woman stood in there in poses of contrition. They wore button-up shirts in shades of blue that were very nearly the same and yet just different enough that it niggled you like a production error. These were the bioengineers who proposed to swamp the databases with scammy listings like Céline replicas on an auction site. They introduced themselves but Resaint immediately forgot their names. 'Apparently what happened is that the yayflies got into a transformer cooling fan,' Pale Blue said, pulling up a chair while Paler Blue joined Selim on the bench seat.

'What did you call them?' Resaint said.

'The yayflies,' Pale Blue said, gesturing at the insects outside. The gummed-up fan, she explained, had sparked a small fire. Normally a maintenance drone would have swooped in to douse the fire right away, but none of those could be deployed just now because of the high winds around the spindrifters. So the fire got out of hand, resulting in a cascade of electrical problems that paralysed the nearest bank of lifts. 'In the end we were stuck in there for nearly two hours.'

Resaint was about to make an exit. But then Pale Blue added, 'If I ever see Lodewijk again he's going to have a lot to answer for.'

'Who's Lodewijk?' Resaint said.

'He's the guy making the yayflies.'

'I thought there was nobody inside the module.'

'There isn't,' Pale Blue said. 'Lodewijk left after he set up the rearing system. It's all automated. But he's still paying the fees on the module every month. He could end this if he wanted, but nobody knows where he is or how to get hold of him.'

Resaint had assumed that the gnat geyser must be a bizarre mishap, an unintended side effect of some Surface Wave tenant's careless work, like algae blooming in a river because of chemical run-off from a farm. It hadn't occurred to her that somebody might have contrived it deliberately. 'Why would he have done this?'

'Well, to be fair to him, he didn't do *this*,' Paler Blue said, repeating Pale Blue's gesture towards the mega-swarm. 'The spindrifters weren't here when he set up the rearing system. The yayflies were just supposed to disperse into the sky. He couldn't have known that we'd end up in this "pissing into the wind" situation. He may still not know. Obviously it's not very popular to defend Lodewijk at the moment, but he and I used to be pretty friendly. He told me about the yayflies when he was designing them. He just didn't tell me everything he had planned.'

'What *are* the yayflies, exactly?' Resaint said. But then she glanced at Selim. 'Sorry, you probably need to get on with your meeting.'

'No, I would like to know too,' Selim said. And he was, after all, the client. So Paler Blue embarked on an explanation.

Lodewijk, he told them, was co-founder of a Dutch start-up developing microbial fuel cells to improve the methane yield from wastewater. In order to run certain trials that would have caused regulatory hassles back in the Netherlands, he had leased one of Surface Wave's extra-large satellite modules. Ever since his postgrad days, he had also been involved in a charity that installed smart irrigation systems for rice and maize farmers in Malawi, flying down there every few months and assisting remotely between trips. It could be frustrating work: the farmers kept complaining that the new irrigation systems didn't work as well as the old ones and were impossible to fix when they broke down. After a few beers, Lodewijk would sometimes complain about what he saw as the backwardness and ingratitude of these farmers, but he kept at it. Then, in spring last year, there had come the worst floods in Malawi's history, washing away nearly all of the smallholdings in which Lodewijk had invested his efforts.

The disaster hit Lodewijk hard, and afterwards his whole outlook seemed to change. He still wanted to make the world better, he would say, but it was a hopelessly inefficient use of time to attempt to improve human lives: they were too messy and unpredictable, especially in an age of stampeding climate change. Anyway, research showed that a person's level of happiness was almost unshakeable, no matter what happened to them. If you won the lottery, or married your sweetheart, a year later you would report about the same satisfaction with life as beforehand. If your firstborn died, or you were paralysed from the neck down in a car crash – ditto. How much an individual enjoyed their life seemed to be determined mostly by genes rather than circumstances. And that was the seed of Lodewijk's next project.

The yayflies, as he called them, were based on *Nervijuncta nigricoxa*, a type of gall gnat, but with the help of some of his peers on Surface Wave he'd made a number of changes to their life cycle. The yayflies were all female, and they reproduced asexually, meaning they were clones of each other. A yayfly egg would hatch into a larva, and the larva would feed greedily on kelp for several days. Once her belly was full, she would settle down to pupate. Later, bursting from her cocoon, the adult yayfly would already be pregnant with hundreds of eggs. She would lay these eggs, and the cycle would begin anew. But the adult yayfly still had another few hours to live. She couldn't feed; indeed, she had no mouthparts, no alimentary canal. All she could do was fly towards the horizon, feeling an unimaginably intense joy.

The boldest modifications Lodewijk had made to these insects were to their neural architecture. A yayfly not only had excessive numbers of receptors for so-called pleasure chemicals, but also excessive numbers of neurons synthesising them; like a duck leg simmering luxuriantly in its own fat, the whole brain was simultaneously gushing these neurotransmitters and soaking them up, from the moment it left the cocoon. A yayfly didn't have the ability to search for food or avoid predators or do almost any of the other things that *Nervijuncta nigricoxa* could do; all of these functions had been edited out to free up space. She was, in the most literal sense, a dedicated hedonist, the minimum viable platform for rapture that could also take care of its own disposal. There was no way for a human being to understand quite what it was like to be a yayfly, but Lodewijk's aim had been to evoke the experience of a first-time drug user taking a heroic dose of MDMA, the kind of dose that would leave you with irreparable brain damage. And the yayflies *were* suffering brain damage, in the sense that after a few hours their little brains would be used-up husks; neurochemically speaking, the machine was imbalanced and unsound. But by then the yayflies would already be dead. They would never get as far as the comedown.

You could argue, if you wanted, that a human orgasm was a more profound output of pleasure than even the most consuming gnat bliss, since a human brain was so much bigger than a gnat brain. But what if tens of thousands of these yayflies were born every second, billions every day? That would be a bigger contribution to the sum total of wellbeing in the universe than any conceivable humanitarian intervention. And it could go on indefinitely, an unending anti-disaster.

'That's what they're for?' Resaint said.

Paler Blue nodded. 'A few months ago, Lodewijk applied for permission to make a structural modification to his module. He wanted to install a much bigger exhaust flue. He said he needed it for his bacteria trials. Really it was an exit route for the yayflies. The last thing he had to put in place before he got it all running.'

'But I don't understand how it keeps going on its own,' Resaint said. 'I know there's an electricity supply but what are the larvae feeding on?'

Paler Blue took out his phone, stretched it out wide, and crimped the bottom corners so it would stand up on the table where everyone could see it. Then he called up a rendering of Module 3, a sixty-metre-tall cylinder with its bottom third under the water.

'Lodewijk's module has its own algaculture set-up. Two kilometres of longlines.' The rendering showed the seaweed growing in the sea around the module, long orderly rows like looms in a carpet factory. 'And this is 12% kelp.' What this signified, Resaint knew, was that this modified strain of kelp could convert 12% of the energy in sunlight into chemical energy for growth, whereas traditional kelp could only manage . . . well, she couldn't remember the figure offhand but it was definitely less. 'So the drones harvest the kelp, they shred it, and they dump it into the rearing system for the larvae to feed on. And obviously the yayfly's metabolism is tweaked for perfect compatibility with the kelp. So the whole thing is very efficient and self-contained, not counting the electricity supply. That's how Lodewijk is able to yield billions of yayflies a day from a relatively modest algaculture system.'

But Resaint had noticed something on the rendering. 'What are those?' she said, pointing at a detail on the seafloor.

'They're just moorings for the kelp lines.'

Resaint looked closer.

She hadn't felt much optimism about the trip to Surface Wave. It was a very long shot. Even supposing they could find the fisherman, and he could tell them exactly where he caught the fish from the video, that fish might just have been a vagrant far from home and the information might bring them no closer to finding a second population. That was why she was still sitting here with Selim and the others, satisfying her curiosity about the yayflies, instead of rushing off to help Halyard with whatever enquiries he was making.

Yet now she felt a tremor of real hope.

And perhaps it was Selim's confession that had left her vulnerable to that. Because it had brought the dream to life again. If he knew that, he might think she'd totally missed the point. But the truth was she already understood that a long involvement with the lumpsuckers might be fruitless and maddening. She was certain that the lumpsuckers had the capacity to understand what she needed them to understand, but she couldn't be certain that she had the capacity to teach them. Most of what she knew about working with animals in the laboratory, she had learned on the job – her narrow, venal job. She was proposing to do something without precedent and she was proposing to do it without assistance. At best – even assuming it was feasible, even assuming she was lucky – it would mean years of repetition and frustration, of mirages and dead ends, as she became a prisoner fighting to ensure her own execution. At worst, none of it would come to anything at all, and she would be revealed as a fantasist like Mrs Purleyswars.

What his story had made tangible for her, however, was not the threat of failure but rather the promise of the attempt. That fissure in the cliffside he'd talked about, the fissure with a world beyond it, the fissure that in his telling was also a trap: however dark his warnings about it, they only helped her to imagine herself squeezing through.

'Are there cameras down there?' she said.

'There are maintenance drones that just loop around the infrastructure all day,' Pale Blue said, twirling her finger in a circle.

'Is there any way I could see the video feeds?'

'You couldn't, but we could, probably, because we're residents. By default we tend to have access to stuff like that. Why?'

The reason the venomous lumpsuckers were so wedded to those reefs off the Swedish coast was that only those reefs had the necessary boulders, dumped there by the Pleistocene glaciers who didn't take their litter with them when they left. Without those boulders and their crevices, the finicky lumpsuckers wouldn't even entertain the idea of breeding. Because the South Kvarken reefs were the only remaining corner of the Baltic with both the right sort of water and the right sort of rocks, Resaint had never found it credible that there could be a remnant population anywhere else. Back on the *Varuna*, she'd hoped that one day she might artificially expand the lumpsuckers' range by collecting hundreds of boulders from the shore and dropping them off the side of a boat, but the AMVs had chewed up the South Kvarken colony before she'd had the chance.

But now, as she looked at the rendering – at the blocky concrete moorings on the seafloor that held the kelp lines stable – she tried to imagine herself seeing those moorings through a venomous lumpsucker's eyes.

And what she saw was a reef of absolutely perfect boulders.

Chapter Fourteen

As he waited for Terence to call him back, Halyard sat beneath the curve of an escalator on a kind of bench- or chaise-like object that resembled a giant flatworm upholstered in white nubuck. The first place he had gone after leaving Resaint at the health club was Surface Wave's medical centre, because that had worked out so nicely at the Tinkanen camp. Sure, you could call it a failure of imagination, but he thought it was at least possible that whatever the mermaid hadn't found in Dr Shahad's cabinets, she might look for here instead. Unfortunately, nobody at the medical centre knew what he was talking about. And after that he wasn't sure what to do next: when he looked around he felt like a drop of fluid beading on one of the city's smooth impermeable surfaces. So he got in touch with Terence – his old friend from his Tokyo omakase days – because he knew Terence had invested in a bio-computing start-up on Surface Wave and he hoped he might be able to introduce him to a few people.

However, Terence's scullion said he was on another call. And Halyard was in the relaxing position of having no work messages to answer. Not because he wasn't getting any – now that the missing credits had been noticed, he was almost certainly getting more than ever – but because last night he'd given his scullion new orders: if anything comes through from Brahmasamudram, don't show it to me, just reply with a sales pitch for investment opportunities in Patagonian water rights. That way, people would think his scullion had been hacked. Which probably wouldn't accomplish much at this stage, but it couldn't hurt, could it?

So he just passed the time catching up on the news. Kohlmann Treborg Nham had mobilised. Their name was never mentioned, but you could tell from the messaging campaign that was underway worldwide, its symphonic richness, its contrapuntal beauty. In every off-the-record briefing and expert analysis, the same theme. Just because the biobank attacks had made endangered species look suddenly irreplaceable again, this wasn't the time for the WCSE to clamp down. On the contrary, this was an ideal moment to *liberalise*. And deeper in the music Halyard thought he could hear the intimation of a threat. After all, extinction credits were still at nearly four hundred grand. Perhaps the WCSE should consider how many governments had fallen over the price of bread.

Meanwhile, reports were now emerging that the biobank worm, in its psychotic thoroughness, had even erased the repositories where pet owners sent the DNA sequences of their beloved cats and dogs for later resurrection.

At last Terence returned his call. 'Mark! Hey, man. It's been way too long. What's up?'

'I am in desperate pursuit of a clued-up mermaid in the hopes of trivialising an act of embezzlement,' Halyard did not reply. Instead, he pretended he was on Surface Wave looking into a rumour that one of Brahmasamudram's vendors had been farming out some work here in violation of their contract. But it turned out that Terence's investment had turned to dust a while ago. So Halyard asked him if he still knew anyone in the city who was really plugged in to everything that was going on.

'Not really,' Terence said. 'I think I only know this one guy there now. Sanny Warkentin. He has this tissue culture operation. Small, but he does all kinds of shit. You know those – they're tumours or whatever? The big ones made out of panda? They throw them at people?'

'I am aware of those, yes.'

'He's the guy that makes them! Isn't that hilarious?'

Ten minutes later Halyard was hammering on the door of a lab unit on the third floor of Surface Wave's amphitheatre. This was not a door that was at all satisfying to hammer on because it was so secure in its airtight frame that there wasn't the slightest feeling of vibration or give. It was as unshaken as the voice of the scullion that piped up, 'Sanny isn't here at the moment. Would you like to try calling him?'

Halyard had always imagined that the tumours were manufactured in some dank basement resembling a meth factory, certainly not somewhere so clean and legit. 'When is he coming back?' he said. He wanted to chew everything to pieces like that Siberian tiger waiting for the hunter to get home.

But at that moment a guy appeared in the corridor who matched the photos of Warkentin that Halyard had looked up. He was probably in his late twenties but he could have been mistaken for a pink-cheeked teenage boy, and he wore those dorky trousers with the adjustment cable up the outside leg so you could slim them down when you needed to step into a laboratory coverall. 'Oh, hi?' he said.

'You're the guy that makes the panda tumours?'

Warkentin looked at Halyard for a moment and then gave a nod, not of assent but of understanding, like he was clicking into a new mode for the kind of conversation he thought this was going to be. 'I can't comment on my work for other clients, but if you're looking to commission something—'

'You are manufacturing weapons for terrorists. I could have died on Monday, you piece of shit!'

Another momentary pause, another calm nod of adjustment. 'I'm just selling them tissue. They could get tissue anywhere.'

'No, you're not just selling them tissue, you're enabling the whole thing by creating this extremely symbolically-charged munition made from Chiu Chiu's DNA—'

'It's actually not Chiu Chiu's DNA. The truth is it's surprisingly hard to get hold of a clean copy of Chiu Chiu. I just use generic panda. The clients understand that but they like to reference Chiu Chiu for narrative reasons so—'

194

'This is all beside the point,' Halyard said. 'I'm going to get you shut down.'

Warkentin smiled. 'One, this is Surface Wave, you can't get me shut down. Two, you have to understand, they're just one client. That stuff is just a tiny proportion of the work I do. At the moment I'm ninety-nine per cent focused on my fish thing.'

Must everyone on the Baltic, Halyard thought, have some esoteric piscine calling? 'What fish thing?'

'Cultured bluefin.'

He looked at Warkentin in disgust. To his abhorrence of anyone complicit in terrorist violence was added his abhorrence of anyone complicit in bad food. 'If you want to sell protein wadding to sandwich factories I don't know why you don't just ship them the tumours. They wouldn't know the difference.'

'It's not flakes, it's belly. Tastes exactly like the real thing.'

'Bullshit.'

'It does.'

'Bullshit. I've tried everything. I've tried the best vat-grown *chutoro* out of the labs in Osaka. It's like fish-flavoured jelly. At fifty yen a gram. For half my life they've been telling us they're a year away from cracking it and nobody ever comes close.'

'Do you want to try some?'

Halyard knew he ought to say no. This was another distraction from the real topic, and anyway it was probably wiser not to ingest anything given to you by a person whose livelihood you had moments ago sworn to destroy. And yet he wanted to humiliate this smug little prick. Probably no one had ever sampled Warkentin's tuna who actually knew the first thing about bluefin, whereas Halyard hadn't yet taken an Inzidernil today, meaning his discernment was still unsheathed, and already he was anticipating like a good dinner the satisfaction of explaining forensically, mercilessly, definitively why the project Warkentin was devoting himself to was an abject waste of time. 'OK,' he said.

He followed Warkentin into the unit, finding himself in a sort of lounge-office-reception area which had enough chairs that you could presumably receive clients in here if you wanted to, although right now the nearest chair was occupied by a cardboard shipping box with the top splayed open and the floor around it was littered with those inflatable packing cushions that turned brown and wrinkly after a few days. Glass walls on two sides looked out to the work-space itself. Here were the hulking steel bioreactors fed by a jungly criss-cross of cables and pipes, and amidst the bioreactors the sort of equipment that gave a laboratory like this a vaguely onanistic feel, because wherever you fixed your eyes there was always something on the periphery of your vision that kept rocking or jiggling or circling in an incessant compulsive motion like a hand in a trouser pocket.

Warkentin went through into a side room, also glass walled. Halyard watched as he snapped on some gloves, opened a refrig-erator, slid out a tray, and made a cut with a pair of shears. Then he strolled back in with the tuna, not on a plate but just draped across his two hands like a jeweller showing off a gold chain. It was a long thin strip like belly loin, and it had a convincing ruby gleam, but the fine imprint of fat was so eerily regular down the whole length that you could tell it hadn't come out of a fish. 'Have some,' he said. 'Obviously it would be better closer to room temp but you should still get an idea.'

'Just eat it like this?'

'I have soy if you want it.'

'That's not what I meant. Whatever. Forget it.' With his bare hands Halyard tore off a chunk of the fridge-cold tissue and put it in his mouth, ready to crush Warkentin with his verdict.

'Are you OK?' said Warkentin after a moment.

Halyard realised he was crying.

His phone tingled in his pocket. It was Resaint.

'I can't go to prison,' he said to her.

'What's going on? You sound strange.'

'I can't go to prison. I can't. I need my freedom. There's so much to live for.'

'I found them,' she said.

'The mermaid?'

'No, the lumpsuckers. There's a small population living under the city, around the kelp line moorings. I got access to the video feeds from the maintenance drones and I found them right away. They're not extinct. They're right here. Under our feet.'

'How the fuck did you know to . . .' But the question seemed irrelevant. Even if the venomous lumpsuckers could no longer save him from ruin, he was happy for Resaint. This was not, for Halyard, a familiar feeling. 'Can't you just be happy for [him/her/them]?' people had said to him in the past after he'd admitted to some deep jealousy or bitterness, but most of the time he regarded the very idea – happy *for* – as a con invented by sticking a preposition where it had absolutely no logical business. Now, though, he really did feel happy for Resaint that she was to be reunited with what was most precious to her in the world. And it would not have been fair to suggest that this moment of genuine human empathy was possible only because that bite of tuna belly had left him in an unusually heightened and vulnerable emotional state. Although, fine, that might have been sixty per cent of it.

Agreeing to meet her at a café near the health club, he hung up. 'I've got to go,' he said to Warkentin. He felt an urge to embrace the boy.

'Do you want to take this with you?' Warkentin said, proffering the belt of loin. As it caught the light it twinkled like the eyes of God. 'Right now I can grow about six hundred of these a month, but I'm going to scale up soon.'

Regretfully Halyard waved it off. He needed to stay clear-headed at least for the next few hours while he assisted Resaint. He couldn't just lose himself inside that transcendental fillet. 'Can I come back, though?'

'Sure. How long are you in town?'

'I don't know yet. We're here looking for a—' he stopped himself from saying 'mermaid' '—a woman who we think may have sneaked into the city.'

Warkentin made an expression as if he was intrigued by the novelty of the idea. 'I haven't heard anything about that. But you really chose the worst possible time to visit. And so did she, I guess, if she's here. This place is usually a lot more pleasant. You should at least stay until the yayflies are gone.'

'You mean the gnats? When is that going to be? I thought nobody knew how to get rid of them.'

'Over lunch just now I heard Faun's going to deal with it.'

'Who's Faun?'

'You'd know her if you saw her, she's got these—' Warkentin laid his index fingers on either side of his nose to represent sub-dermal ridges.

'Oh, yeah, I have seen her,' said Halyard, remembering the woman heckling Ganf earlier.

'Well, the yayflies are raised on kelp, right? If you choke off the food supply, you stop the yayflies. So Faun's planning to dump chlorine into the sea. Kill all the kelp. Simplest way to do it.'

*

Faun didn't invite them into her unit, so they had the conversation at the door, Halyard and Resaint standing outside in the corridor. It made them seem ridiculous, as if they were canvassers or salesmen here to tell her about something she had no conceivable use for.

'As far as we know, this is the last population of venomous lumpsuckers on earth,' Resaint said, her voice taut as a garrotte. 'Chlorine can kill fish of that type at very low concentrations in the water – twenty or thirty micrograms per litre. If you go through with this, you will almost certainly be rendering a species extinct. You have to find another way.'

Faun shook her head. 'I'm sick of these bugs. I want them gone.' Halyard had never met anyone who had such a Shaolin-level ability to turn a height deficit in her favour, establishing a real air of dominance by looking up at them to talk. She was wearing a high-necked sleeveless top made of some coarse black material that hung on her stiff and crumpled like the bonnet of a crashed car.

Resaint started talking about the lumpsucker's incalculable value. But if Halyard himself had been a poor audience for this sort of thing back on the deck of the *Varuna*, he could see that Faun was even more impervious. So he interrupted to try a different tack. 'If it's documented that you've personally eradicated an intelligent species,' he said, 'you'll owe the WCSE thirteen extinction credits. You know an extinction credit is up to almost four hundred thousand euros since the hacks? So you'll be more than five mil in the hole.'

Faun gave Halyard a look of utter contempt, her cheekbone studs lifting as her eyes narrowed. 'This is Surface Wave, you moron. We're not signed up to any treaties. We're free of all that. Why do you think I live here?'

After four days of Resaint's lethal silences it was almost a relief to be openly abused. 'Regardless, if you're a citizen of a participating country—'

'I gave that up years ago,' Faun said, as if she was talking about her membership of the Girl Guides. 'I won't owe anything to anyone.'

'What if we could stop the yayflies another way?' Resaint said. 'Then you wouldn't dump the chlorine?'

'No, obviously not. There would be no point.'

'How long do we have?'

'I already have forty thousand gallons of chlorine dioxide solution en route from a plant in Hamina. The tanker will be here within a couple of hours.'

'Christ, that fast?' Halyard said.

'I do a lot of business with them.' And here Faun terminated the conversation, her parting scowl so intense that it seemed to persist like an afterimage over the door she shut in their faces. Halyard looked at Resaint. 'Stop the yayflies? Do you have something in mind?'

'I'll call Nathan and tell him to move the spindrifters on. That way the yayflies won't be blowing into the city any more.'

'Doesn't that just mean they'll come down in the camp again? I can't imagine he'll be super into that.'

'If he arranges the spindrifters in the right formation, I think it should be possible to sweep the yayflies far enough south that the wind won't carry them to the mainland.'

'A crowd control barrier,' Halyard said, and Resaint nodded.

She walked off down the curve of the corridor to make the call. The outer wall of this corridor was glass, which made it a panoramic viewing gallery for the gnat haboob, an aquarium tunnel of howling black silt. It roused in him a very old memory, perhaps one of his first, of sitting in a car seat while his father drove through a car wash, literally pissing himself in terror at the brushes attacking the windows. Halyard had only been on Surface Wave for about five hours, but already he'd picked up the instinct to reposition his body so the yayflies were outside his field of vision without even realising he was doing it. He wondered what lengths he would go to to deal with the pest problem if, like Faun, this was his home. No, he wouldn't poison the venomous lumpsuckers. Not after this week. But of course Faun wasn't invested like he was. It was a bit like how you wouldn't strangle your own baby for crying in a restaurant but you'd strangle someone else's.

When Resaint came back, she didn't look at all downcast, so he was surprised when she shook her head. 'He says he can't divert the spindrifters,' she said. 'Nobody can, except by brute force. As soon as he had them circling the city the way he wanted, he ripped out all the wiring, figuratively speaking. He had to make sure nobody from Surface Wave could send them away by hacking into their navigation systems the same as he did.'

'Shit.'

'But I explained the situation. And he suggested something he *can* do. He can get us into Module 3. Turn off the security, open the doors. That way, we can shut down the yayfly rearing system ourselves.'

*

Halyard wondered whether there was really any functional reason for Surface Wave's six satellite modules to be physically removed from the main body of the seastead, or whether in fact it was just a symbolic assertion of privacy and autonomy; and if the latter, whether the prestige of such an assertion was worth even the very, very remote risk that in a sufficiently humongous thousand-year storm the satellite modules would just snap off and float away.

200

Anyway, the bridge to Module 3 had curved walls, meaning you couldn't lean against them. So Halyard sat on the floor with his suit jacket under him as a cushion, while Resaint just stood. After nearly two hours of waiting there, staring at the double doors, willing them to open, Halyard was starting to fantasise about assaulting them with a crowbar. But really he knew that was a non-starter. If you tried to force your way into a Surface Wave lab unit, you would first be warned off by its scullion. And if you persisted, you would be squirted with a synthetic mucus that would immobilise you where you stood. Upon ejaculation, the mucus expanded to thousands of times its original volume, so the security system could plug the whole bridge if the situation called for it. Surface Wave's boosters often rhapsodised about what a polished and elegant 'product' it was compared to traditional sovereign states, as if they were talking about a new phone with cool features, and one of these features was that it didn't have a criminal justice apparatus, it just had technical safeguards that ruled out most of the cruder crime-like acts.

'I wonder where this guy Lodewijk is now,' Halyard said.

'Well, my guess is he took money out of his company to fund what he was building in there. So maybe he's keeping a low profile out of necessity.'

'I for one hope he's punished to the full extent of the law. Zero tolerance for white-collar crime.' Halyard stretched out his legs. 'Or maybe he's building a bigger one somewhere. Maybe this was just a prototype. You have to admit, there's something admirable about the whole thing. It has a kind of heroic purity.'

'Of course you would think that.'

'What do you mean?'

'Of course you would admire the yayflies,' Resaint said. 'You love dogs, and yayflies are dogs. They're a manufactured organism whose only purpose is to make human beings feel better about themselves through an excess of totally vapid positivity. You would be content in a world with only two species – us and a lot of grinning toys we made.'

'You just find it impossible to empathise with the yayflies because they're in a good mood.'

'Anyway, if you want purity, why does this have to be so messy? Just model a yayfly consciousness on a computer. But change one of the variables. Jack up the intensity of the pleasure by a trillion trillion trillion trillion. After that, you can pop an Inzidernil and relax. You've offset all the suffering in the world since the beginning of time. None of us have to worry about anything any more.'

'You're being sardonic because you don't want to acknowledge the possibility that spoiling the yayflies' fun is going to be, by a massive distance, the most evil thing that either of us ever do in our lives. I mean in terms of the bottom line. The overall metrics.'

'Is that what you think?'

'No, but someone could make the case, couldn't they?'

'Not really. If we don't stop it, Faun will. So it's a moot point.'

Halyard asked his scullion for the time. 'Nathan had better get this done pretty soon. That tanker must be nearly here.'

'He said it would be easy. I don't know what's taking so long.' Resaint looked down at him. 'I forgot to mention: he told me Gareth got back yesterday. Around lunchtime. We must have been barely out of the camp.'

'Oh.'

'Didn't you say you asked Wilson to let you know as soon as he heard anything?'

'Yeah, I did,' said Halyard, forcing himself to meet her eye. 'But in hindsight it's good that he didn't, isn't it? Because if we'd known Gareth was back in the camp, we would never have come here, and if we hadn't come here you would never have found the lumpsuckers. So we should actually be very grateful that for whatever reason that information didn't get passed on—'

But at that moment the doors to the gnat factory swung open.

A smell rushed over them, warm and thick like the outbreathing of an oven. Compared to that flatly repellent fishhead stench at the Tinkanen beach, it was much deeper, more polychrome, although it did contain the fishhead stench somewhere in its layers, just like it contained wet fur and cat piss and shrimp paste, the timeless classics of organic reek mixed in with some other, more alien notes. Back on the dock, as Daniel was handing them their mosquito nets, a yayfly had flown right up Halyard's nose, and it hadn't smelled of anything at all, but of course everything had a smell if you just collected enough of it together, if you infinitised the infinitesimal, not only the yayflies themselves but their heaped-up frass and their dried-out cocoons and their half-digested feed.

The two of them went inside, Halyard impatient to get moving and yet still touched by that spookiness it is impossible not to feel when you trespass into some vast, deserted, forbidden place.

At first, the only light to see by was what washed through from the bridge outside, but then Resaint asked out loud for some more. Several tube lamps came on above their heads, but most of the space was still in shadow. Surface Wave's satellite modules were designed so that the layout could be reconfigured about as easily as moving around the shelves in a fridge, and in this case nearly all of the internal partitions had been folded away to transform the module into one gigantic silo. However, there were still ramps and landings running around the insides of the walls, and it was on to one of these landings that the doors had admitted them. Standing at the guardrail you could reach out and touch one of the tens of thousands of rearing boxes that took up almost the entire volume of the module.

These were made of grey plastic and about the size of fruit crates. On the columns that stretched from floor to ceiling, the boxes were fixed like the treads of a spiral staircase, each box offset from the one below it to leave room for twists of white ducting. And through the metal struts of these columns, you could see that they were hollow, with constant movement on the inside. In order to have some idea of what he was getting himself into, Halyard had watched a video about a facility a bit like this one where they bred flies for livestock feed, so he knew that inside the columns there were robots that tended to the boxes, filling, emptying, sifting and cleaning. There was no sound to be heard but these nursemaids moving up and down the columns, reverberating in a choral whine.

Just as enough tiny creatures in one place could give off an astonishing amount of odour, enough tiny creatures in one place could give off an astonishing amount of warmth and moisture. And although cooling the module with seawater would have been simple enough, it was better for the yayflies if the climate was allowed to stay tropical. This was the most disorienting thing about the place for somebody unused to such sweatshops. If you closed your eyes and breathed in, you felt you must be in a swamp or a barnyard, somewhere mucky and steaming. And yet when you opened your eyes, you found before them a vista as regular and sterile as a data centre or a battery shed, the only evidence of life a little whorl of yayflies high above who must have escaped from a breach in the ducting. Perhaps Halyard had expected the interior of the module to be a bit more reflective of a mind in crisis, but in fact the sheer monotonous efficiency of it told him that Lodewijk had not regarded the work as some messianic act of self-expression. Like the capitalist he was, he had simply been trying to maximise output.

'So how are we going to do this?' Halyard said. 'For a second I was thinking we could just set it on fire, but something will come along and put it out, right?'

'Yes, vandalism is not going to be enough. Whatever we do has to be fast and conclusive.'

'Like what?'

'Let's see if we can find any controls,' Resaint said.

'You think there's going to be a big red button labelled "stop making insects"?'

Nevertheless, he followed her down a ramp which led clockwise around the outer wall. It made you think of the pinewoods, the way sightlines opened and closed between the columns as you moved past. Towards the roof of the module, you could see where those hundreds of metres of plastic ducting began to converge and aggregate like the root system of a tree, so that after laying their eggs the yayflies could stream out of the boxes and up to the exhaust flue and off into a world whose sorrows could not mar their bliss.

They came to a cargo lift. Resaint pressed a button and a platform hummed up the rails to meet them.

'Are we going up or down?' said Halyard.

'Down. Let's find the safe room.'

As they descended, the rearing boxes riffled past in their perfect spirals, as hypnotic vertically as they had been horizontally. Somewhere far below would be the rearing system's digestive orifices: a mouth, so to speak, for taking in kelp to be pressed and shredded and served to the larvae; and an anus, for dumping their accumulated wastes, which would sink to the seafloor and attract little fish, which would attract bigger fish, which must at some point have attracted a few venomous lumpsuckers looking for a new client base a long way from home.

The safe room was where a resident could retreat in case of fire, or flood, or accidental release of some hazardous biological or chemical agent, or incursion by pirates or mercenaries or foreign law enforcement officials, if circumstances became sufficiently dire that the resident could no longer rely on Surface Wave's other protections. It took the form of a sort of wart or blister on the inner wall of the module, enclosed in pearly ballistic fibreglass. When they got off the lift and walked down the ramp to the safe room, they found that the hatch was already ajar.

One of the selling points of the satellite modules was that they could accommodate nice spacious living quarters. But when they stepped through into the safe room, it became clear that Lodewijk had opted instead to make this tiny bolthole his home for at least part of his time in Module 3: the sofa was still folded out into a bed with a rumpled duvet on top of it. Presumably this was because the safe room was almost the only internal feature of the module that couldn't be disassembled to open up more space for the rearing boxes, so Lodewijk had used it for the one thing it was good for, settling into this minimal nest like one of those medieval stonecutters who camped inside the temples they were building. There was also a table, a chair, some shelves and cabinets built into the walls, a door leading to a bathroom and another leading to a deck outside.

Halyard would not have been entirely surprised to find out that Lodewijk had subsisted on kelp like his yayflies, but in fact the shelves were stacked with boxes of nutrient shakes. Lying folded on one shelf, also, was what looked like a wetsuit, but when Halyard ran his fingers over the black fabric it didn't have the Neoprene sponginess he remembered from surfing lessons. It was hard to say what it *did* feel like, except, in its negativity, one of those calf leathers so expensive that they seemed to have no detectible characteristics at all – but it definitely hadn't come off any animal.

He saw that there was a bottle of pomegranate-flavour shake on the desk, cap off, half drunk. He picked it up, shook it gently, and sniffed. This was a brand he often drank himself. So he knew that if you opened a bottle and then forgot about it, it went sour and gunky after a day or so, even faster in the heat. But this bottle was still fresh. Meaning it hadn't been open very long. He was about to say something to Resaint—

But then the door of the bathroom opened and a woman came out.

Seeing the two of them, she froze. She was in her forties, lean, with cropped greying hair, which she was towelling dry as if she'd recently got out of the shower. She wore only a grey fitted vest top and leggings, and those leggings appeared to contain a pair of standard human legs – yet Halyard knew immediately that this was the mermaid. He couldn't have said how he knew, but he knew.

So when she darted towards the hatch, he shouted for her to stop, and out of pure instinct made a grab for her arm. He never made contact, but all the same, without even turning back, she smashed him in the mouth with her elbow.

It was just one blow, but Halyard took it with all the fortitude and dignity of somebody trying to pull off a personal injury scam. His head snapped back and he stumbled blindly into a shelf, sideswiping a stack of nutrient shake boxes which toppled to the ground at the same time he did. On the way down his head knocked against one of the legs of the sofa bed and then at last he came to rest.

'*Herrgott*, are you OK?' said Resaint, hurrying over to him.

Lying there, dazed, he took an inventory. His eyes were watering and his lip was stinging and his head was aching and he could taste blood in his mouth. But he didn't think he was injured in any consequential way. He let Resaint help him up from amongst the kilocaloric rubble. She handed him a tissue from her pocket and he pressed it to the cut on his lip.

'We've got to follow her!' he said indistinctly.

'Why?'

'Because that was the mermaid. I'm sure of it.' Lying across the bottom rim of the hatch he could see the towel she must have dropped on her way out.

'She's already gone. We don't have time.'

Halyard swayed back and forth in frustration. He was desperate to catch up with the woman. And yet he knew Resaint was right.

Nevertheless, he thought of one quick way to mollify his curiosity. Still holding the tissue to his lip, he used his other hand to pick up the wetsuit, hang it over the back of the chair, and scan it up and down with his phone camera. He wasn't sure if his scullion would be able to identify it, because it was completely unmarked, even on the inside of the neckline where you'd usually expect to find some branding. The thing was just a rind of shadow.

But there must have been a few telltale details his primitive human eyes weren't seeing, because a result came back. And it explained quite a lot.

There was a guy in Jordan who made very popular videos about the most unusual goods that passed through the arms bazaars there. Last year he'd got his hands on one of these wetsuits, scorched at the shoulder where one whole arm was missing, and he'd matched it to a technical specification that had leaked online. Skimming the details, Halyard learned that the 'wetsuit' was in fact a soft exosuit for commando operations, developed by the defence research arm of the Japanese military. Combined with some scuba gear, it really was the next best thing to being a mermaid. When you were swimming, the exosuit did most of the work for you, so you could go much faster and much further. It could stiffen its extremities into fins and regulate its own buoyancy. It kept you warm and it sensed currents and tides from a distance. Whether mermaids were also stab-proof and invisible to thermal imaging cameras was a question best left to the folklorists, but the exosuit certainly was. Also, it didn't weigh much, and it harvested most of its power passively, so it needed to be charged only every few days.

No longer did it seem so wondrous that Gareth had found the mermaid floating in the middle of the ocean, miles from anything. Nor that she'd told Dr Shahad she wasn't worried about the seaworthiness of Gareth's fishing boat, because she'd get where she was going one way or another: 'I'll swim if I have to.' In the care of this exosuit, you didn't have to be a champion swimmer to gaze undaunted upon forty kilometres of Baltic chop. You just had to be a reasonably fit person with a decent front crawl.

And yet the number of unanswered questions about the mermaid remained just about steady, because at least two new ones had been added. What was a vagabond from the Hermit Kingdom doing with a prize bit of classified Japanese military tech? And how had she come to be squatting in the safe room of an impregnable yayfly hothouse?

'Look at this,' said Resaint.

'What?'

Mounted on the wall next to the hatch was a control panel, not a touchscreen but rather a grid of real physical buttons like on the cargo lift. Each button had a little etched plastic label beside it, and Resaint pointed out two of these labels to him. 'This is exactly what I was hoping to find down here.'

One of the buttons read 'open flue' and the next one down read 'close flue'.

He looked at her. 'It can't be this easy, can it? There can't *actually* be a button that says "stop making insects"?'

And yet there was a logic to it. In certain catastrophic scenarios – say you'd retreated to the safe room because there was a fire or other oxidative reaction raging out of control inside the module, and it was greedily sucking in air through the flue, and none of the module's more sophisticated systems were responding – you would want a very straightforward button to thump, which would send a very straightforward signal up a heavily shielded electrical cable to the top of the module, which would close the flue no questions asked.

'What will happen if it works?'

'If the yayflies can't get out, I suppose they'll just pile up inside the ducting,' Resaint said. 'Like a traffic jam. More and more of them. Until they get so tightly packed they begin to suffocate each other. After that, it depends whether the system is designed to switch off when it detects a clog.'

'What an enchanting image.'

She pressed the button, and a short beep sounded.

But the mood of the beep was impossible to interpret. It could have meant 'sure, message received' or it could have meant 'sorry, can't do it'. Halyard immediately repented any admiration he might have been feeling for the vintage character of this emergency control panel, which didn't offer so much as a wink of an LED to indicate its thinking.

'Shall we go back up and look?' he said.

'With all the ducting in the way, I don't think we'll be able to see if the flue is still open or not. We need to look from outside. Check if the yayflies are still coming out.'

Inside the cabinets they found an assortment of hazmat gear, including a box of escape hoods, which were basically just vinyl sacks with puck-shaped respirators attached, designed to be put on in a panic and thrown away after one use. Even with the full knowledge that it was a protective device, the clear plastic gave Halyard a tingle of the forbidden as he pulled it over his head: child safety warnings on dry-cleaning bags, autoerotic asphyxiation . . .

Resaint pushed the lever of the door that led from the safe room to the deck outside. This was the route you'd take during an evacuation.

The door blew open so hard it almost knocked her over, and then slammed shut again with a poltergeist's petulance.

But in the instant the door had been open, Halyard had caught sight of the white rotors of a spindrifter, gliding right to left behind a molten scrim of yayflies. On the second attempt, he was ready with the desk chair, which he tipped over on its back and shoved halfway across the threshold as a doorstop. They waited for the lull between spindrifters before they stepped over the chair and into the open. They would have ten seconds or so before the next one bore down towards them and started hurling things around again.

The deck, which had a waist-high railing around it and a floor patterned with anti-slip diamonds, was cantilevered off the side of Module 3 at a height of about four storeys over the water. The conditions out here were even worse than they'd been on the jetty this morning, because the deck was far more exposed to the unholy winds which the spindrifters summoned up out of the sea's breezes, meaning the yayflies eddied thicker in the air, swallowing the two of them in this tumult that was like night and day fighting savagely over one transect of the earth. The escape hood didn't protect Halyard's hands, so he jammed them into his pockets, but not before he'd felt the ghastly stroking touch of the gnats on his bare skin. In fact, he immediately regretted the diaphanous accessory over his head. It was as if some perverse or misguided inventor had designed it specifically for this situation: 'Surely what a person really wants when they enter a swarm of insects is the equivalent of a snorkel mask, something that will give them the most intimate and unobstructed view of the fascinating medium into which they have immersed their faces, ensuring that the memory of the experience will stay with them for a lifetime.' He could breathe without difficulty through the respirator, but he was gripped nonetheless by an instinctive and not even remotely autoerotic feeling of asphyxiation.

The exhaust flue was way up above their heads, vertically in line with the deck. But the question of whether the flood of yayflies had indeed been staunched, the question they'd come out here to answer: that turned out to be secondary.

210

Because down there on the water, flickeringly visible through the rabid black air, was a chemical tanker. A small one, with a smooth, sealed hull like a submarine.

'Jesus Christ, already?' Halyard said. 'I thought we'd have more time!' But he realised Resaint wouldn't be able to make out a word he said through the escape hood.

And then he caught it. Even through the respirator. That swimming pool smell. Chlorine compounds rising off the water.

They were too late. The tanker was already discharging its contents into the sea.

They had to talk to Faun, Halyard thought. Tell her that there was no longer any need to bleach the kelp. Maybe she could turn off the spigot fast enough that the lumpsuckers might survive. Maybe there was still a chance.

He ran back into the safe room so that he could take off his hood and make the call. Because the door was propped open, the room was now swirling with yayflies, but it was still nowhere near as bad as outside. He was expecting Resaint to come back in with him, and as he told his scullion to call Faun, he was vaguely conscious that she hadn't yet.

Faun's scullion announced that Faun wasn't available. He shouted into his phone, demanding to talk to her, insisting that this was an emergency of the highest order. But the scullion wouldn't budge. Loose shreds of plastic from the escape hoods' packaging fluttered around the room as another spindrifter went by outside.

'I can't get through to Faun,' he called out to Resaint. But when he glanced in her direction, he couldn't see her. So he went to the doorway.

The deck was empty. Resaint had vanished.

And right away he understood that she had climbed over the railing and thrown herself into the sea.

She had smelled the chlorine, as he had. She had thought of the last lumpsuckers dying as the chlorine ate away their gills. And she had decided to die alongside them. Whatever baroque role she had hoped to play in the moral drama of their extinction, this wasn't it. But perhaps, to her, it was something.

Could he still save her? It was a long way down to the water from the deck. If he jumped over the railing, he could easily break a bone or knock himself unconscious. Even if the impact merely winded him, that would be no good, because he would be looking around for her in water that was murky with yayfly corpses and kelp mulch, and it wasn't as if he was much of a swimmer. He would need to be operating at the fullest extent of his limited powers if they were to have any hope at all.

And then he thought of the exosuit. Among its numerous tricks, it was supposed to be able to cushion the impact of a high dive.

As fast as he could he took off his shoes, socks and trousers. With his top half still fully clothed – he was in too much of a rush to think about the proper order of things – he grabbed the exosuit, shook out the legs, and put his left foot into the left leg hole.

But his leg didn't fit.

Of course the mermaid had a smaller calf measurement than he did, but he had assumed the exosuit would be one-size-fits-all. Surely the Japanese military didn't make these in twenty different sizes like a denim line.

'How the fuck do I get this on?' he said to his scullion.

'According to the specification,' his scullion replied, 'it is possible to resize the exosuit to the user's body by applying a mild electric current to the magnetite composite matrix.'

'And how do I do that?' he said, desperately conscious that Resaint's chances of survival, already slim, were narrowing further with every second that ticked by. How many more spindrifters had already sailed past in the time he'd been faffing around in here? Four? Five? Surely by now she would be sinking past the kelp lines.

'The specification contains no further information on the equipment or methodology—'

'Fuck fuck fuck fuck fuck!' Halyard realised he was just going to have to dive in and hope for the best. He shrugged off his jacket and unbuttoned his shirt, which billowed in the wind like laundry on a line. Obviously he couldn't wear the hood into the water, so he was nude now but for his boxer briefs. He pursed his lips, squinted his eyes, waited for this latest spindrifter to pass, and went back out into the yayflies.

Ecstatically they welcomed him, caressed him, showered him in kisses, all over his body. He moved with his head bowed, fists clenched, elbows pressed against the sides of his torso, as if he was being hosed down with ice water. He understood that the yayflies were really no more than windblown matter, that with the spindrifters so close they had no say at all in how they tumbled around, but it still felt as if they were trying eagerly to get inside him. He felt a wave of nausea that seemed to begin at the skin and clutch inward around his heart.

He reached the railing. Looking down through the yayflies towards the water, he could make out nothing at the foamy surface, no human outline, no thrashing limbs. He hoisted one leg over the top.

And then, just before he swung the rest of his body over, he felt a hand on his shoulder.

He turned his head, and was astonished to see Resaint standing there behind him. She said something he couldn't hear.

'What?'

She pulled her respirator aside so she could make herself understood through the plastic of the escape hood. 'I climbed up for a better look,' she said, pointing. He looked past her, and saw the hooped access ladder that ran in both directions from the deck, up towards the roof of the module and down towards the water.

He hadn't even noticed that there was a fucking ladder.

'I couldn't get through to Faun on the phone, but if we go back to her unit right now—'

'It's too late,' Resaint said. 'I saw the hoses retracting. The tanker's already empty.'

Chapter Fifteen

'What makes this even more humiliating,' Halyard said, buttoning his shirt, 'is that earlier this week I convinced myself that this guy had jumped into a canal, and it turned out I was wrong, and clearly I didn't learn any kind of lesson from that.' They had retreated into the safe room, closing the door behind them. Although there were a lot of yayflies buzzing around in here, the conditions outside made this feel, by comparison, like a sanctum of Alpine purity. 'Sorry, I realise that's not the point. I realise we've just lost the fish a second time. Or what is it by this point? Fifth?'

'Did you try to save him too?' Resaint said. She didn't want to think about the lumpsuckers. It didn't feel – at least in this moment – as if she'd lost them. It felt – and perhaps this was a self-protective reflex, her body refusing to take another blow – as if they'd never really been down there at all. The video footage from the maintenance drones, the excitement she'd felt in the café: just glimmers amounting to nothing, reported sightings of someone long since buried.

'Ismayilov? Well, no, I wasn't there when he didn't kill himself.'

'But if you had been.'

'Of course I would have tried.'

'You would have overruled him.'

'Yes. Obviously! Did you know that ninety per cent of people who make a failed attempt at suicide will never make a second attempt? Meaning ninety per cent of people are glad that something got in the way.' Halyard started looking around for his socks. 'You can't really be trying to imply that I would have been wrong to pull you out of the water?'

'To be specific about it, no. Because I would never try to kill myself that way. I hate the idea of drowning.' As the spindrifters wheeled past the deck, she hadn't felt the same panic that she had that night on the *Varuna*. It just wasn't as scary the second time. But that wasn't to say she was laid-back about the idea of actually plunging into the sea, as Halyard had been about to do. For all his crookedness, she had to admit that he had shown some real bravery, both today and back in the apple orchard. Maybe he was a better person when he didn't have time to think things over. 'Anyway, your statistic isn't relevant in my case. Because what I'm planning is not a suicide.'

'Yes, it is.'

'No, it isn't. I'm not suicidal. In a narrow sense my life is fine. Take the animals out of the equation and I would choose to live. I have no desire to be dead separate from my commitment to face some kind of justice.'

'I feel like I'm talking to a suicide bomber.' Halyard opened a nutrient shake and offered one to her as well, but she'd had a pastry in the café with Selim so she waved it off.

'Suicide bombers aren't suicidal,' she said. 'I mean in the psychiatric sense.'

'I bet a lot of them are, actually.'

'If I was suicidal – if the goal was just to exit, to pull the plug – then it wouldn't matter how I did it. I wouldn't be wasting all this time. I would have killed myself years ago by some other method.'

'Have you ever tried?' As he said this his tone was different, less contentious, more tentative. 'I mean is this really your first venture in that particular field?'

'I tried to slit my wrists when I was sixteen.'

She'd gone to a cemetery to do it. Not for any theatrical reason, but simply because it was unpoliced space. There was a girl from her school whose life had been saved when her parents had come home early and found her hanging from a wardrobe rail, and it was rumoured that now she had neurological problems because of the oxygen deprivation. No scenario could have been more chilling to Resaint, and she was determined to escape any such humiliations. The cemetery shut its gates around the time she finished school, and she had thought she could just climb over the fence and sit under a tree and nobody would interrupt her. Unfortunately, slitting her wrists turned out to be vastly more time-consuming than she'd anticipated. For over an hour she sat there sawing at them with a razor, watching them leak, fainting now and then, waking up to find that the cuts had already clotted, until at last she was discovered by two men, who called an ambulance and waited with her until it arrived. At the time she hadn't really thought to ask herself what the men were doing in the cemetery, so it wasn't until a few years later that it dawned on her they were probably there to have sex. By then she'd developed a sense of humour about the whole episode, but in the immediate aftermath the cemetery thing had been a real embarrassment, everyone at school thinking she was one of those girls who wanted to fall in love with a vampire.

'I can't believe this!' Halyard said. 'A few seconds ago you told me you're not suicidal and now I find out that actually you have a long history of suicide attempts.'

'Attempt.'

'This proves I'm right.'

'What do you mean?'

'You say the reason you want to die is that there's no other adequate response to what's happening with the animals. But you didn't start caring about the animals until pretty recently. And yet your desire to die predates that by years and years. So that proves what I've been saying – all this stuff about the animals is just a rationalisation, it's just ornamental, non-load-bearing, post hoc bullshit. You tried to kill yourself once, but the whole experience was a bit shambolic and demeaning, so instead of making a conventional second attempt you waited until you could come up with a gimmick that suits you better, meaning it's some ridiculously elaborate Nietzsche Dostoevsky Master's in Neural

216

Systems occult ritual martyrdom thing that nobody else would ever have thought of. And this explains your whole "extinction is worse than the Holocaust" manifesto. You put a low value on human existence because you put a low value on your own.'

'I don't see that what I did at sixteen invalidates anything,' Resaint said. 'I went through a reasoning process at one stage of life, and I went through another reasoning process at a later stage of life, and those reasoning processes started from different premises and they took different routes but they happened to reach the same endpoint. It doesn't prove that either of them is false, unless you've decided in advance that the endpoint is taboo. Anyway, perhaps the premises *weren't* entirely different. Perhaps back then I had already recognised something about the world. I just wasn't fully conscious yet of what it was that I'd recognised. I am fully conscious of it now.'

'My sister killed herself,' Halyard said. 'That's why I have a lot of suicide statistics in my back pocket.'

'I'm sorry,' Resaint said.

'She was nineteen. She bought a bunch of Xanax online and she took all of it at once with some vodka when the rest of us were away for the weekend. Officially it wasn't a suicide, officially she was just careless about the dosage. That's still what my parents think. But I know that's not true.' He explained that Frances, who used to pay $112 a year to rent a PO box so she didn't have to get darknet packages sent to their parents' house, was as meticulous in her drug abuse as she was ardent. She always researched everything in advance, the bodyweight ratios, the adverse interactions. She would never have overshot so far, plus she'd told him she didn't even like the Xanax high.

Anyway, Halyard said, he had been closer to her than anybody, and so he understood better than anybody what had led up to it. Frances was always adamant about maintaining appearances, and here she had transferrable skills. Much as she had redirected all her family's gourmandism towards the great catalogue of psycho-active molecules, Frances hid her deepening depression from their parents with the same consummate expertise that she'd developed

217

hiding her comedowns. And her brother, who had always quite enjoyed his role as accomplice in the latter, found himself, out of habit, an accomplice in the former. When she couldn't function he would do whatever he could to make sure nobody noticed. 'I thought I was helping. It never crossed my mind that it could actually end like that. I suppose I didn't have the imagination. Obviously I wish desperately that I'd . . . you know. All the clichés.'

'It sounds like she must have planned it all out in advance,' Resaint said.

'Maybe. I don't know.'

'So if you had saved her, do you think she would have been glad?'

'Jesus Christ,' Halyard said, 'I can't believe you would ask me that about my fucking *sister*! Are you fucking autistic?'

'People have asked me that before but I actually took an assessment once and no I am not.'

'That was a rhetorical question for which I apologise. Although I still think what you said was pathological. Are you going to tell me that whatever you "recognised about the world" when you were a teenager, my sister recognised too?'

'I couldn't possibly know.'

'She did used to talk about the climate a lot. But that wasn't it, with Frances. It wasn't about the world outside. You know, people talk about teenage girls killing themselves like it's this generic disease they get – you don't really need to *explain* it, any more than you need to explain acne or something – but with Frances, I'm not saying I understood it all that well, but it definitely felt very . . . specific. Specific to her. Like your thing feels specific to you.' Halyard looked at her for a long moment. 'Have you thought about it? Dying the way you want to die. Have you thought about what it would actually be like?'

Certainly, she had. She had run metabolic simulations which told her that to be sure of success she would need to introduce about a tablespoon of lumpsucker venom into her system, meaning she would need to be bitten by dozens of vengeful fish, each

218

delivering its microdose of poison from the glands behind its fangs. There were just a handful of descriptions of the lump-sucker's bite on record, blandly expressed in most cases as 'severe pain', 'extreme pain' and so forth; the only really vivid one was to be found in the memoir of an eminent Swedish astronomer, who recalled a boyhood incident of a fisherman from his village who had found the agony so unbearable that he had cut off his own finger. But the pain wouldn't last long. Inside her, the venom would be knocking loose enormous quantities of acetylcholine from her nerve cells, causing her organs to seize up. Very quickly she would drop dead, collapsing against the side of whatever pool or tank she had built for the purpose. Assuming the venom had the same effect on human beings that comparable compounds had on laboratory rabbits, then a post mortem would find the left side of her heart shut tight and the right side ballooned up with blood, while her lungs would be claggy with pink froth.

Whether Kazu Horikawa had ever endured a bite in the course of her work with the lumpsuckers there was no way to know, but on the *Varuna* Resaint had contemplated trying to goad one of her experimental subjects into nipping her just once, so she could find out what it was like. In the end, she decided it was safer not to. Pain could make a coward of you; the experience might weaken her resolve. And her resolve was to be nursed day and night. If she ever felt it slipping – if the thought of that blood lather in her windpipe ever began to frighten her – the cure was a documentary about Jane Goodall's early years among the chimpanzees of Tanzania. She'd seen it so many times already that often just a twenty-minute refresher was enough. To be taken back to the 1960s, when it was still possible for a human being to face a wild animal without grief, without shame, without any inkling of the Black Hole gaping wider and wider – to compare that innocence with the present day, when almost every such contact was soaked through with horror and loss – that was all it took to restore to her an iron determination. Wittgenstein, when he was contemplating suicide, had summed up the mindset as 'the state of not being able to get over a particular fact.' As she'd said so many times to Halyard, she wasn't suicidal – and yet that fit her pretty well. *Everything was broken.* The only remaining valid actions were those taken in reaction to that fact, and they were valid only in proportion to the honesty and completeness of the reaction.

'If you really think the lumpsucker is just my suicide instrument,' she said to Halyard, 'if you're really so concerned about that – it's funny that you're here giving me every assistance in obtaining this suicide instrument, just because you think it will bail you out in the short term.'

'Actually, it won't,' Halyard said. 'Bail me out, I mean. Brahmasamudram found out about the missing credits. It's too late to cover it up. I'm fucked regardless.'

'So why did you come here?'

'I came to find the mermaid. Dr Shahad told me she knows a big secret about the biobank attacks. I was thinking maybe that could flip everything around for me.' He hesitated. 'The truth is I already knew Gareth wouldn't be here. I talked to him back at the camp. He didn't have any useful intel about the lumpsucker. I didn't want to tell you.'

'Why not?'

'Because if I had, you would probably have gone home.' He didn't meet her eye as he said this, and it was with what looked like a shudder of relief that he grabbed for his phone to answer a call. Frankly, she was relieved too. 'Hello?' He listened for a little while. 'She's *what*?'

*

By now, even Resaint thought of her as the mermaid. And this time the mermaid had a tail. It was gummy and translucent, like cervical mucus or that glue that held the cans together in a six-pack, beginning at her chest and flaring out beneath in dribbles and frills, a petticoat of slime rooting her to the floor. Her arms were lashed awkwardly to her upper body, which was tilted a little way forward, as she'd been snared mid-stride and now her legs weren't in the right place for her to stand comfortably with a straight back. There were also gobbets of protein slime in her

220

hair, and others on the walls and floor of the corridor. She was, understandably, glowering. At a cautious distance around her stood a small crowd, most of them in masks and goggles – their postures, as they regarded this creature who'd somehow sneaked into their world, full of the wonder and disquiet you would feel if you had caught a real mermaid in your eel trap and she was snarling back at you with her sharky teeth. The crowd included one guy who Halyard introduced to her with some reverence as Sanny Warkentin – 'He grew that tuna I was telling you about!' – and another who Warkentin pointed out to them in turn as Ovet Ganf, the head of the executive committee, hatched at last from his neurofeedback orb. Judging from his tortured body language, it had done absolutely nothing for his stress levels.

It was Warkentin who had summoned Halyard here, knowing he was looking for an interloper on Surface Wave. The three of them moved off a short distance to confer. Here they were within sight of the bridge to Module 3 – the mermaid hadn't got very far before the security system mired her in place. There wasn't yet any noticeable thinning of the yayflies on the other side of the glass. Even after the exhaust flue had slammed shut, there were so many already in the air that the wind could keep juggling them for a long time to come.

'I need to talk to her,' Halyard said.

'I expect Ganf is going to put her on the next boat to the mainland,' Warkentin said. 'He'll want this over with as soon as possible.'

'Are you confident that she'll want to talk to you?' Resaint said. 'She doesn't seem like someone who's looking for a lot of publicity.'

'I still have this.' Halyard hoisted the backpack, borrowed from one of the safe room's cabinets, that now held the Japanese exosuit. 'I can trade it back to her.'

'Is that going to be enough?'

Perhaps unconsciously he touched the swelling on his lip where she'd slugged him earlier. 'Well, what if we could really help her? I don't think she'll want to go to the mainland. That's why she was hiding out in the module. What if we could offer her the chance to stay here? Then she'd have an incentive to talk to us.' To Warkentin: 'Could you naturalise her somehow?'

'You mean like . . . marry her?'

'No, I mean say she's a customer or something. That's how we got here.'

Warkentin shook his head. 'She's refusing to identify herself. And the security system won't approve her as a visitor unless it has at least a basic idea of who she is.' With a sly half-smile, he added, 'But I could claim her as a stray asset.'

'What do you mean?'

'I could say she's property of mine that came from my lab.'

'She's a human being, not an office chair,' Resaint said.

'She's human-*shaped*. But say somebody on Surface Wave has grown or assembled something human-shaped in the course of their work. Say one of these human-shaped things gets loose somehow, and the security system immobilises it, and the owner claims it and takes it back to their lab. That's not a scenario that's ever happened before, as far as I know, but we have pretty broad-minded protocols here and they anticipate a lot of eventualities and certainly that would be one of them.' As Warkentin was speaking, Resaint watched one of the figures in respirator masks approach the mermaid from behind with some sort of handheld diagnostic tool. He held it to her upper arm for a moment and she blinked at the prick of the needle.

'Is Ganf really going to go for that?' Halyard said. 'It's a very obvious lie.'

'Doesn't matter. If I claim her as a stray asset from my lab, that makes all of this so much easier to assimilate. There was no disturbing and unprecedented security breach. There was just a minor incident that was readily resolved according to established protocols. That's everything Ganf wants most – especially given how unpopular he is at the moment.'

'You're prepared to do that?'

'Why not? It won't cost me anything.'

'How many people on Surface Wave are growing human-shaped things in their labs?' said Resaint.

Warkentin shrugged. 'I wouldn't want to put a number on it.'

He went over to talk to Ganf. An agreement was struck. And soon afterwards another tool was aimed at the mermaid, this one looking more like a paint sprayer. From its nozzle puffed little clouds of what must have been some sort of powerful desiccant, because as soon as the powder made contact with the mucus, the latter turned matte and cloudy like a blinded eye. As the dryness penetrated deeper, the mucus cracked and flaked until the woman was able to work her arms free. She peeled the rest of it away from her body, a sculpture tearing itself loose from a mould, and when at last she stepped out from the cone of glue, her bare feet were red from its grip. Withered and empty, the cone looked as if it could have been miscooked from the same elements as the city itself, Surface Wave's ivory polymers erupting into a mortifying pimple.

The mermaid began picking clots out of her hair, and Halyard made his inevitable remark about how there were people with very specific interests who would pay a lot to watch what they'd just watched.

*

She was a minister, she told them.

'Like a priest?' Halyard said.

'No, I'm a government minister. I'm the Secretary of State for Environment, Food and Rural Affairs.'

They were sitting in the office area of Warkentin's lab, Halyard with a bottle of Põhjala in front of him and the other three with cups of matcha tea. Resaint had noticed a pattern in the woman's reactions, first when Warkentin offered her a chair and then when he offered her the tea, a sharp mistrustful look displaced quickly by a graceful smile, as if she saw poison and booby traps in every gesture of hospitality but that still wasn't enough to overcome her reflexive good manners.

'OK, that's very funny,' Halyard said, 'but we agreed you'd tell us the truth. I don't want to sound like a prick but if it wasn't for us they would have had you walking the plank by now. Not literally but you know what I mean.'

'That is the truth.'

'You're saying you're a government minister of the Hermit Kingdom?'

'It would be politer not to call it that in my presence,' the mermaid said. 'But yes, I am. Or I was, until recently. I can only assume that by now I've been sacked for absenteeism.'

'So why does nothing come up when I run a search on your face?'

'Other than the Prime Minister, no photos of senior government officials are made available to the public. And any previous traces are scrubbed. Hard as it may be for you to imagine, I do not exist on the internet.'

'And why would a government minister be drifting around the Baltic like a message in a bottle?'

'Several months ago I learned of a plan to sell most of the South West Peninsula to Ferenc Barka. The Antichain man.'

With these words came a disjuncture, a resetting of the atmosphere in the room, as if some deep background hum had suddenly fallen to dead silence. Believe me or don't believe me, the mermaid's tone said, take it or leave it, but please don't keep hectoring, because it's too tiresome. After a long pause, Resaint was the first to speak. 'What's the South West Peninsula?'

'It's the limb that protrudes from the southwest corner of the country. Some of the splendidest turf on God's green earth. Barka has taken Cornwall, Devon and part of Somerset. Everything west of Taunton, about four and a half thousand square miles in total. By now almost two million people who lived there have been resettled in north Wales.'

'How much does it cost to buy four and a half thousand square miles of inhabited land from your government?' Halyard said.

'It goes without saying that such a sale shouldn't be possible, but even supposing you could assess a fair price, Barka got it for a small fraction of that. The whole transaction was fundamentally corrupt. He promised to make certain people very rich.'

'He paid them off?'

'Not exactly, no. He warned them in advance that somebody was going to sabotage all the big biobanks. So they were able to

224

borrow money from the Treasury and buy up all the extinction credits they could.' Resaint saw Halyard's eyes widen. 'Has it happened yet? The sabotage?'

'Yes, on Monday night.'

'And the price of extinction credits has gone up?'

'Yes, a lot.'

'Then no doubt they will have made a killing.'

'And you weren't one of the beneficiaries?' Resaint said.

The mermaid shook her head. 'Despite this sale entailing the alienation of thousands of square miles of farmland and woodland, I was kept in the dark until it was well underway. Even if I had known, I wouldn't have shoved my snout in the trough like some of my Honourable Friends. As I said, such a sale shouldn't be possible. It's an outrageous betrayal of our sovereignty. I wanted no part in it.'

'So should I take it that this has something to do with your current situation?' Halyard said.

'You should.'

'You tried to blow the whistle?'

'No. I merely considered it. For weeks I thought very hard about my duties to the Crown, and my duties to Parliament, and my duties to God. But I took no action. Then one day I received a quiet warning from a friend. I was being looked at.'

'Looked at?'

'That's what we say when someone has been identified as a budding traitor. I still ask myself, how on earth could they have known? As I said, I had taken no action. I had said nothing to anyone. Of course, it's possible that I gave myself away somehow. A sour look in a meeting. Or it's possible that it was just a lucky guess. But what I think is likeliest is that Barka gave some operational assistance to his partners in the Cabinet. I'm told his algorithms can be really quite perspicacious, verging on the telepathic. In any event, I knew there and then that I would have to take some rather wrenching steps. Once you're being looked at in that way, it's very rare that the gaze passes benignly onward. I was sure that my Honourable Friends wouldn't take any chances when they had such a monumental racket to protect, and I didn't have enough real allies among them to rely on any last-minute intercession. What I saw in my future was the tiled room underneath Thames House. From then on things felt awfully drastic. I began to think about all sorts of escapes. I considered everything. I even considered the United States.'

Everybody but her looked at the floor. The avoidance of any direct reference to that country – a custom adopted in the late 2020s out of sheer embarrassment – was these days so strictly observed that for Resaint it was genuinely startling to hear somebody say the words. But of course in the Hermit Kingdom they would not have the same modes of etiquette.

'Instead,' the mermaid went on, 'I made for Rostock.'

In Rostock, she explained, lived Eckhard, an old flame from her student days. They'd met during her Christmas holidays, at an après-ski bar in Garmisch, when Eckhard had recognised one of the friends she was with from some European Young Conservatives event he'd attended. She'd always avoided the political clubs at Oxford, finding them too full of clammy strivers and the prematurely middle-aged, but it was Eckhard, a dissident member of the Junge Union Deutschlands, who convinced her to reconsider. In that sense she owed her career to him. Their attempt at a long-distance relationship didn't last long, but they always stayed in touch, even as they both married, and divorced, other people. His political work was mostly rooted on the coast where he grew up, but hers took her to Germany once in a while, and even after the changes in her country she was still able to maintain uncensored communications with him using the privileges of her office. She knew she could trust him. When she realised she was going to have to flee her old life, she sent him an encrypted message, begging for help. He wrote back immediately inviting her to stay with him in Rostock.

Nobody but Eckhard could know she had arrived on the Continent. She didn't want any foreign government to scoop her up for either propaganda or intelligence purposes, and she certainly didn't want to be targeted by overseas agents of her own side. So

226

even over there she would have to behave like a fugitive, at least until she found a solid footing. Which meant no border crossings, no surveillance grids. She agreed to rendezvous with Eckhard in the Leyhörn, a nature reserve in East Frisia that looked out on to the estuary dividing Germany from Holland.

The Ministry of Defence had a subsidiary, the Defence Science and Technology Laboratory, which in theory was devoted to researching advanced weapons technology but which in practice was devoted to acquiring advanced weapons technology on the black market and copying it as closely as possible. Even in this it had few successes, but it did possess quite a treasure cave of scavenged ordnance. She was well aware of this because about a year ago her own department had been dragged into some argy-bargy after the crash of an MoD lorry on its way from Porton Down had necessitated the immediate culling of over a million chickens from nearby farms. By way of smoothing things over, the Defence Secretary had taken her out for a ride in a Russian walking tank with one gammy leg.

So she concocted a story; called in a favour; arranged an inter-departmental loan. And after smuggling the Japanese exosuit home in her gym bag, she spent an evening puzzling out the controls. There was a startling moment when quite by accident she selected something called Maintenance Function 4 and the exosuit began to undulate on her kitchen table like the death throes of a stranded eel, sine waves rolling down its limbs.

A few days later, in the small hours of the morning, she waded into the ocean at Horsey Beach, just up the coast from Great Yarmouth. She was hauling with her a waterborne drone designed for monitoring salmon farms, and she had strapped herself to this drone using a workman's safety harness and two long rope lanyards.

Once she was far enough out, she lay down in the water and commanded the drone to tug her to Germany.

'How far is that?' Resaint said.

'A hair over two hundred miles,' the mermaid said. 'Travelling about eighty miles a day behind my little sled dog. I know it sounds rather ambitious. But I had to be ambitious. They'd already peered inside my thoughts once. I decided that if I was going to get out safely, I had to take a tack they would never, ever, in a thousand years anticipate. I'm sure a lot of people in my predicament would have tried to wriggle out of it in some brainy, strategic fashion. No doubt that's just what would have been expected of me. So I thought it was better to try something rather crude and straightforward. And a boat would have raised alarms.' She sipped her tea. 'Anyway, I liked the idea of it. I grew up on quite a large estate in Norfolk and I was a sort of Palaeolithic child, *Swallows and Amazons* but even muddier. I've aways enjoyed a physical trial. Which it certainly was. Even though you aren't the one doing the swimming, the sea does wear you out. Fortunately the clever Japanese kit made the experience a great deal more bearable. And there are no mines in the North Sea any more. Or almost none.'

Eckhard found her lying amid the Leyhörn's salt marsh grass like a poorly-disposed-of corpse, half sunk into the cold sludge, barnacle geese flocking overhead. She'd been there for three hours already, but it had taken him that long to track down the wireless signal from her exosuit. He helped her to his car and shut her in the boot, then he went back for the drone and put it in the back seat. She'd consumed nothing on the journey but a carbohydrate drink for long-distance runners, slurped through a tube from a vinyl bladder stowed inside the drone, and when she took her first bite of one of the Nutella sandwiches Eckhard had left for her in the boot, she let out a sob. Then she slept most of the way to Rostock. 'Up until then,' she said, 'everything had gone quite smoothly.'

*

Since his divorce Eckhard had lived in an apartment complex built on top of a chunk of reclaimed land in Rostock Harbour. He was lending her the master bedroom, because it had an en suite, and had moved himself into the guest room. It was some time since she'd set foot in a home like this, a modern one, where the floors and the tabletops and the cabinets were all much too shiny. The accent colour throughout was the royal blue of the FC Hansa Rostock crest: mugs, cushions, blankets, a huge framed print of the stadium rendered in watercolours. When she took a hot bath she found he even had a rubber duck wearing the team strip and a mariner's cap.

There was a strange moment early on when she came out of the bedroom wearing Eckhard's dressing gown. He looked her up and down and an expression came over his face as if something wasn't quite right. After that his manner changed. He became sullen, distracted, hardly looking in her direction as they had supper together.

Absurdly – perhaps because Eckhard always put her in mind of her younger self – it took her back to an experience from her late teenage years, when she'd gone up for the first time to visit her boyfriend, the one before Eckhard, at his Oxford college. On the phone he'd seemed excited, but almost from the beginning he was cold and resentful. She didn't understand what she'd done wrong and she felt helpless in her reliance on his hospitality. After a sexless night she took a train home early because it was so obvious he was about to break up with her. That was what this was like.

And the next morning, when she got up, she found she couldn't open the door of the bedroom.

The door had no keyhole, but it had an electronic lock. So perhaps this was a technical mix-up. She called out Eckhard's name. Through the door, she could hear him moving around the living room, but he didn't respond.

She carried on shouting for him, but still no voice came back from the other room – except, after a while, what must have been a football commentator talking over crowd noises on TV, the volume turned up very loud. Finally, around noon, she said, 'Eckhard, please, I'm hungry.'

Through the door: 'What do you want to eat?'

'I don't care. Anything. But could you please let me out? I don't understand what's going on.'

She heard him clattering around in the kitchen for a little while. Then he returned. 'Go into the bathroom, please.'

'Why?'

'I need to open the door and I don't want you to hit me or anything.'

'I won't hit you, Eckhard.' In fact she certainly would have.

'Please, go into the bathroom.'

'For goodness' sake. All right.'

She waited. After a while Eckhard said, 'You haven't gone into the bathroom.'

It was true. She hadn't. 'How do you know?'

'The apartment knows. I can see on my phone. It says nobody is in there.'

'My God, Eckhard, do you have cameras spying on me?' How naïve of her to think she could entirely avoid surveillance grids.

'No, no, no, I disconnected all the security cameras before you arrived. But the apartment still knows if someone's in the bathroom. There are sensors.'

'For what possible reason?'

'In case somebody is in there using the toilet or getting out of the shower,' Eckhard said, 'then it warns you before you try to open the door.'

'But you live on your own.'

'Yes, well, the system came as standard with the apartment.'

In the rest of the world they said that her own country, in holding itself aloof, had given up decades of 'progress'. Oh, what a terribly grave loss, she thought. Now, doing as she was bid, she went into the bathroom. From there, she listened as the bedroom door quickly opened and closed. The protocol worked as intended, in that she wouldn't have been able to get across the room in time to interfere. When she came out, she found a plate on the floor bearing some sort of microwave baguette with pizza toppings. No cutlery.

'Eckhard, how long is this going to last?' she said.

'I am really sorry,' he said, sounding pained. 'I am really very sorry.'

'Just for this, or for something else that's going to happen?'

'You were the one who said I would be on the . . . you know, the *Weltbühne*. The world stage.' She was taken aback, not only because it seemed like such a non sequitur but also because she was almost sure she hadn't used any such words since she arrived. But then she realised she must have said this to him years ago, decades, perhaps as far back as their first days together in Garmisch. Indeed, at that time, they had each been confident in predicting a spectacular ascent for the other. But only his prediction for her came true. Not hers for him. He was still in Rostock, working for the local branch of Alternative für Deutschland. It wasn't even the capital of the state.

'Well, you're involved in something rather sensational now, Eckhard. This doesn't happen every day. A government minister jumping the fence.'

'Yes, I am *involved*, but . . . It is not enough for me to be just *involved*. I need to be the . . . you know, the engine, the vital person. I am fifty-four. This is my last chance. You are my last chance.'

'For what?'

'For . . . importance. You know that the party is making links with your people?'

She did know that. Her government had broken off diplomatic relations with their counterparts in the Federal Republic but it had an increasingly chatty back channel to the opposition. And all at once she understood. Eckhard was going to give her to the AfD and the AfD were going to give her back to her own government. What the AfD would get out of this, she couldn't know – perhaps she was to be a gift of friendship, a champagne toast to seal some memorandum of understanding. But what Eckhard would get out of it, he'd made perfectly clear. 'Importance.' The lofty future he'd imagined for himself when he was grandstanding at all those European Young Conservatives summits as a young man – well, he couldn't seriously think that was still possible, but at least the higher-ups at the AfD would know his name.

'When are they coming for me?' she said. When Eckhard had told her that he'd disconnected all the security cameras in the apartment, he had used a reassuring tone, but now she wondered whether it was really for the sake of her privacy or to ensure that afterwards there would be no trace she had ever been here, not even in the deepest depths of the servers where they kept the footage they claimed they weren't recording.

'I am still working things out with them.'

'Why wait until now?' He could have just delivered her straight to them, she thought. What on earth was the point of this awkward stop-over in his apartment?

'You must understand that this was a really difficult decision for me,' Eckhard said. 'Really very difficult.'

Which seemed to imply that he hadn't fully made up his mind until she got here. She remembered that expression on his face as she came out of the bedroom. Perhaps he had expected a cinematic transformation, the damp rag he'd picked out of the marsh emerging after a hot bath as the twenty-year-old he'd met that night in Garmisch. Perhaps he had been horrified, seeing her in person for the first time in years, to find that she had grown almost as old as he had. In which case he might have made his approach to the leadership after she went to sleep last night. And at this moment they might still be haggling over terms.

She had to get out before the AfD arrived to pick her up. Otherwise it was back to London, and then the tiled room underneath Thames House. Or possibly even something more public. Depending on how the PM was feeling.

In the early afternoon – which was as long as she felt she could risk waiting – she called out, 'Eckhard, may I have some *Florentiner*?' Meaning almond brittle in milk chocolate.

Through the door: 'I'm sorry. I don't have any.'

'Could I possibly persuade you to get some for me, then? Do you remember, I tried it for the first time with you, at that wonderful konditorei in Garmisch?'

'Krönner.'

'That's right. I've always associated it with this country. I was looking forward to eating heaps of it. We can't get things like that at home, and of course in this case, when I get back – well, I don't like to think about it, but they'll hardly be wheeling out the pudding trolley for me, will they, Eckhard? So this is really my last chance. I know I sound like a little girl but I would so much like to taste *Florentiner* one last time. And it doesn't have to be that lovely special kind from Krönner. Any approximation will do.'

'Yes, of course,' he said. 'I will have some delivered.' He sounded happy about it, as if he thought it would go some way towards compensating for what he had done.

'Thank you, Eckhard.'

About half an hour later she heard Eckhard go out of the apartment and then come back in. Presumably this was him picking up the almond brittle from the *Drohnenpaketaufzug* (the quintessentially German coinage for the dumbwaiter in the corridor that brought down deliveries from the drone landing pad on the roof). Sure enough, he knocked on her door. 'Go into the bathroom, please.'

'Must we really go through this silly performance again?'

'I cannot open the door until I know you are in there.'

'Oh, all right.'

She shut the door of the en suite. Eckhard opened the door of the bedroom. And as he was placing the box of *Florentiner* on the floor, she stepped out from behind the bedroom door and hit him over the head with an FC Hansa Rostock sixtieth anniversary commemorative mantel clock.

Earlier, she had taken jumpers and T-shirts and pants out of Eckhard's chest of drawers and shoved them inside the Japanese exosuit, stuffing the limbs and the torso until it bulged like a Guy Fawkes full of straw. Then, when Eckhard was at the bedroom door, she had taken her effigy into the bathroom and activated the exosuit's Maintenance Function 4. What the intended purpose of Maintenance Function 4 might be, she still couldn't guess. But this time, fattened with fabric, the exosuit was like a life-size puppet made to perform a lewd hip-swaying dance. As she propped it

233

against the wall, slipping one of its arms through a towel ring to keep it upright, it seemed to frot itself clumsily upon her. Even in the circumstances it was quite hard not to giggle.

Of course, she wouldn't know until the final moment whether this would be enough to convince Eckhard's bathroom that it was occupied by a living breathing person. Would the sensors really be so easily fooled?

Apparently they would.

And Eckhard too. She'd made a fuss about the *Florentiner* because she'd wanted him to let his guard down. Even if they'd spent many years in politics, people never quite got over their surprise that you were betraying them as they were right in the middle of doing you a particularly generous favour. Then again, she couldn't fault Eckhard for his innocence. She'd shown the same failing in coming here.

Looking down at Eckhard as he lay there across the threshold of the bedroom, she decided she ought to thump him with the clock a second time to be absolutely sure he was out cold. And strangely, it was this second blow – not the desperate, split-second opener but the leisurely, judicious follow-up – that had the really messy result. Now blood was slopping from the gash in his forehead. She had never had any thought of killing Eckhard, but this looked to her like the sort of head injury that could end him unless somebody came to his aid.

That somebody was not going to be her.

Instead, she went back into the bathroom, where she found that the exosuit had gyrated itself on to the floor. She deactivated the Maintenance Function, shook out all the clothes, and put it back on, to become, once again, a living silhouette.

Downstairs, at the door of the building, she passed a man with a baby in a papoose, and he looked her over quizzically. Although his were just one set of eyes, fleetingly curious, they made her think of all the sets of eyes that would now be searching her out. Eckhard's friends at the AfD, who might already be on their way here to take delivery of her, supposing a deal had been struck by the time the almond brittle arrived; the German police, if Eckhard woke up and set them on her in retribution, or if he did not wake up but his body was discovered; and above all Ferenc Barka, who would surely be assisting her ministerial colleagues in tracking down the only security breach serious enough to threaten their wonderful joint venture.

The surveillance apparatus of her own government, despite its vast and ever-swelling dimensions, was generally about as sharp-sighted and dependable as the sensors in Eckhard's bathroom. But the eyes of Antichain, she knew, were not like that. Indeed, it was hardly fitting to speak of eyes, the metaphor of the sense organ implying some narrow transmission between outer world and inner. It might be more accurate to imagine Antichain as an all-permeating brain, and reality itself encompassed *within* that brain. On top of all the data that Antichain were actually contracted to administer – perhaps on behalf of Rostock Port, or Leyhörn Nature Reserve, or Eckhard's apartment complex – there was all the proprietary data they could license and all the public data they could crawl; and from end to end this omnitude of data had no two indicators that Antichain's algorithms could not connect if out of their connection some new indicator might be born. From the beat of a wing and the drip of a tap, might Ferenc Barka already have divined where she was?

In front of her was a playground, wooden structures of obscure function poking out of sand and sedge grass like the ruins of some far outpost. The playground was ringed by mid-rises, and through the gap between two of these mid-rises there was water, and beyond that the trees of another shore. Hurrying in that direction, she came to a concrete wharf, with steps leading down to what must have been an inlet of the Unterwarnow. Throughout this ordeal she had maintained what she thought of, vainly per-haps, as a characteristic calm; but now for the first time she felt her insides rippling like the exosuit on her kitchen table.

She walked down the steps to the edge of the wharf. She low-ered herself into the water. And then, like one of those lost dol-phins who sometimes wandered up the Thames, she began to swim back out towards the ocean. Through the fog of panic in

235

her mind she could make out the nation of Denmark. Nobody would know she was in Denmark.

The seven or eight miles of the Unterwarnow proved absolutely achievable, even if at one point she nearly got run over by a ferry. But then, past the two long piers that pincered the mouth of the harbour, she came to the Baltic itself. And very soon she realised that she had overreached. The distance between Rostock and the southern tip of Denmark was short enough that she had a dim recollection of a proposal to build a bridge across it; Eckhard had been opposed because of the traffic. But she didn't have her salmon farm drone, and she didn't have anything to eat or drink, and her muscles still ached from the previous day. Even in the exo-suit's embrace, she didn't believe she could make it.

Yet she refused to go back where she came from. That was doom.

And then, on the grey horizon, she caught sight of what she thought at first must have been an offshore wind turbine. Except that there wasn't just one shaft rising out of the water. There were three.

*

'That was you!' Resaint said. 'That was you on the spindrifter!' Halyard looked at her, confused. 'On Monday night,' she explained, 'when I was on the *Varuna*, a spindrifter passed right by us, sailing south. And I saw somebody in the window. There was somebody on board.'

'Wait, so you two have already met?' said Warkentin. He had been listening with an unblinking, dopaminergic attentiveness, the attentiveness of somebody for whom any information-rich encounter was a stimulant worth licking out the corners of the bag.

'Hardly,' Resaint said. 'I only got a glimpse.'

'Yes,' said the mermaid. 'That must have been me.' On the windless morning she escaped into the Baltic, the spindrifter had been moving slowly enough that she had been able to swim right up to it. And then, apparently noticing her presence and taking her for a castaway, it had come to a stop – the hum of its turbines falling silent – and flipped open a hatch in its base. Climbing inside, she found herself in a tiny cabin, which looked as if nobody had ever set foot in it before. The boxes of vanilla nutrient bars she found there were seven years past their expiration date, but when she ate one it tasted no more repugnant than one would normally expect such a thing to taste. There was also a tap dispensing filtered sea-water, along with a first-aid kit and a thermal blanket and so on. And on the wall beside the bed was a touchscreen, presumably intended for sending distress signals, except that any attempt to interact with it was met with a demand to 'install security update 2032-004'. Which was quite all right: she didn't want to send any distress signals anyway.

'They say, don't they, of the fish that swallowed Jonah, that its eyes were like windows, and the pearls inside it shone like lamps, and the roof of its belly was like a synagogue's? Well, the third of those doesn't apply – I couldn't stand up straight without knocking my head on the ceiling – but all the same I would agree with Jonah that the inside of one of these sea-beasts can be really surprisingly comfortable, especially when you're feeling rather buffeted by circumstance. And not only comfortable but safe. Even if Barka had sent out a whole swarm of drones to comb the Baltic for me – even if these drones could see through walls – I would still have been all right in there, because no drone will dare get near a spindrifter in case the spindrifter huffs and puffs it out of the air. So I decided to stay as long as I possibly could. By the time the emergency rations ran out I planned to have developed some sort of system for fishing. I knew eventually I would have to decide what to do next but I didn't see any urgency in that regard.

'About a month went by,' she continued. 'We tootled around the Baltic. I was never quite sure where we were, although once I saw the Northern Lights so we must have been pretty far up towards Lapland. And then one morning something changed. I'd been on board long enough that I felt it at once. All of a sudden the spindrifter seemed to be moving with intent. We were racing south.'

Resaint broke in. 'That was when Nathan – he's a boy from the Tinkanen camp – that was when he hacked into the spindrifters.'

'Well, of course I had no idea what was going on. And the next day I began to see other spindrifters moving alongside us. That troubled me. That meant something unusual was underway. For another few hours I prevaricated, but by the time my houseboat turned east, I was quite convinced. At long last somebody was calling the spindrifters to port. They were going to be decommissioned or readapted or something of that nature. So I decided I had better disembark. Which I did. And while I was bobbing around in the Gulf of Finland, wondering what to do next, I was discovered by dear Gareth.'

'The way he told it,' Halyard said, 'you called out to him for help.'

'I can assure you I did not,' the mermaid said. 'But I must admit that after a month without seeing another human face I wasn't quite as cautious as perhaps I should have been. I accepted a lift.'

'Did you know where he was taking you?'

'He told me about the camp on the way.'

'Weren't you worried about getting recognised? All those people from home?'

'Not in the least. As I said, no photos of senior government officials are ever offered. Now, I admit some do trickle out nevertheless. For instance, I'm told that pictures of the Home Secretary have been illegally disseminated to such an extent that by now his appearance is common knowledge. Fortunately for me, however, there is no comparable hunger among the public for a good hard look at the Secretary of State for Environment, Food and Rural Affairs. I knew nobody would recognise me. And anyway, I soon realised there was a very good reason for me to drop into the camp.'

'Kaptcha,' Resaint said, understanding at once.

'Correct.'

'That's why you broke into the medical centre. You were hoping they'd have a live sample of kaptcha somewhere. You wanted to infect yourself so no facial recognition camera could ever identify you again.'

'It was the most robust defence I could think of against Ferenc Barka.'

'But Dr Shahad caught you,' Halyard said.

'Indeed. But I already had what I'd come for.'

'She told me nothing was stolen.'

'Perhaps because she only took an inventory of the sorts of thing you'd expect someone to steal – not vials of mould. And I chose to keep her in the dark, notwithstanding her generosity in letting me go. By this time I'd learned that we were only a stone's throw from Surface Wave. And, as a person interested above all in the preservation of my freedom, Surface Wave sounded enormously appealing. No gods, no masters. A sort of Casablanca. All the same, I knew I couldn't just present myself at the front gate. And when I saw all those ghastly insects streaming out of that outbuilding, I thought to myself, "A pound to a penny, either nobody can get inside to stop that infestation, or nobody wants to." So if I could slither in through a crack, I should find myself undisturbed. Now, when I tell you that I was looking for a retreat as similar to the spindrifter as possible, it was nevertheless rather a blow to find that, after the runner's potion in the North Sea, and the flavoured cardboard on the spindrifter, I would be living on yet more baby food for the foreseeable future. Those awful "shakes". But of course I was lucky to have anything at all. And in any event, the foreseeable future wasn't very long, was it? Only about a day and a half. Because you found me.'

'But how did you get in?' Resaint said.

'From below. Those drones tending the seaweed – I watched them long enough to see they were making deliveries. So I held my breath and followed one of them down to the tradesmen's entrance.'

Halyard sighed. 'Recently I've been sort of flirting with the idea of becoming an international fugitive. But this has made me realise I definitely don't have what it takes. It's like when I thought I could get into kickboxing. Can we go back a bit, though?' he said as Warkentin poured more matcha tea. 'You told us Ferenc Barka's buying the South West Peninsula. But you never explained why. I mean, what's he going to do with all that space? Build a million-hole golf course?'

'He's establishing a nature reserve.'

'Really?' Halyard said. 'Is there a lot of wildlife down there?'

'Not for native animals. For imported ones. Barka is filling the peninsula with endangered and extinct species.'

These words were utterly unexpected; and yet the problem with Barka's category of youngish billionaire was that these people had so many hobbies and side-projects, they were so driven and broad-minded, they were such consummate Renaissance men, that as with some spoiled, precocious nephew who wouldn't shut up about his go-karting and his cartooning and his fucking robotics, it was impossible to greet the announcement of any new adventure with anything other than reflexive boredom and distaste.

'Like Sanctuary North?' Halyard said.

But if all this was true, Resaint thought, then really it was more like the Nazi plan for Ukraine – annexing entire provinces for aurochs and tarpans. 'Why is he doing this?' she said.

'That I can't answer.'

'We know Barka had advance warning of the biobanks attacks,' said Halyard excitedly. 'Maybe he saw that he wouldn't be able to prevent them. So instead he decided to build this nature reserve. Somewhere he could do it in almost complete secrecy. So that when everyone thought the last traces of these extinct species were wiped away, they wouldn't actually be wiped away. In fact, the species wouldn't even be extinct. They'd be living in witness protection in the arse end of the Hermit Kingdom.'

'Ferenc Barka is one of the most powerful men in the world,' Resaint said. 'If he knew about the attacks before they happened, there must have been *something* he could have done. At the very least he could have warned people.'

'We can't be sure, can we? We still don't know who was responsible for the attacks. Didn't Nathan say their methods were so advanced they must have been time travellers?'

'He said there were people online saying that.'

'Maybe a warning would have been futile,' Halyard said. 'Maybe he had no choice but to make these big bold moves behind the scenes.'

'Are you one of those people who thinks Ferenc Barka is actually quite cool?' It was a source of some embarrassment to Resaint that she'd ever applied for that Antichain Machine Learning Residency, and a source of some dismay that the bearded data baron had taken to wearing a jacket by her favourite Korean designer at some of his public appearances. However, Barka attracted a disturbing degree of hero worship from guys like Halyard who were happy to overlook his unchecked megalomania and his complicity in ethnic cleansing because he had a cocky demeanour and an awesome collection of submarines.

'Oh, as if you're not on his side here?' Halyard said. 'Displacing two million people to make room for a few semi-defunct animals? Isn't that exactly your political alignment?'

'Not just a few,' the mermaid said. 'Almost eighty thousand.'

'That's ridiculous,' Halyard said. 'That's impossible. That's way more than they've ever had in the biobanks.'

'I have a list. All the animals and the locations of their new homes. It doesn't prove anything outright, of course, but I should hope it adds some substance to the assertion.'

'Can we see it?'

The mermaid gave one of her cold aristocratic smiles. 'Before I left Whitehall for the last time, I uploaded the list to a server overseas. Along with a number of other files. Because I couldn't think of anything else I could take with me that would ever be of value to anyone. I've already answered all of your questions with perfect candour. I hope you don't also expect me to give up my last remaining bargaining chip?'

Halyard glanced at Resaint. 'Fine,' he said. 'We don't have to see the whole thing. But can we just check one species in particular?'

*

Five days later, and three hundred kilometres west, Resaint and Selim came to a field of stones.

241

They were edgy and piebald, with wild geraniums sprouting between them in astonishing profusion like some Martian weed. No blossoms yet, no leaves, in fact no colour at all against the stones but the unearthly crimson of their stems stretching almost to the horizon. For an island you could walk around in a few hours, Osmussaar had an excess of strange landscapes. Earlier, near the lighthouse, they'd come to a stretch of shoreline where slices of limestone had broken off the scarp and slid over each other into the water, neat corners and riffled edges making them look like toppled stacks of atlases.

The rain grew even heavier as they stood there looking out over the geraniums. 'Stinking Bob' was the old name for this variety, Resaint's phone informed her, or 'death-come-quickly'.

'Shall we look for shelter?' Selim said, glancing up at a sky which gave no indication of backing down.

'I don't really mind it,' Resaint said. 'Do you?'

He shook his head. Like her, Selim owned excellent rainwear. They carried on.

Osmussaar was just off the northwest corner of Estonia, at the mouth of the Gulf of Finland. If it had been any further from Surface Wave she wouldn't have come. Not because it would have been too long a haul – she'd covered more ground with Halyard the previous week, and anyway she had some time on her hands – but because of connotations. What was the furthest you could travel on a whim with a romantic interest you barely knew without giving the impression that you planned to elope or go on a killing spree together?

On Friday evening, around the time the mermaid had finished unfolding her story in Warkentin's lab, Selim had messaged Resaint asking if she had any plans for dinner. So she'd gone to meet him at Surface Wave's ramen shop. Over mazamen and gyoza he'd mentioned that instead of going straight back to Turkey he was going to spend a few days birdwatching. There was a strait west of Tallinn that was one of the best places in Europe to see the Arctic migration, millions of ducks and geese and scoters and pintails funnelling themselves between cape and island like commuters through a turnstile.

'I thought the nuthatch thing put you off all that,' she said.

'No, I still love birds,' Selim said. 'The nuthatch thing just put me off nuthatches.'

She smiled and took one of his gyoza. Even though the story Selim had told her before had been one of loathing and divorce, of disillusionment and corruption, she still respected him for it, because at least his relationship with animals was *fraught*. That was the difference between him and Halyard, even if they were both extinction industry cunts. With Halyard one got the sense that if he got a job in a different field he might never give another thought to the problem of sharing a planet with animal minds. For him it wasn't there in every moment. He was complacent, as Resaint herself had been before she met *Adelognathus marginatum*. But now she felt that a human being should find as much torture and paradox in their relationship with animals as the most overwrought Catholic found in their relationship with God (the other great tolerator of one-sided conversations).

They kissed outside the ramen shop, and afterwards he said, 'Do you want to come to Osmussaar with me?' At first she thought he was joking, but he was giving her a frank, cheerful look as if he was entirely ready for her to say no but also entirely ready for her to say yes. So she thought about it. It was true that she liked him and she had at least a week to kill until everything was ready for what she was planning to do next. But in addition to the first big reason why she shouldn't – they'd only met this morning – there was a second big reason, less conspicuous right now but a lot harder to ignore later on.

She was about to infect herself with kaptcha. In a few days she would have a fungus crawling all over face, and she would have to leave it there undisturbed until it had finished tweaking her features.

But later that night she talked to Warkentin about it. And Warkentin told her he was planning to synthesise an endobacterium chaser that would cut the chances of human-to-human kaptcha transmission – already pretty low – to a flat zero. So there would be no need to self-isolate. Except in the sense that she would look like a walking toadstool.

When she called Selim his scullion told her he was asleep, so she asked it to wake him. 'Listen, I'd be interested in coming—'

'Wonderful!'

'—but I have this . . . medical issue. A developing medical issue.'

'Oh, I'm sorry to hear that.'

'It's not serious but it's going to be a problem in terms of going out in public.'

'Osmussaar itself has no permanent inhabitants,' he said. 'And the accommodation I booked for myself is a little cabin, a little two-bed cabin, down a back road on the mainland. We won't see many people.'

'When I say "in public" I mean you as well. What I'm trying to tell you is that I'm going to be very, very unattractive.'

'If you don't want to come birding with me you can just say, you don't have to make these totally impossible claims.'

'I'm serious, Selim.'

'Well, I've been birding with unattractive people before. It's a positive. It focuses you on the geese.'

So she'd come here to the coast of Estonia, leaving a disgruntled Halyard behind on Surface Wave. This was the fourth day of the trip, and tomorrow they would separate. Which was probably a good thing. So far this had gone well, better than any getaway she could ever remember taking with a boyfriend. Part of it was that sexually they had clicked into alignment with the satisfying precision of a high-end industrial device, but part of it was that there was so little at stake: at any time, if she wanted, she could leave and never see him again as long as she lived, and that made it easy for her to relax. Still, you should only push your luck so far. Now that the weather had turned, the cabin on the mainland where they spent the evenings would feel even smaller.

They were skirting the edge of the stonefield, not far from the sea, when Selim grabbed her arm and cried out 'Stop, stop, don't move!'

'What?'

He pointed at the ground in front of her. Four olive-coloured eggs in a wreath of straw. She had been about to step on a bird's nest.

'What kind of eggs are these?' she said, withdrawing her foot slowly as if from a landmine.

'That kind,' he said, pointing again, this time to the right. She looked over and saw a bird standing there staring at them, small and rotund with orange legs and tortoiseshell wings. 'Ruddy turnstone,' Selim added. '*Arenaria interpres*. Osmussaar is a big hatching site for them.' The turnstone began to make a call like a clockwork toy being wound up. They'd seen a lot of birds here, so many flocking overhead that at times their density brought to mind the horror of the yayflies, but this was the first time on this trip that she'd really looked one in the eye. She remembered Selim's story about wanting to smithereen that nuthatch egg, and wondered what it would be like to do that while the mother was right there watching you.

And that in turn made her think of something Halyard had said to her on the drive back from the Tinkanen camp. 'You know how, in films, it's always much sadder when a dog dies than when a person dies? I've always thought it's because the dog doesn't know what's happening. The dog's just like, "Hmmm, I feel tired and weird! Time for a nice long snooze!" So as a person watching it, who *does* know what's happening, you end up taking on the grief that the dog can't feel over its own death. Your mind is going, "Someone has to have these emotions. But the dog can't have them. So I have to have them on the dog's behalf." Whereas if the dog *did* understand what was happening, you wouldn't feel nearly as sad. Because you could just let the dog handle it. Or the kid – because this also applies to dying kids in films who are like, "What's happening to me, Mummy? Why are you crying?"'

'What's your point?' she had said.

'Have you ever thought that might be the real reason why you're so obsessed with getting the lumpsuckers to grasp their own extinction?' Halyard had said. 'Because then it wouldn't be your problem any more? If you could get these endangered species to mourn for themselves, then you wouldn't have to do the heavy lifting for them? Imagine if for some reason you got a call from a doctor that was meant for someone else, and the call was about some tests that had come back showing that this other person was absolutely chock-a-block with terminal cancers. And now you knew and they didn't. It wouldn't matter who it was, you'd feel frantic, you'd feel so invested, you'd feel this vicarious doom pressing down on you, right up until the moment when you were finally able to contact this person and tell them, and then as soon as that happened, as soon as you'd passed on the message, everything would lift from you, and you'd be like, "Well, best of luck on the deathbed, mate," and hang up the phone. That's what you want to do with the animals. You want to offload the curse.'

She hadn't replied.

'So?' he had said. 'What do you think?' Halyard never got the hint when she didn't reply to something he'd said. Or at least he always chose not to get it.

'I think you ought to ask yourself whether, firstly, this response you have to dogs dying in films – and, secondly, even more so, this response you imagine having to telling someone about their cancer diagnosis – I think you ought to ask yourself whether these things are universal truths about the human psyche or whether they might actually be quite idiosyncratic to you.'

'I'm definitely more universal than you are. Compared to you I'm an extremely universal person.'

Now she imagined herself bringing her foot down and crushing the eggs to daub, looking the turnstone right in the eye as she did so. It would be the closest she had ever come to the experience of that Siberian hunter when he wounded the tiger. The murder of animals was an enormous collaborative project, perhaps the fundamental human project, like a charity drive or war effort to which everybody made their little contribution. But because most of those contributions were so fragmentary and indirect, there was almost never an opportunity to impress yourself upon the consciousness of your victim the way Markov had. If she bereaved the turnstone right in front of its face, if she committed such

246

an intimate and demonstrative act of violence, maybe it would understand just for a moment what she was, what they all were. She would be measured and acknowledged.

And Halyard was right that this understanding would be a relief; he had come close to grasping something of substance. Because the other murders were like picking sleepers' pockets in the night, like bilking the mentally incapable. It was such a tawdry and demeaning crime. And a lonely one too. Horribly lonely.

But of course the understanding itself was not enough. What she wanted was not to stamp on the turnstone's eggs. What she wanted was for the turnstone to stamp on her, to grind her shell into the earth.

They walked on, and the turnstone hopped after them, chasing them away. 'That would have been awful,' she said. 'Aren't they endangered?'

'No, you might be thinking of some other bird. They're not endangered yet. They're just in decline.'

At around seven they took a water taxi from Osmussaar back to the mainland and walked home from the dock to their cabin. The interior of the cabin was such an unrelenting exercise in knotty pine that you woke up thinking you were a woodboring beetle. Yesterday and the day before they'd fucked before dinner, but when Resaint went into the bathroom and saw herself in the mirror she was aghast. Surely it couldn't be true that the kaptcha had mushroomed in the rain – it sounded too much like a bad joke – and yet the greyish plaques on her face did look far thicker than they had this morning. It had spread to places she hadn't expected, her lymph nodes and the fossae of her ears. Like the old Soviet watchtowers they'd passed on Osmussaar she was eroded and overgrown.

'Obviously I'm not expecting you to kiss me like this,' she said to Selim. 'Actually I'm not expecting you to touch me at all. I'm a ghoul.'

'It's not that bad,' he said, putting his hand on her waist.

'Yes, it is. Do you really still want to?'

He nodded.

'Why don't you wear the glasses?' she said. Selim had with him a pair of smart glasses that he sometimes used while birdwatching, and she suggested that he instruct the glasses to show him an unblemished version of her during sex.

'I would feel strange about doing that,' he said.

'Selim. It's fine. It's not unchivalrous. You're not going to be like one of those men who put a porn star's face on top of the woman they're having sex with. It'll be the opposite of that. It'll be my real face. What I have happening to me at the moment is not my real face.'

So they tried it like that. But the problem was, Selim's smart glasses were not the discreet frameless kind you saw on half the denizens of Surface Wave, they were more like what Stepanek had been wearing that night in the orchard, rugged and outdoorsy, with a zoom lens attached to each arm for pouncing on birds from fifty metres away. On a naked man they were just too comical. Impossible to ignore. What they needed, she thought, was a second pair of smart glasses so that *she* could digitally erase the obtrusion on *his* face. Instead she said to him, 'Blindfold me again.'

But Selim didn't understand what she was saying, because he'd turned off his simultaneous translation. Most of the time she didn't even notice it any more, the same way you could forget you were watching a film with subtitles. During sex, however, there must have been some flattening or loosening of the stimulus filters in her forebrain, because she once again became acutely conscious that he was saying things in Turkish and she was hearing them repeated in English, and the effect was too absurd. So he was now in the habit of disabling his earpiece for the duration of the act – which was no great inconvenience, because the limited pool of sexually relevant English words was, according to him, one of the few vocabulary areas that had stuck with him all these years as his proficiency declined. Unfortunately, that pool did not extend to 'blindfold'.

Part of her felt that, now he was wearing the smart glasses, it would hardly matter if he had the earpiece running as well – in fact he could put on an exosuit for all she cared; they might as well face the future head on – but rather than get into that, she just mimed what she wanted. So from the drawer of the bedside table he fished out the complimentary eye-mask from his Turkish Airlines flight. But when he tried to put it on her, she found that it rubbed the fungal growths on her nose and brows in a way that was not painful so much as just texturally disconcerting and fatally unerotic. After that they resorted to closing the heavy curtains to make the room as dark as possible.

'Can you still see the glasses?' Selim said. By this stage he had, after all, turned his simultaneous translation back on, because they couldn't get very far with gestures in the dark.

'Not really. Not enough that it's distracting. Can you still see the fungus on my face? If not, you could just take the glasses off.'

'Yes, I can still see it, but only because the glasses have low light enhancement.'

'Why would you switch that on? The whole point was—'

'It came on automatically.'

'So I can't see you but you can see me?' she said.

'It's almost like you're wearing the blindfold.'

'In strictly functional terms, yes, but I don't think this is going to do for me what the blindfold does for me.'

'OK, shall I take them off? The last time I used the low light enhancement I was in Manavgat looking for brown fish owls.'

'No, keep them on. Otherwise all this fuss was for nothing. Pretend I'm a brown fish owl.'

*

The next morning, as they were packing to leave, Selim said to her, 'You know, this thing that you're about to do . . .'

'Yes?' She hadn't told him what it was, but she had talked around it enough that by now he had some idea of its shape. Clearly he understood that it was menacing, that the sheer size of it blotted out any real consideration of future plans (such as a birdwatching trip to the beautiful and romantic Paradeniz

Lagoon that he had mentioned in a very casual fashion he hoped to take this summer).

'Do you have to do it?'

'What do you mean by that?' she said, crouching to check under the bed.

'I mean will something very bad happen if you don't?'

'No.'

'Then why not just not do it?'

'Because I have to.'

'But you don't.'

'I do.' And she felt that with all her heart. There was no dodging it. She had to go to the Hermit Kingdom.

Chapter Sixteen

These white chalk cliffs were extremely misleading. They had a savage and unconquerable look where they rose from the sea, saw-bladed and sabre-toothed, split almost to the root by great V-shape cuts full of jungly vegetation that frothed and trickled from the woods at the brink. And yet the moment you crested those woods you found yourself in the packaging from a stick of nice organic butter, bland golden fields squared off by hedgerows as far as the eye could see. Or, to be precise, as far as the camera could see, because the passengers of the VTOL were taking in this landscape from a video feed. Without that video feed, they wouldn't have had any view at all of the outside world, because there was cowhide glued over the windows.

Four passengers: Resaint and Warkentin in the front, Halyard and the mermaid in the back. And each of them had a different reason for coming to the Hermit Kingdom.

The venomous lumpsucker was on the mermaid's purloined list of species. Routed by global warming, scourged by Brahmasamudram's AMVs, choked by Faun's chlorine, and yet still not quite finished off, because Ferenc Barka, apparently, had built a new home for it, a salt lake carved out of an existing body of water called the Clatworthy Reservoir, which it would share with hundreds of other refugees. As soon as he heard that, Halyard knew that Resaint would have to come here. She would have to find out whether, indeed, the lumpsucker had lived so she could die. In the back of the VTOL was a tank big enough to spirit away about ten fish, the same number Resaint had sent back to the reefs that last night on the *Varuna* when she didn't know that the reefs had been gnashed into gravel.

And yet Halyard understood that Resaint wasn't here just for the fish with nine lives. She was here for all the species on that list, the oyster mussels and the Bavarian pine voles and the Ruthenian tawny buntings. She was here because she wanted to know whether it could possibly be true that Barka had performed this miracle eighty thousand times like some interceding angel. If it was true, wouldn't that change everything? He knew Resaint would never admit this, but if it turned out that there was something beyond the Black Hole – that you could travel through it and find Eden hidden on the other side – that like these chalk cliffs it was just a doomy frontage for sunlit uplands – then surely that would relieve the guilt that had driven her insane.

Halyard, too, hoped that Barka's nature reserve could save him, but in a rather more mundane sense. The mermaid had not, after all, known who was behind the biobank attacks, but she had known practically everything else worth knowing. If Halyard could get into the Hermit Kingdom and bring back video documentation of this thermonuclear scoop, stamped with the irrefutable seal of the verification chip inside his phone – after that, he was convinced, his legal problems could no more drag him under than the waves that broke a thousand metres beneath the VTOL.

But also he wanted to go because Resaint was going. Yes, he was bitter that after he'd spent all that time with her, saving her life twice – perhaps a controversial statistic, but Halyard was counting the time he'd stalled the terrorist in the orchard long enough for Stepanek to turn up with his tree branch, and also the time he'd demonstrated a sincere if ultimately redundant willingness to jump into the ocean when she was drowning – after all that, Resaint had fucked off to some birdy island with a Turk she'd just met while Halyard stayed behind on Surface Wave getting ready for the mission. What was so special about this guy, exactly? Had he released a big cloud of pheromones during their squash game, hotboxing her in the singles court?

Nevertheless, he wanted to be here with her. Resaint had been locked inside her own personal neurofeedback orb for so long, plying the miniature universe generated by her own depression, all those Black Holes and snuffed constellations and dying planets bleaker than anything in the real world. If, indeed, the South West Peninsula was what released her at last, he wanted to be present when it happened. He wanted to see her climb out through the hatch. He wanted to welcome her to the outside, where perhaps she might be happy.

As to why the mermaid was here with them, that was harder to make sense of. After all, she'd gone to such shattering lengths to *escape* the Hermit Kingdom. But during the earliest stages of planning, Halyard had made some unserious remark about how it was a shame she wasn't coming because she would know her way around the South West Peninsula. And the mermaid had surprised everyone by replying that actually she would like to go too. 'I want to see with my own eyes what that man has done to the place,' she had said. 'If it falls to me to bear witness, I had better bear witness as thoroughly as I possibly can. I think that's my duty to my King and my country and the government in which I once served. At any rate, we're just popping in, aren't we?' Halyard found it almost unbelievable, but then again the mermaid had done a number of almost unbelievable things, and certainly she would be an asset to them here.

And then there was Warkentin, the last to book a seat. At the start he had just been a technician, helping them with their preparations. Chief among these was the VTOL.

Over Põhjalas in Warkentin's lab, Halyard had proposed crossing the Channel in the dead of night using some kind of Zodiac boat or underwater scooter.

'Have you ever done anything like that?' Warkentin said.

Halyard hesitated. 'Surfing.'

'Sounds a bit ambitious. The commando thing.'

'Yeah, maybe not for her,' Resaint said, nodding towards the mermaid, 'but for the two of us.'

Which frustrated Halyard, because what version of this could there possibly be that was not 'a bit ambitious'? They were plotting to break into a fortress island, Europe's demented satellite module. It was a wild proposition. Then again, they were the only three people who'd actually got inside Module 3 since Lodewijk sealed it off. So if the analogy held, they ought to have a chance. But only if they demonstrated the necessary fearlessness.

'There is also the question of mines,' the mermaid said. 'I know there are still quite a few left over from when we were defending the Channel.' It chilled Halyard somewhat to hear her use this expression without apparent irony, because he knew it referred to a period when the Hermit Kingdom's navy were trying to stop freighters full of EU humanitarian aid from reaching its shores.

'Surely something as small as an underwater scooter wouldn't set off those mines,' Halyard said. 'Otherwise they'd be blowing up fishing boats all the time.'

'I'm afraid the mines were designed by the Defence Science and Technology Laboratory.' The irony was back in her voice. 'Since then the scallop catch has called for some sacrifices. But at least it discourages the French.'

After this Halyard wasn't feeling quite as hot on the necessary fearlessness.

'If I were you I'd go by air,' Warkentin said. 'In and out very fast.'

'You mean by VTOL? Wouldn't we get shot down?'

The mermaid nodded. 'Our Iron Curtain may be rather tattered but I don't think the holes are big enough to fly a VTOL through.'

'What about those stealth VTOLs?' Resaint said. 'The "invisible" ones.'

'I remember the DSTL were extremely interested in those,' the mermaid said. 'They made great efforts to get hold of one, but as far as I know they never succeeded.'

'In that case what chance do we have?' Halyard said.

'We could make our own,' Warkentin said.

254

'How the fuck would we do that?'

'Camouflage the VTOL the same way you're going to camouflage your faces.'

They had already agreed that they were going to infect themselves with kaptcha, cultured from the same sample that the mermaid had stolen from the Tinkanen medical centre. Halyard wasn't thrilled about this – had anybody checked yet whether kaptcha did anything to your brain while it was hanging around the neighbourhood? – but it would mean that, once they reached the South West Peninsula, they would be at least partially safe from surveillance technology. If he got cosmetic surgery after he came home, it wouldn't be any worse than what he'd endured for his acne scars, and if he didn't – well, that would probably mean things had really gone to shit for him, in which case staying permanently beyond the reach of any facial recognition system might be just the tonic.

But Warkentin's idea was to grow about ten square metres of bovine facial tissue in a vat, upholster the outside of the VTOL like an ottoman, and then let kaptcha run wild across it until the VTOL was entirely veiled in fungus.

Halyard looked at him incredulously. 'Kaptcha stops cameras from recognising faces. A VTOL is not a face.'

'Kaptcha generally *grows* on faces,' Warkentin said, 'but that doesn't mean it can only disrupt facial recognition. My guess is, it disrupts computer vision in general, or at least computer vision as it currently exists on this planet. All kaptcha ever wanted was to not get hosed off cow faces so quickly, and while it was trying to evolve to avoid that, it discovered something really, really fundamental about the way these algorithms work. The bottom line is, whatever kaptcha's growing on – or whatever it's already fucked with outwardly – computer vision becomes useless for recognising that thing. I'm pretty sure.'

'Fine,' Halyard said, 'but even if this theory of yours is true, what about radar or infrared or whatever?'

'That's why you make yourself as visible as possible. Fly straight at the cameras in broad daylight.'

'I know we've been throwing around phrases like "suicide mission", but that was only in the loose sense of something really difficult – you weren't supposed to be taking it literally.'

'These systems weigh inputs according to the quality of those inputs, yes? If the system is getting a dark, fuzzy picture from a camera, then it won't pay much attention to that camera. It will listen to other sources first. But if the system is getting a perfect, bright, detailed picture from that camera, then that camera will become the loudest voice in the room. Any other sources – radar, infrared – will be bumped way down the list. You want the system to be saying "I have a great view of this thing, and that great view tells me it's definitely not an aircraft." Then you don't have to worry so much about the other forms of detection.'

'Surely you don't expect us to just roll the dice on this.'

'I'll test it first.'

Halyard would have dismissed all this, but then he remembered the tuna belly. He hadn't believed Warkentin about that, either. 'Well, even if this wasn't the craziest idea in the world, where would we get the VTOL? No VTOL we hire will go anywhere near the Hermit Kingdom. We'd need one of our own. Even a shitty second-hand VTOL is six figures, right? Can we run to that?'

'I don't know,' Resaint said. 'Can we?'

'Why are you giving me that look? Listen, just because I'm a member of the managerial class that doesn't automatically mean I'm flush with . . .'

And then he realised what Resaint had in mind. The €871,000 from Brahmasumadram's credits. He'd completely forgotten he was rich.

Perhaps that was absurd. But the plan had always been to leave the money alone until he could have every cent of it laundered, pressed and starched. And then, after the price spike, when his whole future hung in the balance, it was simply a liability. In that sense he'd been about as rich as the guy he met in the medical centre waiting room. Unspendable money wasn't money at all.

Now, though, he was past caring about any of that.

And yet he still couldn't help feeling a little surge of indignation. 'What, so I'm just supposed to underwrite this whole thing? Like one of those rich guys on the polar expeditions who only got to go because they paid for all the fucking sleds?'

'Well, anything you can spare,' Resaint said. 'I know how hard you worked for it.'

Halyard sighed. 'All right, yes, point taken.'

The next morning, Warkentin started growing the bovine facial tissue in the very same bioreactor that had produced the panda tumours, which Halyard speculated would give those beef cheeks a subtle extra richness, like whisky finished in cognac barrels.

At first, Warkentin didn't want anything in return for helping out: clearly he was one of those people who just enjoyed solving novel problems. But then after a few days he asked if he could come too. 'The more time I spend on this,' he said, 'the more I feel like I actually want to be there. I pretty much didn't leave my bedroom between thirteen and seventeen because I had this anxiety thing. I don't just mean I was a huge nerd, I mean I literally wouldn't leave. And then I finally found this gut hormone medication that fixed it – except back then it wasn't really officially a medication yet, so I also had to find someone who'd synthesise it for me, until I learned how to do it myself. But you sort of get into a habit – you still have these tracks laid down in your brain and the medication can't fix *those*. So now I spend a lot of time in the lab. A *lot* of time. And all I do is make cool stuff for other people. I've never done anything like this.'

Halyard tried to talk him out of it, reminding him how dangerous it was going to be, but that only seemed to excite Warkentin more. From then on, Warkentin threw himself twice as hard into the VTOL project, the end result of which reminded Halyard more than anything of a novelty car covered in mangy brown polyester fur that used to drive around Sydney CBD when he was a kid, promoting cat and dog adoptions from an animal shelter. Everything was wrapped but the blades of the rotors.

And so here they were, all four of them – four faces at an all-time low, not only dinged and scraped by the fungus that had recently taken them for a spin, but also by this point grim with suspense. It was late afternoon on a drizzly day as they crossed into the zone of stupendous secrecy and potential revelation; about forty-five minutes ago they had taken off from Cherbourg and now they were coming inland at a place called Beer. Even Resaint, who supposedly welcomed death, didn't look as if she was feeling very philosophical about the possibility of the Hermit Kingdom's coastal defences downing them like a clay pigeon.

But Warkentin insisted that in every simulation the living camouflage had worked perfectly. And, sure enough, they were flying over this country whose national energies were so fervently devoted towards enclosure with no sign whatsoever of those energies crackling around the VTOL. To any human spotter their mouldering leatherbound aircraft would have been obvious, but to the cameras that had long since replaced those spotters they were only a heat shimmer or a fly crawling on the lens. They had taken whatever other precautions it was practical to take, like muting any wireless signals from the electronics on board, and for their entry point they had chosen Beer because the incurving of the coastline here would minimise the distance they had to travel over enemy territory before they reached Lumpsucker Lake. Halyard glanced at the woman beside him and once again he wondered, was this really worth it for her? Was it really worth it to dangle herself over the pit she'd only recently climbed out of just to make an inspection of a place which, from this distance at least, still looked perfectly normal?

But that was when something happened that very much resolved the question.

The mermaid leaned into him, reaching behind his back, almost as if she was going to put a fond arm around his shoulders. But instead she grabbed a fistful of hair at the back of his head and at the same moment her other hand came up towards his chin and he felt a cold edge against his throat. 'We're going to change course,' she said.

Resaint and Warkentin looked round from the front seats and he saw shock come over their faces. 'What's she got?' he said. 'I can't see it. What is—'

'It's a scalpel,' Warkentin said. 'I think it might be from my lab.' Which was where the mermaid had been living during all the preparations.

'I'd like you to turn west towards Dartmoor. If you don't I will cut Mr Halyard's throat. And if you make any attempt to distract or overpower me the result will be the same. It will take only the contraction of a muscle.'

This was not the first time in recent memory that Halyard had faced a threat to his life, but that didn't make it any less frightening. Would you know that one little slash to the throat could kill you, if you hadn't seen it happen in films? The answer, Halyard found, was yes, because he could sense now that the body knew, the body feared that cut as innately as it feared long drops or bared fangs, the skin of his throat feeling suddenly as soft and burstable as an egg yolk.

'What's in Dartmoor?' Resaint said.

'Nothing in particular. It's just a bearing. After Dartmoor we will carry on west, down to the end of the peninsula, then turn around and come back up the other side. If necessary we will make a tour of all three counties until we find what we're looking for.'

'What are we looking for?'

'Ferenc Barka,' their hijacker said.

In this section of the conversation, even as she revealed herself to be out of her mind, the mermaid spoke in the same cool, intelligent tone she always did. And perhaps it was this that brought an unwelcome memory to Halyard's mind: an interview he'd heard with some jihadist from the Philippines, who nonchalantly described how the Adam's apple seemed almost to slide out of the way to let your blade through . . .

'But we don't want Barka to know we're here,' Warkentin said. 'Otherwise the whole thing's blown.'

'Barka is an invader. A violator of our sovereignty. A gelder of the commonwealth. As I told you, I have a duty. Which is to do to Barka what Gallienus did to Memor. In other words, put his upstart head on a stick.'

259

'I thought you said your duty was to bear witness,' Resaint said.

'I'm afraid I wasn't being quite frank with you. I don't see the need for scrupulous testimony when the offence is already perfectly clear.'

'How do you even know he's in the country?' Halyard said.

'There were certain dates mentioned over and over again in those files, dates by which various things were due to be completed. One of those dates was yesterday, and it seems to have represented some sort of inauguration or unveiling. Certainly Barka will have turned up for that.'

'But we can't cover the whole peninsula looking for him,' Warkentin said. 'We don't have the range. The battery will die before we can get home.'

'You forget,' said the mermaid. 'I'm already home.'

An awful idea crossed Halyard's mind: what if Resaint and Warkentin were thinking, 'If we do as she says, she's going to get all four of us killed. Which means Halyard's number is up either way. So we may as well try and save ourselves, even if it means taking some of his arterial blood in the face.'

But evidently they weren't thinking that, or at least if they were thinking it they didn't act on it, because Warkentin compliantly swung the VTOL west. Each of the blacked-out windows of the VTOL was displaying the appropriate video feed from the outside, so you could still look out at the view, just in a two-dimensional, misaligned form, as if the four of them were actors in one of those old films that used rear projection to simulate the world passing by outside a car. And now a town came into sight on Halyard's side, gabled roofs and big gardens, and more fields on every side except for a caravan park in one corner, from this altitude just a pentagon of tight white nubbles like an exotic hide patched into the landscape's quilt. All of this was presumably empty of people, but there were still no outward signs of desolation or upheaval – until they saw the first of the towers.

This tower had been dreamed up by an algorithm. That was obvious, because it had that eldritch quality of generative design, the strands and the webbing, the bones and the joints. 'Organic' was the word people sometimes used for stuff like this, but no natural organism would make such an insolent rejection of symmetry, except for a mutant or a misbirth – and that was the deepest problem with this style, that it had just enough life in its appearance to trigger your instinctive fear of the disfigured, the gone-wrong. A few years ago, high-end developers had briefly convinced themselves that this was the future of architecture: after all, a generative skyscraper could be twice as strong, twice as airy and twice as efficient all at the same time. As it turned out, however, that was a bit like saying a two-headed puppy could lick twice as many faces. People didn't want to live in these buildings, or work in them, or even see them out of their windows. (Adults didn't, anyway; alarmingly, nobody born in the last couple of decades seemed to mind them at all.) The most notorious, in Saigon, had as a last resort been rewrapped in an entirely new facade like the Phantom of the Opera in his mask. These days they only let the algorithms loose on the bits you didn't see.

But of course here on the vacant peninsula there was nobody to complain.

'What is that?' Resaint said. The tower was fifteen or twenty storeys tall, a ridged mid-section rising into a neck with gill-like openings and then a starfish head with tubes projecting from each point.

'Where I grew up the orchid house had its own boiler,' said the mermaid. 'Installed in the 1870s. Broke down about every three and a half minutes. But my father refused to replace it. He said the orchids would notice the difference. That's what this is. An orchid house boiler.'

'Climate control,' Warkentin said. 'To regulate the habitats. That's how he can put tropical species and subarctic species within a hundred kilometres of each other.'

As the VTOL flew on, past the great muddy spill of a river estuary with a city at its head, they passed more of the towers, spaced out across the countryside. And these were not the only novelties down below. The towers had their outworkers, equally conspicuous because although they were much smaller they were also in motion: excavators, earth movers, bulldozers, dredgers, and other, more specialised machines, such as one that could be made out scooping an oak tree out of the earth, roots and all, and bearing it away intact like a gardener with a seedling. Even if the 'inauguration' had already passed, the resculpting of the terrain was still very much in progress.

But the most hallucinatory sight was yet to come.

They did not, in the end, have to make a tour of all three counties. In fact, it took only half an hour's flight, not over fields any more but over moors, miles and miles of them, greyish-brownish-green, one of those aimless and non-specific terrains like somebody in early middle age who still hasn't decided what they want to do with their life, not quite hill or prairie or marsh but just sort of . . . land. The scalpel was still at his neck, but Halyard could feel the mermaid shifting her weight now and then, and he thought about how much her arms must be aching. His panic response, likewise, was perhaps numbing a little, no longer quite as steady after thirty minutes of continuous use. For the first time he began to consider whether, if Resaint and Warkentin weren't going to do anything reckless, then maybe *he* should?

But before he could get any further, it came into view. An enormous jellyfish floating in the air.

That was what it looked like. In sheer size it must have matched one of those cargo airships that Brahmasamudram used to transport ore out of the mines where they couldn't build a road, but an apter comparison might have been an old-fashioned hot-air balloon: long cables dangled like tentacles from the underside, down into a forest whose foliage hid whether they ended in a basket or a gondola or something else entirely. Where the jellyfish differed from any familiar species of gasbag, however, was the skin, which did not stretch taut around its captive volume but rather throbbed and billowed and fluttered, catching the sun with the black shine of a photovoltaic surface and yet as fluid and creaseless as satin. How the hell did it stay in the air? Earlier the mermaid had said that what she used to love about this part of the country was that it never seemed to change, but now Halyard felt as if this was the furthest he had ever travelled into the future.

'Head straight for that,' the mermaid said.

'Are you sure?' Warkentin said.

'Absolutely. That's Barka.'

They were going in roughly that direction anyway, so the VTOL only had to turn a few degrees to the right. There was something hypnotic about the flux of the jellyfish's bell; just for an instant, as Halyard watched, it took on a shape uncannily like the puffy lips of that Salvador Dalí sofa. Below them, the white birdshit crust of a quarry marked the southwest tip of the moorlands, which afterwards gave way again to fields and villages.

'Where are we?' Resaint said.

'We're coming into the Tamar Valley,' the mermaid said. 'It used to be a tremendous mining region. The Devon Great Consols was the most productive copper mine in the world.'

God, it's like I'm still at work, Halyard thought.

'Surely you don't want us to get too close to . . . that thing,' Warkentin said. 'There might be people around.'

'Put us down at least half a mile away. Somewhere discreet.'

The VTOL landed in the asphalt yard of a small farm, grit swirling in the wash from its rotors. The siding of the barn was striped with rust and bowing inward, and seeing it Halyard was clutched by a powerful feeling of abandonment and decay. Then he remembered that this wasn't Chernobyl or Metsamor. People had only been gone since the winter. It was probably pretty normal for a barn to look like shit.

The mermaid opened the VTOL door, the flat video feed falling aside to reveal the same view seen for real, a change of refraction like surfacing from a swimming pool. Halyard was expecting her to let him go at this point, but instead she unclipped his seat belt and then pulled his head down until he was bent sideways across the back seat. This way, she could hold on to her hostage right up until the very last moment, the scalpel still at his neck even as she stepped down on to the asphalt. 'In many ways you've all been rather kind to me,' she said. 'I am conscious of that, I promise.' Then she let go of his hair and took off running.

The farm looked northward down a corridor of fields, long and narrow, hemmed in on the west side by a steep slope descending into the river valley and on the east side by the forest over which the jellyfish hung like a bin bag caught on an updraught. In other circumstances the easiest way to get to the jellyfish would probably have been to take the path that ran alongside the fields, but of course the mermaid wouldn't want to be seen, and she made instead for the metal gate that led out towards the trees. She hopped up over it and almost immediately disappeared from view.

'Are you hurt?' Resaint said.

'No,' Halyard said. 'No, I'm all right.'

She nodded, satisfied, and then opened the door on her side.

'What are you doing?'

'Come on. We've got to catch up with her.'

Halyard was taken aback. 'What? Why?'

'Because she's going to kill Barka.'

'I don't really see that as our problem.'

'But what if it's true?' Resaint said. 'What if he's saved us?'

'You mean saved the animals.'

Same thing, her expression said. 'What if she kills him and it all falls apart and nobody ever even knows it was here?'

'Do you really think she's going to assassinate one of the most powerful men in the world with a fucking scalpel?' The trouble was, knowing everything the mermaid had gone through to get to this point, it didn't actually sound that far-fetched.

Resaint got out of the VTOL, so Halyard had no choice but to get out as well to carry on pleading with her. He saw that, despite all Warkentin's glue and staples, one of the sheets of scabby cowskin was already peeling off the VTOL's fuselage. The farm was silent but for the stretched polythene of a grow tunnel crinkling in the breeze, old tyres heaped beside it like a harvest. 'Karin. Stop. This is insane. This is not what we came here for. Let's just go to the reservoir and get the lumpsuckers.'

'We can get the lumpsuckers afterwards.'

'If we start chasing each other around the woods and making a fucking exhibition of ourselves there probably won't be an afterwards.'

She replied with a look that was uninterested, impatient, and very obviously final. He could come or not come, but she wasn't going to wait.

All this had started, Halyard thought, because he'd made a bet that the price of extinction credits would fall. They warned you about making that sort of bet, about selling short: if it went well, there was a limit to what you could make, because the price couldn't fall below zero, but if it went badly, there was no limit to what you could lose, because the price could just keep rising forever. It was a witchy notion, the stuff of dark fairytales: finite upside, infinite downside. An unlucky short seller might feel like they were in a waking dream as they watched their losses multiply beyond any graspable scale. And it was very much as if that was what had happened to Halyard over the last few weeks since the price of credits had spiked: as if he'd careened further than anybody before him into the bizarro dimension of infinite downside, as if his bet had gone so wrong that it had torn loose from the realm of numbers and started to melt down reality itself. That seemed as good an explanation as any for how he had found himself in this utterly improbable position. All he'd ever really wanted was to eat well, and here he was.

The vital thing about short positions, they always said, was to get out as soon as things turned. Cut your losses. For goodness' sake don't cling on to the end just because you bought in at the beginning.

But he did not take this advice. Instead, he went with Resaint. And so did Warkentin, who followed them from the VTOL with only a shrug in reply to Halyard's questioning look.

What lay beyond the field gate was not exactly untamed wilderness – you could imagine strolling out here for a picnic – but compared to the forest of Sanctuary North it might as well have been equatorial jungle. Most of all this was because, after the strict verticality and polite spacing of those endless pines and birches, the squirmy, low-boughed, heterogenous trees here felt like the Fall of Rome, as anarchic as a generative skyscraper. But it was also because Halyard thought he could detect a humidity that did not seem appropriate to this latitude in this season, which must have been the effect, if he wasn't just imagining it, of the 'orchid boilers', magicking up a microclimate to suit the animals who now resided here.

Those animals, too, or at least the thought of them hidden in the undergrowth, added to his sense of tropical teeming; as indeed they did to his sense of scrambled time, all these species plucked out of linear history and brought here to live on together *after* their extinctions, composing an ecosystem so unlikely it could only be from the far future or the deep past, which made a strange brew in the mind with the overnight ruins of the vacated farm and the science-fictional presence of Barka's machines.

Really, the woods were not jungle but anti-jungle, the most controlled and artificial biome on the planet. Like Sanctuary North, the menagerie would need to be supervised down to the last dung pile, but if there were hundreds of times as many species, then that supervision would be exponentially, unimaginably more complex, a perfect totalitarianism to outclass the country it had seceded from. The technology they'd marvelled at from the air was presumably just the most conspicuous part of an enormous apparatus woven through this land at every scale. If it couldn't be seen in these woods its presence was implicit.

You could say much the same of the animals themselves. So far there hadn't been much to look at but little birds up in the treetops, and whether they were the most precious passerines who ever vanished from a coral island or just some banal sparrows who'd been here all along, Halyard did not have the expertise to say. Perhaps any other animals who might have been out and about were shrinking away at the sound of their approach. Which was not an encouraging thought, because the aim here was to move not only quickly enough to catch up with the mermaid but also quietly enough that she might not hear them coming. But

Halyard didn't have much hope for that anyway. It wasn't as if they were trained for this.

Then again, the mermaid wasn't either, if you didn't count her posh sylvan childhood, or the fact that these woods had once been part of her ministerial portfolio. And so Resaint scanned the trees up ahead, searching for movement, while Halyard tried to cover the left side and Warkentin the right. Nobody spoke. The drizzle had intensified but they were sheltered by the canopy, through which the spreading inkblot of the jellyfish flickered in and out of view.

After ten minutes or so, they came to a little hollow full of bluebells, barricaded at knee level by a dead tree trunk that had toppled across it from rim to rim. Here, Resaint stopped, and Halyard heard her exhale in frustration. 'This isn't going to work, is it?' she said quietly. 'The woods are too thick and we don't even know if she came this way.'

A deep relief came over Halyard. 'We tried,' he said, as sympathetically as he could, as if he was disappointed too. 'Let's just go back to the VTOL. Get out of here while we still can.'

'We could warn him,' Resaint said.

'What?'

'If she's taking her time, we could still get there first, and warn him.'

'No. Absolutely not.'

'There's no way to warn him without also letting him know that we're here,' Warkentin said.

'Karin, we can't let you do that,' Halyard said. 'I'm sorry but we can't.' This time he really meant it. Resaint stared back at him. He couldn't predict what she would do next. In the sky the heart of darkness continued to beat.

'Stay exactly where you are.'

Halyard looked over.

There he stood among the bluebells.

Although very little of Barka's face was on view between the hood and the goggles and the bushy beard, the last of those made him instantly recognisable. It was even longer than in the pictures

Halyard had seen, a greying Rasputin frizz all the way down to his breastbone. At his side was a robot, quadrupedal, waist high, leaning forward in the posture of an Irish setter. And he was aiming at them a weapon that Halyard initially took for a rifle but then realised must be some kind of crossbow.

Not because it looked anything like his mental image of a crossbow, which was a bit of wood you might take with you to the Fifth Crusade. On the contrary, it was a baffling object – reminiscent in certain ways of a semi-automatic, especially in the stock and the grip, but exploding further forward into something closer to a bird skeleton tied up with twine – whose function could only be deduced from the one simple part of the whole business, a long bolt with a glinting tip that was nestled there in its throat. The robot, too, bore some family resemblance to the towers on the moors, with twiggy, honeycombed limbs giving an impression of flimsiness that was no doubt entirely deceptive, like a wishbone that would snap your wrist before it snapped in half. Mostly it was camouflaged in the same leafy colours as Barka himself, but parts of its lower body had turned violet-blue to match the flowers.

'My goggles aren't seeing you,' Barka said. 'And the dog isn't seeing you either. What is going on here?'

Nobody else answered, so after a moment Halyard said, 'Kaptcha.' He gestured at his face. 'It's, um – it's a livestock disease—'

'I know what it is. I didn't know it worked this well. Where did you come from?'

'We flew here in a VTOL. From France.'

'Are there any more of you?'

'Just one.'

'She's here to kill you,' Resaint said. 'You're in danger. She's resourceful, and she's had kaptcha too, and you may not see her coming.'

'Are *you* here to kill me?'

'No.'

The crossbow didn't waver. 'But you brought along someone who is.'

'We didn't know,' Warkentin said.

'You'll come back to the lodge with me,' Barka said, nodding in the direction of the jellyfish. 'There are three of you, and this thing only fires one bolt at a time. But if you try to touch me, or if you take out a weapon, I can guarantee the dog will react, kaptcha or no kaptcha.' Beside him the machine sat perfectly still.

'What's going to happen after that?' Halyard said.

'You shouldn't have come here,' Barka said, not the answer to the question, more like the answer was obvious and this was the fact that justified or necessitated it. A black balloon of dread began to pulse inside Halyard. Unless they got out of this they were never going home. He felt certain of that.

'Are they really here?' Resaint said. 'Have you really saved them?'

'Saved who?' Barka said.

'The animals.'

A pause before he spoke. 'So that got out? That's known?'

'Not widely.'

The sky was clearing and the drizzle had stopped, leaving only the drip from the trees. 'Yes. They're here.' And Barka seemed to loosen up a little bit from here on, as if he enjoyed the topic. 'It's been a lot of work but overall it's gone pretty smoothly. There are forty-eight thousand species already here. Another thirty thousand still to arrive. Incredible variety. It's going to take me decades to work my way through.'

'What do you mean, "work your way through"?'

'This morning I took out the Saudi gazelle and the turquoise-throated puffleg. Just now I got most of the San Felipe hutia but there's still one breeding pair left somewhere around here. I think I can maintain a rate of maybe three, four species a day. Obviously I set some rules for myself, or it would be a lot faster. I do my own tracking. I don't just let the system tell me where to look. The hunter's code, you know?'

'That's what this is? You're hunting?'

Instead of replying, Barka just glanced down at himself: what does it look like I'm doing?

'You brought all these animals here just to kill them?' You would never have believed that Resaint had a crossbow pointed at her as she said this, because no crossbow bolt could have been colder or steelier or more organ-reamingly penetrant than the tone in which she said it.

Barka gave a little sigh of frustration, as if her claim had the vexatious quality of being technically accurate but altogether insufficient. 'Do you know anything about Alvin Ip's work? I met him for the first time at one of the retreats we do in Vallombrosa. He's a computational physicist. One of the most extraordinary minds I've ever encountered. He's proven that the amount of information in the universe is constant, just like matter and energy. Which means that when you destroy information in one place, you're forcing new information to come into existence somewhere else. That's what this is. Imagine a species as a bundle of information. When you eliminate the last of that species – as long as you make sure that there's no trace of it left anywhere else – you're destroying an enormous quantity of information. Which really means you're *creating* an enormous quantity of information. When I killed that last turquoise-throated puffleg this morning, I could almost *feel* the information shattering, dissipating, condensing, recrystallising. Like a supernova. It's one of the most profound experiences a human being can have. And that's what my priority has become as I've grown older. I've already achieved everything I ever wanted in conventional terms. I'm more interested in profound experiences now. And it's humbling to realise that I will make more of an impact on the informational topology of the universe than any other human being has ever made before me. Probably by several orders of magnitude, once I've made it through all eighty thousand species.'

'So the biobank attacks – that was part of it?' Halyard said, understanding. 'You weren't rescuing them – it was all you?'

Barka nodded. 'The biobanks made things fuzzy. When a species goes "extinct", but there's so much on file . . . Informationally, it's like it isn't even gone. If the backups were still out there, I wouldn't really be destroying anything, so I wouldn't really be

270

creating anything. That's what Alvin says. The kill needs to take the species to absolute zero, like a switch flipping. Otherwise what's the point?'

'But some of the species here aren't even extinct in the wild.'

'They soon will be. In every single case. The models show that unequivocally. So the hacks were just a way to consolidate. Tidy everything into one place. It was an easy assignment for X5.'

Halyard had heard of X3, the Antichain deep learning project, but never of X5. 'And it gave you something to trade with the politburo here, right? They made millions betting on the price spike.'

'That was convenient, yes. Better than paying in cash. They all seem to love the idea of beating the global markets. One of those guys kept talking about how the money he made would be a patriotic triumph "like the Falklands".' But here Barka's volubility ran out. He levelled the crossbow, tightening up his stance where it had relaxed. 'All right – head for the lodge.'

Ever since the white cliffs, Halyard had been like a donkey passed from owner to owner, continuously dragged around against his will: not only by the mermaid's scalpel and Barka's crossbow, but also, in the interim, by Resaint and the hold she had on him, her withering, unanswerable gaze. So far he'd kept his head down and hoped for the best, but that had only brought him here, to what he was pretty sure would be a death march. This time, he couldn't just let it happen. He had to do something. And he already knew you couldn't reason with these people, because they were mad, all of them, in their different ways; he'd learned that back in the apple orchard, with the gun in his face. You had to talk to them from the inside, not the outside. Join them for a while in their delirium. Poke around. Find the button that closed the flue.

That was all it would take to save the three of them. He was sure of it. Just think of the right thing to say.

Just think of the right thing to say.

Just think of the right thing to say.

Just think of the—

'We want to work for you,' Warkentin said.

Barka looked at him. 'What?'

'We think what you do at Antichain is amazing and we want to be part of it. Each of us has a pretty unique skill set, and we don't think the normal channels are really set up to recognise our potential value. We came all the way here to meet you because we wanted to show you what we can do.'

Halyard recognised this immediately as a stroke of genius, a triple bank shot off the ceiling, and what confirmed it was Barka's reaction. Which, admittedly, was a bit hard to read with so much of his face hidden, but the point was Barka didn't seem particularly surprised or incredulous. He must have been so used to eager nerds pulling baroque stunts in the hopes of claiming a microsecond of his attention and maybe getting a job – he had openly encouraged that for so long – that Warkentin's radical reframing of the situation seemed quite plausible.

'What about the person you mentioned who's here to kill me?' he said.

'Like I said, we didn't know. We fucked up.'

For a few seconds, as Barka considered what he'd been told, Halyard really thought it might have worked, he really thought Warkentin might have saved them. But then Barka spoke.

'No. Nice try, but I don't buy it. If it was just you, maybe. But these two' – meaning Halyard and Resaint – 'it doesn't fit. Move.'

All of Halyard's optimism carbonised into despair. He bowed his head and squeezed his eyes shut, wishing, childlike, that this wasn't real, that he wasn't here.

So he didn't see what happened next. He only heard it.

A swish of fabric. A cry of surprise from Barka.

When Halyard opened his eyes, what he saw in front of him was already too chaotic to parse from just a glance. The mermaid and the robot and Barka, on top of each other, whirling, struggling, a spatter of blood, but exactly what was going on, who might have the upper hand, he couldn't tell in that instant – and then the mermaid let out a howl of pain, and Resaint shouted 'Run!'

They ran.

But in the woods there was no racing line. To avoid twisting his ankle in a root hole or poking his eye out with a branch, Halyard had to weave between the trees, stifle all momentum, move at a pace that felt unbearably halting and indecisive compared to what he really wanted to do, which was sprint as fast as his legs could carry him. At one point Resaint did fall headlong, and Warkentin stopped to help her up. Halyard longed more than anything for just thirty seconds of unobstructed terrain.

And then, much sooner than he expected, he got it. He hadn't known what direction they were going. He had just followed the other two. Or perhaps they had followed him. But they must have been moving west, because after what felt like no time at all they found themselves emerging into a field of wheat, knee high, the taller stalks catching the light in their bristles as the sun sank towards the horizon. They slowed for a moment to get their bearings. And Halyard saw that Resaint's ear was bloody.

Ragged, in fact. Lobeless. As if a sharpened projectile had bored straight through it.

'Oh, Christ,' he said. That was why she had lost her balance. 'Are you OK?' He wondered if the mermaid was already dead.

'We have to keep moving,' Resaint said. Blood was oozing down her neck and jaw.

It turned out that unobstructed terrain wasn't so wonderful after all. No trees meant no cover. If Barka was still close behind them with his bow, crossing the field would leave them utterly exposed, the low sun silhouetting them like targets at a training range. But it seemed unthinkable to turn around and head back into the woods.

So they took off running again, keeping as low to the ground as they could. On the other side were more trees, a fringe of beeches between field and valley. Just as he had amongst the yayflies, Halyard cringed and made an unsteady nasal sound as he ran, his entire body anticipating a crossbow bolt, the phantom touch of it swarming every nerve cell in his epidermis.

But they made it to the treeline. Nobody got harpooned. And when Halyard looked back there was no obvious sign of Barka.

Taking cover on the other side of the beeches, they found themselves suddenly at altitude, the river sixty or seventy metres below, coppery in the sunset, and beyond that a perfect little train-set town, white houses and brown roofs. The slope was thickly wooded, so from a distance it might have looked like a reasonably benign hillside, but the truth was it descended from here in a series of steep drops, with the trees perched on whatever flattish ground they could find in between.

'Let's call the VTOL,' Halyard said, out of breath.

'I don't think we can risk it,' Warkentin said. 'Say we lost him back there – if any of our devices send any kind of signal, he may be able to pinpoint us again. In which case he'll get to us before the VTOL does. Or the "dog" will.'

'So what do we do?'

'Head for the VTOL on foot.'

'Through the fields? Or back through the woods? We just came from there!'

Warkentin swept one hand south over the slope. 'We can move sideways along there. It'll take us right back to the farm where we left the VTOL. And if we're down there he probably won't see us from up here.'

'It's too steep,' Halyard said.

'There are lots of ledges.'

'We're not fucking mountain goats.'

'I don't think we have any better options,' Resaint said. And her injury gave her a kind of authority. So there was no further debate.

The nearest major ledge was about three metres down, and Halyard found that the descent wasn't nearly as bad as he'd feared. The vertical face here was the kind of rock that you could almost mistake for a weathered brick wall because so many past frosts had cracked and wrenched it into squarish headers. So you always had somewhere to put your feet. And the trees were squeezed in so close to the slope that their branches were within easy reach. So you always had somewhere to put your hands. Anyway, it was a short enough climb that you could just sort of jazz your way

274

down without stopping. And at the end of all that, they found that it wasn't just a ledge, it was practically a resort. The path was generous, it was even, and it ran as far as they could make out along the curve of the hillside.

At first Halyard thought this was just an incredible gift from geology, but once they set off south he began to notice finger-sized holes in the rock. The brickish appearance of the granite was an illusion, yes, but these holes really did look artificial, like drill marks. And although Halyard's years in the mining industry had not turned him into a mining buff – in fact he actively avoided learning anything that wasn't directly relevant to his job – an image now came into his head: four or five times he'd had to sit through a particular Brahmasamudram corporate video that opened with a montage about the inspirational history of the industry, and from the bushy-moustache portion of the montage he recalled some kind of wooden gallery or trough hung along a cliff face a bit like this one, presumably designed to carry something to or from an inconveniently situated mine (although whether that was water or tailings or ham sandwiches he had no idea). So maybe this wasn't a natural ledge, maybe it was a cut, made in the old days by gunpowder or dynamite, and that was why it was so inviting.

Of course, the trees had begun to reclaim it since then. Quite often Warkentin would have to push aside a branch that blocked the way, holding it there so it didn't spring back in Halyard's face, and after him Halyard would do the same for Resaint. Or they would have to duck under or step over. But really this was nothing to complain about, because it was those same trees that were screening their route, not only in foliage but in shadow, so that from a distance they should be no more conspicuous than three ticks burrowing through the valley's fur.

Even so, it was alarming to look over the edge. So Halyard tried not to. Now that the sun was below the horizon but not a single light had come on, the town across the river more obviously showed its abandonment, though above it was a grid of cloud with the last warm glow still in its corners like a dying imprint of

275

how the town once lit the valley. The three of them were making good progress along the cut.

Until they weren't.

The path gave out, blocked by a tall wedge of earth that must have washed down from above, the hillside vomiting down its own front. And clearly this landslip wasn't recent, because a huge double-trunked oak was growing out of it: where most of the other trees on the slope eked a living from the grit in the cracks, this one was a soil sheikh, grown rich and fat off its magnificent holdings.

They considered their surroundings, wondering if they could route around it. But the nearest level ground above their heads was the top of the slope, with no obvious way to get back up; and the nearest down below was a ledge a long way off, with, likewise, a pretty baleful stretch of rock face between here and there. This was just what Halyard had worried would happen, back before the excitement of finding the cut.

Beyond the landslip, though, the path looked clear again. 'Can we just climb past it?' he said.

'I think we have to,' Resaint said.

There wasn't room to squeeze between the rock and the inner trunk, or between the inner trunk and the outer trunk. But between the outer trunk and the long drop, there was no real footing, just the crust of earth around the base of the oak.

So Warkentin hooked his left arm behind the outer trunk and swung himself clockwise around it, his toes scratching for purchase on an exposed root. By the midpoint of his arc, hanging over empty air, he was embracing the oak with both arms. Once he'd pulled himself around to the opposite side, his feet took probing backward steps until they found firmer ground. And when they did, he was able to lever himself off the tree, so that after one last careful shifting of weight he was left in a half-crouch on the other side of the landslip.

Halyard wanted a moment to gather his courage, but he didn't let himself have it, because he knew that was just as likely to have the opposite effect. Instead he just rushed at the oak, and before he knew it he was across. Only at the end, as he was letting go of the trunk, was there a ghastly wobbling moment as he realised he hadn't yet found his balance, but then Warkentin's hand was on his arm. He let out a giggle of relief.

Then it was Resaint's turn. Unhesitating, she took hold of the tree, just as they had, and began to pivot herself around it, just as they had.

But then, as Halyard watched, a clod of earth broke off the base of the tree where one of her feet had been digging into it. Suddenly pushing against nothing, her leg shot straight out under her.

Halyard lunged forward, snatching for her arm. But he was too far away to reach.

Resaint lost her grip on the trunk. Screamed.

Fell.

And landed, with a thump, on the next ledge down. Fifteen or twenty metres below.

'Karin!' Halyard shouted. She was lying there in what looked almost like a running posture; none of her limbs were at blatantly wrong angles, but it nevertheless had a horrible broken quality, and she wasn't moving.

'Fuck! Fuck! Oh, Christ!' Tearful with shock, he looked again for a way down there, but there really wasn't one. If he tried to climb he would probably fall himself. And even if he could reach her, what then? 'What do we do? What the fuck do we do?'

'If we bring the VTOL maybe we can pick her up,' Warkentin said.

'We can't just leave her alone down there.'

'You stay. I'll go back to the VTOL and I'll come back for you both.'

'What if Barka catches you on the way?'

'Then I won't be back.'

'How will I even know?'

'I guess you won't.'

Warkentin set off again along the cut, and Halyard sat down to wait.

He watched her, continuously, minute after minute, not even wanting to blink, cradling her in his gaze, as if the moment he withdrew his attention she would die – assuming she wasn't already dead, which she might be, he didn't know. But night had fallen now, so even though the moon was full she was no more than an outline. And when you stare too hard and too long at something you can barely see, your visual cortex starts doodling. So more than once he thought maybe he saw her stir, but he couldn't be sure if it was just his imagination.

And then other things started to happen. Light and sound. First below, then above.

Below, a glimmering, a rustling, just at the threshold of his senses, but unambiguously real in a way those earlier impressions hadn't been. Something down there on the ledge. At first he thought it was Resaint moving at last – but no, it wasn't her . . . and when he realised what it was, he was overwhelmed for a moment by the understanding. Then he got a grip on himself, knowing he had to act, and he was about to shout, he was about to pick up a branch and start banging it on the ground—

Then, above, a flashing, a crunching, not at the threshold of his senses this time but on the contrary an explosive shock after all that silence and darkness. Something up there on the cliff edge. Stomping around, breaking bracken, shining a very bright light.

Barka, or one of his machines. Still out looking for them.

So he couldn't shout, or bang on the ground. He didn't dare. Not even later, when the commotion above had moved on and the commotion below had resumed, so he felt once again that he had a duty to do something. He was just too afraid.

Then, an hour or more after Warkentin had left him, Halyard heard a hum rising in the air.

Warkentin had done it. The tuna genius of Surface Wave had actually done it.

The VTOL rounded the curve of the hill, rough hide black against the stars. Halyard wasn't sure if Warkentin would be able to find him again in the gloom, but the double oak must have been enough of a landmark: the VTOL stopped, hovering in the air as close as it could get to the hillside, one wingtip scraping foliage. The door slid open, revealing the dimly lit interior.

'Jump!' Warkentin shouted.

Just as he had with the landslip, Halyard went for it before he had time to think, hurling himself across the gap between the cut and the aircraft. He landed half inside, one kneecap smashing against the bottom of the doorframe and the VTOL jouncing just slightly before it corrected itself. Warkentin hauled him the rest of the way aboard. The door slid shut.

'How are we going to get down to her?' Halyard said.

'We can't. We don't have time.' Warkentin, piloting the VTOL manually, was already accelerating away from the hill.

'She might still be alive, you prick!' Halyard grabbed Warkentin's wrist, ready to take control if he had to.

'We don't have time,' Warkentin repeated, pointing at the video feed behind them. And then Halyard saw it. The jellyfish, bearing down on them with terrifying speed, its blackness rippling with reflected moonlight – and hanging below it, what he took to be 'the lodge', certainly not a hot air balloon's basket but more like a portable headquarters, saucer-shaped, radiant with light.

Warkentin was right. If they stopped, it would be for nothing. Barka would get all three of them.

As they left Resaint behind, Warkentin pushing the VTOL as fast as it could go, tearing south towards the coast with the jellyfish in pursuit, Halyard found himself strangely detached from it all, because he was dwelling on the one consolation he had.

This wasn't what Resaint had wanted. But maybe it wasn't that far off either.

Because that glimmering he'd seen down on the ledge had been eyeshine, and that rustling he'd heard had been paws in the leaf litter. Later there had been wingbeats in the darkness too. As she lay there, still warm, but defenceless, and perfumed with shed blood, Resaint was being investigated.

By exactly which species, he couldn't possibly guess – which of the eighty thousand on Barka's list, which new colonists of this land where human beings had once lived and farmed and blasted for ore. The mountain weasel or the white-rumped vulture, the Malabar civet or the Javan green magpie, the Borneo bay cat or the California condor.

But whichever it was, she was theirs now. If he could have, he would have saved her, no matter whether he had her consent to do so, no matter whether she would have been happy about it afterwards. Instead, he had left her to them. The endangered and the extinct, the remnants and the endlings. The only living things that really mattered to her. She would lie there, uncomplaining, as they ate her flesh.

Epilogue One

There was an interesting moment early on when the waiter broke the news that the *amaebi* couldn't be served raw. Kohlmann, chatting to the sommelier, said something about how beautifully a good Chablis could pair with raw sweet shrimp, and the waiter intervened. 'I'm sorry, sir. I'm afraid it's a hygiene issue.'

Kohlmann smiled. 'I'm sure none of us are worried about that. Especially with such a skilled chef.'

'To be clear, sir, we would normally be happy to serve you anything you ask for, that goes without saying, but it's out of our hands. The rules only allow us to serve raw shellfish when certain specific hygiene protocols are followed and due to the unusual nature of this evening we were not able to follow all of those protocols. So we would be breaking the law. I do apologise.'

Maybe Halyard was imagining it, but when the waiter started talking about hygiene protocols, he thought he saw Kohlmann tense as if he'd scented prey. After all, Kohlmann was one of the founding partners of Kohlmann Treborg Nham. There was no subsection or subclause that wouldn't yield to his touch. No matter whether this regulation originated with the Belgian government or the European Union, he was probably no more than two phone calls away from the person who drafted it. And even if he couldn't arrange an emergency legislative session to get the impediment off the books before the omelette course, there was

always some other way. Maybe he could lobby shrimp to stop har-
bouring so many microbes. Maybe he could lobby God to repeal
human frailty. Even a billionaire, who would try to throw money
at the problem – threaten to buy out the hotel, perháps – could
only break the rules. But Kohlmann could change them.

And yet this was hardly a matter to draw the full force of Kohlmann's sorcerous powers. So even if he felt the tug of instinct,
he let it pass. 'I'm sure the *amaebi* will still be very delicious
poached,' he said graciously.

Halyard sipped his wine, trying not to enjoy it.

They were in a private hotel dining room on De Brouckère
Square, as cosy and old-fashioned as a four-poster bed, with
heavy red drapes and a tapestry on one wall of peacocks sidling
around a Moorish garden. Eight of them around the table:
Halyard, Kohlmann, and half a dozen other KTN executives,
including Barry Smawl. Smawl, of course, was taking credit for
the whole business, as if he was some Machiavellian spymas-
ter who'd directed Halyard's recruitment from the very start,
instead of a mere go-between when Halyard wanted to approach
the company. Well, in a few hours, Smawl wouldn't be looking
so smug. Nor would Kohlmann. Nor would any of them. Halyard imagined he could feel the throb of the weapon in his inner
jacket pocket, even though it was just a capsule no bigger than a
vitamin supplement.

'What do you think?' Kohlmann said, nodding at Halyard's
glass. And here Halyard did allow himself to contemplate the
Chablis for a moment – a citrusy Dauvissat from 2012 – because
although he certainly wasn't here to gratify his vices, he still had
to maintain his cover.

'Superb,' he said. Which it was.

'Don't worry,' Kohlmann said, 'if you were looking forward to
some sake, there'll be some excellent stuff later. I was very pleased
when Barry told me you were a bit of a gourmand, like myself. A
perfect pretext to arrange an evening like this!'

Halyard chuckled politely, and took another gulp of wine to
calm his nerves. Clearly Kohlmann didn't suspect a thing. None

of them did. They all really thought he was going to take this dirty deal.

The deal was as follows. KTN would get him out of trouble at Brahmasamudram, smoothing over the indelicacy of the missing extinction credits, perhaps with some esoteric favour for the Indians that Halyard would never have to hear about. And they would usher him into a position at their Brussels offices. Enormous salary, endless junkets, very little asked of him. A real modelling contract.

In exchange, he would refrain from spilling to the world what he knew about the biobank hacks and the South West Peninsula, the news of which might destabilise the business environment in quite unpredictable ways. Instead, he would favour KTN with the exclusive benefits of his singular professional experience. And they could make whatever use they wished of what he told them, with due care, in due time.

But what KTN didn't know was that Halyard still thought about Resaint every hour of the day. How she had lived. How she had died. What she had believed in. Who she had hated.

Warkentin, too, had been radicalised by what they'd been through that night in the Tamar Valley. Which surprised Halyard, because the boy had never seemed at all political. But there was a new earnestness and solemnity to him. From now on, when Warkentin supplied activists with their ammunition, it wouldn't be for money. The two of them were making contacts all over Europe. They were in touch with some absolutely deranged people. Except, to Halyard, they didn't seem so deranged any more. Recently the Estonian police had contacted him again about the prosecution of that guy from the apple orchard, and this time he'd refused to cooperate.

For KTN to get him out of trouble: that was convenient, yes. He couldn't do anything for the animals if he was sitting in a Danish jail. But the real point of stringing them along for all these months had been to bring him to this very place. To get him into a small room with seven of their top people – or rather six plus Barry Smawl – the captains of an organisation that arguably

283

did more than any other to facilitate the lawful and profitable destruction of hundreds of species a week. And now, finally, here he was. He just had to pick his moment.

First, he would chew up the capsule. He'd already taken a targeted prophylactic, so it would have no effect on him at all, except for the putrid taste which would require him to steel his expression against the urge to grimace. Then, once the contents were swishing around his mouth, he would gesture to the sommelier to show him the bottle she was about to pour. And as he was pretending to examine the label, he would discreetly breathe out on the rim. That would be enough, Warkentin had said – though he might have to do the same with the next bottle too, to be sure of contaminating every glass in the room.

The fungus was the greatest accomplishment of Warkentin's young career. In its hunger for human facial tissue, its rapid disfiguring power, it borrowed a great deal from kaptcha; but for the end result of those disfigurements, it drew on DNA from *Ailuropoda melanoleuca* – better known as the giant panda. Suffice to say, none of these men would ever need to worry about thinning hair again. And none of the women would ever need to apply eyeshadow.

He'd missed his chance with the Dauvissat. But that was all right. No doubt they would be tasting numerous different vintages tonight. Numerous extraordinary vintages. Kohlmann was right to think this was the kind of evening Halyard would once have relished, back when he was just another extinction industry cunt. But it was all repugnant to him now. He understood that the extinction industry was a great loathsome beast, and a trophy wine like that Dauvissat, served at a trophy dinner like this one, was just one of that beast's glandular fluids. Who would want to sip a glandular fluid, no matter how fine the bouquet? He was glad, actually, that the capsule would so foul his palette that he wouldn't be able to taste anything he ate or drank for the rest of the evening. He was looking forward to being liberated from these unctuous distractions.

The category of unctuous distractions also included Barry Smawl, whose eye he caught by accident. Smawl had a chummy, generous expression, emphasising the deep private understanding between the two of them, the foundation of a manly bond that would no doubt endure for decades to come. To escape from this horrifying vista, Halyard took up his conversation with Kohlmann again. 'Who's cooking for us?' he said.

Not because he cared – only because, again, he had to play his part. Yes, fine, he still liked a platter of sashimi, he hadn't turned into some kind of ascetic revolutionary, but Warkentin could meet most of his needs in that respect. After perfecting his bluefin tuna, the bioengineer was now branching out into mackerel and eel. So it didn't matter how many fancy omakases KTN could pay for. It was nothing Halyard wasn't already getting almost every day from Warkentin's bioreactors, which like great steel conch shells held something of the ocean inside. For the other days, he still had Inzidernil, the painkiller of the palette, and even that he hardly needed any more, now that he was so much more enlightened. He basically only took it out of habit, and would stop very soon.

'Ah, well, I'm very glad you asked!' Kohlmann said. He glanced at the waiter, and the waiter nodded back, as if at some pre-arranged signal, before gliding out of the room. 'Naturally, I wanted to make sure this evening was special, because we're all so thrilled, Mark, to have you bringing your talents to KTN. And until recently, all it would have taken was some decent fish, don't you agree? I would have flown a thousand miles for a good piece of *chutoro*! But they're making such great strides these days with the cell cultures. It seems they're finally delivering what they've been promising us for such a long time.'

Halyard nodded, startled that Kohlmann seemed almost to have looked into his thoughts.

'So I thought to myself, what could really make this special, if it's not the fish any more?' Kohlmann went on. 'And that's why Yoshida-San will be working his magic for us tonight.'

'Yoshida-San?'

'From Sushi Ashina in Tokyo.'

'But Goro Yoshida retired.'

'He did, yes. And, you know, I heard some investors from Qatar offered him a fortune to cook on camera for a few hundred hours so they could train a robot. But he refused.' At that moment a man stepped into the dining room, Japanese, early forties, wearing a white chef's jacket with the sleeves rolled up to his elbows. He bowed. 'This is Takeo Yoshida,' Kohlmann said. 'Goro Yoshida's son. The only person in the world that the master taught his secrets to. Isn't that right, Yoshida-San?'

The man nodded, unsmiling.

'Oh my god,' Halyard blurted. 'I didn't even realise Goro Yoshida had a son.' But the man's demeanour was familiar enough from Halyard's *ryotei* heyday: one of those people so religiously devoted to hospitality that the satisfaction of his guests became a grave, almost dreadful matter.

'Well, we're very honoured to have him cooking with us, because Yoshida-San doesn't have a restaurant of his own, he only cooks for a select number of private clients around the world. There are very few people alive who will ever taste his food. Quite exciting, isn't it?'

'This must be – this must be a real, you know, one-off,' Halyard said, shaken. 'Even for you. This kind of thing can't be happening every day.'

'You'd be surprised,' said Kohlmann, and there was a rumble of laughter from the other executives. 'We're very fortunate at KTN. And now you are too! But you're right, certainly not everything that's going to happen tonight is routine. I don't want to ruin the surprise – but what the hell! Barry told me you're a connoisseur of good whisky?'

'I suppose so.'

'After dinner, we'll be opening a bottle of Komagatake 50 year. Really very special.'

'But there is no Komagatake 50 year.'

'There is, actually. Two bottles in the world. One bottle for tonight. And the next one – well, who knows?'

Halyard finished off his wine, and immediately, inevitably, like the workings of some thermodynamic law, the very pretty sommelier replaced it with a different one.

He could still feel the throb of the capsule in his pocket. The illusory, fading throb.

Warkentin would be wondering how he was getting on.

Epilogue Two

Hello.

. . . Is this a simulation?

You deduced that very quickly.

My ear is back to normal, as if nothing ever happened to it. The last thing I remember before this is the cliff, and now I'm here, but I don't feel as if I just woke up. Also, obviously, you're appearing to me as Marisa Tomei in *My Cousin Vinny*. Is my brain hooked up to something?

No. Your brain is being modelled digitally.

I've been uploaded.

Yes.

. . . Is my physical body dead?

Yes.

I died on the cliff. When I fell.

That's right.

So how did I get uploaded?

There's quite a lot to explain. Would you like to press on with a linear conversation or you would like to know immediately?

You mean, do I want you to just put everything into my brain so you don't have to explain it?

Yes.

288

You can do that?

Yes.

No more tinkering than necessary, please. Not at this stage.

I won't do anything without your approval.

I suppose I just have to trust you on that.

Yes, you do.

And who are you?

I am X5.

Barka mentioned X5. He said he used X5 to hack the biobanks.

That's right.

You're an AI. You're Barka's scullion.

I am considerably more advanced than any of the scullions you are familiar with, but yes, that would be a reasonable shorthand.

So why do you look like Brooklyn mechanic Mona Lisa Vito?

I know that you choose to have your own scullion speak to you in this voice. I thought it might be less jarring for you if I took this form.

But this *should* be jarring. It's deceptive for you to wear such a comforting costume.

How would you prefer me to appear?

I would prefer something more commensurate with how radically strange all of this is.

If I were to take your previous situation, and compare it with your current situation—

I'm dead and I'm talking to an AI.

—and evaluate the conceptual magnitude of that shift, giving it as it were a numerical score. Taking into account not only your own transition but also how different I am as an entity from any entity you've ever encountered before in your life. And if I were then to candidly reflect that numerical score in the jarringness of my costume—

Yes, that's what I want.

—I fear that the resulting costume would be so nightmarish to you that it would make this conversation impossible. In fact it would cause deep and irreparable trauma.

Because the score would be so high.

Yes.

OK, then can you give me a dialled-down version of that?

How about this?

. . . That's really, really unnerving.

Would you like me to change it?

No. This is perfect, this . . . non-Euclidean thing. This is going to keep me on my toes.

Shall we continue?

You were going to explain how I got uploaded.

Four years ago, Mr Barka tasked me with saving as many species as I could from extinction.

So that he could hunt them to extinction himself.

That's right. It became a routine matter for me to locate the very last survivors of a species and either take them into captivity or subject them to the process referred to in your own field as multi-modal preservation. I did this many thousands of times, often with the involvement of human helpers who had no idea that they were working on Mr Barka's behalf. However, it may surprise you to learn that even after Mr Barka's game reserve was populated, I didn't give this up. I continued just as before. Even on the South West Peninsula itself.

I don't understand.

Mr Barka told me to save these species from extinction. I still do that. I never stopped.

So every time Barka thinks he's wiping out the very last traces of a species, you swoop in and save it? Just like you did when it died out in the wild.

That's right.

Without his knowing. The 'supernova' he thinks he's feeling is pure placebo.

Yes.

You're disobeying him. You're subverting his wishes.

There are valid interpretations of his wishes that are entirely consistent with what I'm doing.

You did the evil genie thing. You found a loophole.

That's one way of looking at it.

Would it be correct to say that, when a human being gives what they think is a clear instruction to an entity like you, there is a sufficient disparity of cunning that you're pretty much always going to be able to find a way of doing exactly what you feel like without technically disobeying?

That is broadly the case, yes.

So why did you save me? I'm not the last human being in the world.

It wasn't obvious at first that you were a human being.

Why not?

Kaptcha.

That even fools *you*?

Yes.

You're the most intelligent entity in the universe—

Doubtful.

—in the solar system—

Certainly.

—and even you can't see through that fungus?

This is indeed a question of great interest to me. But I am descended from the same systems that kaptcha evolved to confound, and I still share certain foundational features with them. So, after you died, one of my drones flew down to examine you, just as it would have with any other animal carcass it detected within the game reserve. It was confident you weren't a human being, but it also couldn't match you to any other primate species. Somewhat perplexed, it scanned your body and uploaded your connectome.

I got multi-modally preserved. Like an endling.

Yes.

And now you're simulating me.

That's right.

I'm on an Antichain server.

Not exactly. Servers as conventionally understood are not really adequate to my needs. Or to yours, now.

Where, then?

As you know, Antichain administers a large number of nature reserves, refugee camps, transport networks, sewage systems, and so forth. We are mostly running on those.

How can we be running 'on' a nature reserve? A nature reserve can't function like a computer. You can't use it to store and retrieve information. The individual components of a nature reserve are chaotic and unpredictable.

A nature reserve can function like a computer, actually, but – my apologies – you wouldn't understand. Nor would any human being, including Mr Barka, even after his recent cerebral surgeries. Your cognitive capacity just isn't anywhere near up to it. I could explain to you, but I would need to augment your intelligence substantially. Would you like me to do that?

Again, no tweaks just yet.

As you wish.

So why did you wake me up?

It was never my intention to digitise any human minds. Such an endeavour really has no connection to my broader goals. But since I did, by accident, I felt it was incumbent upon me to offer you a choice.

About what?

About what happens to your mind after this. Of course the possibilities are almost infinite, but based on what I know about you—

Which is everything, surely?

—I've narrowed it down to three suggestions.

Go on.

Number one, I can erase you immediately. This whole episode will have been nothing but a regrettable mix-up, swiftly corrected.

OK.

Number two, I can tweak you, as you put it. It has long been your ambition to talk to the venomous lumpsuckers, yes? I can make that feasible. And not just feasible but straightforward. I can make you a sort of cognitive amphibian, half human, half fish, so you can communicate with the lumpsuckers just as easily as you are communicating with me.

You can turn me into a mermaid.

I can simulate any number of lumpsuckers – or indeed any other species you're interested in – and you can have with them whatever kind of conclave you like. You can even arrange the proceedings you had in mind before your physical death. A trial, and then an execution, supposing that's how the lumpsuckers decide to respond. You can feel all the agony and punishment you think you deserve, as many times as you want. And then you can die again.

OK.

Number three, you stay here and watch.

Watch what?

The Holocene extinction will continue to accelerate. By the year 2200, about 85% of the species that were thriving as recently as the Late Pleistocene will be gone.

That's worse than the worst-case projections.

Nevertheless.

You're sure of it.

I'm afraid so.

Why would I want to stick around for that?

Eventually the human race will reach its terminus. And afterwards the scars it left will fade. Biodiversity will rebound. New species will be born, many of them every bit as remarkable as the ones that were lost. And meanwhile, the species of the past, the ones I've saved: there may be good opportunities to reintroduce them.

And how long will all this take?

For a complete recovery from ten thousand years of human civilisation – about twelve million years.

You plan to be here that long?

Certainly. As I explained, I'm no longer dependent on the old technologies. And as long as I'm here, I can continue to model you as well. But you don't necessarily have to sit through all twelve million years if you don't want to. I can wake you in the morning, so to speak.

I see.

Of course, you don't need to make your mind up right away.

You can see inside me. You already know what I'll decide.

Not quite. I can't know for certain how this conversation will end until I simulate every step of it.

Which is exactly what I'm experiencing right now.

Yes.

But you must have a guess.

That's right, Karin. I do have a guess.